H
A
AMAZON, AND
OTHER FABLES

Edited by
Mark Graham, Rob Kitchin,
Shannon Mattern and Joe Shaw

Meatspace Press

How to Run a City Like Amazon, and Other Fables
Edited by Mark Graham, Rob Kitchin,
Shannon Mattern and Joe Shaw

Publisher: Meatspace Press (London, 2019)
Weblink: meatspacepress.com
Design: Carlos Romo-Melgar and John Philip Sage
Format: Paperback and pdf/e-book.
Printed by: TradeWinds (Second Print)
Paper: Popset Virgin Grey
Typefaces: Arial, Founders Grotesk, Helvetica Neue, Helvetica Textbook, HTRACLA Capitals, Monument Grotesk, Union.
Length: 350 pages
Language: English
ISBN (paperback): 978-0-9955776-7-1
ISBN (pdf, e-book): 978-0-9955776-8-8

Contributors (alphabetically): Manuel B. Aalbers, Tooran Alizadeh, James Ash, Sarah Barns, Gavin Brown, Ryan Burns, Matthew Claudel, Jeremy W. Crampton, Ayona Datta, Martin Dodge, Leighton Evans, Jessica Foley, Jennifer Gabrys, Mark Graham, Tony H. Grubesic, Edward Helderop, Kara C. Hoover, Andrew Iliadis, Kurt Iveson, Glenn Kaufmann, Rob Kitchin, Agnieszka Leszczynski, Sophia Maalsen, Shannon Mattern, Harvey J. Miller, Cian O'Callaghan, Nancy Odendaal, Dietmar Offenhuber, Alison Powell, Lizzie Richardson, Gillian Rose, Jathan Sadowski, Kalpana Shankar, Joe Shaw, Harrison Smith, Monica Stephens, Linnet Taylor, Jim Thatcher, Pip Thornton, Anthony Vanky, Alberto Vanolo, Alan Wiig, Katharine Willis, Matthew Zook.

Support for the design and printing of this book came from Maynooth University and the European Research Council (ERC-2012-AdG 323636-SOFTCITY). Meatspace Press wishes to give thanks to The Alan Turing Institute under the EPSRC grant EP/N510129/1 and the University of Oxford for incubating this project.

HOW TO RUN A CITY LIKE AMAZON

Mark Graham, University of Oxford
Rob Kitchin, Maynooth University
Shannon Mattern, The New School
Joe Shaw, University of Oxford

In an article to promote their new book— 1
'A New City O/S'—Stephen Goldsmith (a former Mayor of Indianapolis and Deputy Mayor of New York) and Neil Kleiman (Director of the NYU/Wagner Innovation Labs) contend that cities should act more like Amazon to better serve their citizens.[1] They argue that cities will be more efficient and productive if they become data-driven, using analytics and machine learning to parse data about citizens and city services/infrastructure into insights that provide a responsive, tailored experience. Just as Amazon's online shopping platform provides a means to order everything

1 Link: https://nextcity.org/daily/entry/cities-should-act-more-like-amazon-to-better-serve-their-citizens

a household might need and deliver individually-specific recommendations, a city administration can function as a marketplace for services and be accessed through a single point of entry. The complex systems architecture that would enable this 'friction-free experience' would also provide a means for the administration to manage itself.

At first sight, Goldsmith and Klei- 2
man's argument seems appealing—who doesn't want to live in a more efficient and responsive city? On reflection, however, the article prompts some critical questions. Goldsmith and Kleiman are not simply using Amazon's systems architecture and business model as a metaphor for how cities might be run. Rather they are promoting the twin ideas that cities should be *run like businesses* and city services and infrastructure should be *run by businesses*. In a city 'run like a business', the ethos and logic of city government shifts from a bureaucracy serving citizens for the common good, to a technocracy that adopts business models and practices to serve individual consumers. In a city 'run by businesses' the provision of services and essential infrastructure transfers from public to private delivery.

Both ideas have gained much traction over the last half century and form key tenets of urban neoliberalism, in which there is a transformation from the practices of urban managerialism to urban entrepreneurialism. That is, there is a shift from city administrations that manage an urban commons and seek to deliver services and infrastructure largely through their own endeavours, to cities that compete with one another for resources and investment, and services and infrastructure are opened up to market forces through deregulation, outsourcing, public-private partnerships, and privatisation. Here, the city is no longer the place that enables markets to function, but the city itself—its components and its administration—become a collection of markets. 3

This translation from public to private, from managerialism to entrepreneurialism, has been driven by arguments from the Right that city administrations are inefficient, wasteful, and lack sufficient knowledge and expertise for managing systems in an increasingly complex world, and competition between private suppliers produces value for money, innovation and choice. In turn, the move towards entrepreneurial approaches alters the mode of 4 urban governmentality (the rationality, practices and techniques through which people are governed) and the nature of citizenship. Here, there is a shift from citizens having defined civil, social and political rights and entitlements, who are disciplined to act in prescribed ways, to consumers with autonomy to choose from a suite of public service options dependent on desire and budget, who gain rights through acting responsibly, and are nudged to act in the interests of state and capital. What little changes are the underlying notions of stewardship (for citizens) and civic paternalism (deciding what's best for citizens) in how states and companies view their relationship with residents with respect to how cities are run.

The latest phase of urban entre- 5
preneurialism is the attempt to produce smart cities; that is, to use digital, networked technology to manage cities and deliver urban services and utilities. Technologies such as urban control rooms, city operating systems, urban dashboards and performance management systems, sensor networks, smart grids, and intelligent transport systems, it is argued, will break-down internal administrative silos, produce better coordination, and leverage insight

and value from data to produce more effective and efficient delivery of services. They will also improve security, safety and quality of life, and create improved resilience and environmental sustainability. The new markets created will foster local innovation, economic development and entrepreneurship. Further, shared economy platforms and thousands of urban-living apps are already transforming services such as taxis, tourist accommodation, housing, food distribution, work space, and indeed how work is organized and undertaken. Smart technologies are explicitly designed to be disruptive innovations; that is, to radically transform how established activities are organised and performed. For the corporations who develop them, the aim is to disrupt how the state operates and to create a new market for their products and services, or to disrupt existing market actors.

As many critics have argued, the 6
neoliberalisation of city governance and the creation of smart cities raises a whole series of social, political and ethical questions. These include concerns about profit being placed before people and the environment, widening inequalities between citizens, a loss of rights,

and the erosion of democracy, fairness, justice and accountability, the privatisation of public assets and corporatization of surveillance, the application of predictive profiling and social sorting to deliver differentiated services, and a transfer of risk and liability from the private to public sector. In turn this raises normative questions about what kind of city do we want to live in? Do we really want to reside in cities run like or by businesses?

It is these questions that this book explores. Our challenge to the contributing authors was to imagine what cities might be like if they were run using the technologies, business models, and ethos of specific companies. In other words, we asked them to extend Goldsmith and Kleiman's thesis beyond Amazon to consider how the city might be governed and experienced, the consequences to citizens if the city was run by or in conjunction with Uber, Disney, Twitter, Tinder, Ikea, and so on. We gave authors free-rein to select any company they wished as long as we avoided duplicates, with most selecting tech companies, many of which produce smart city technologies.

Many companies are actively involved in partnering with cities or are delivering urban services, though others simply serve urban consumers. In every case, other similar companies could have been chosen, and the selections are designed to provide a thought experiment or grounded discussion of urban entrepreneurship. In the cases where product or corporate names may be trademarks they are only used for the purpose of conducting a thought experiment or identification and explanation without intent to infringe. 8

We also gave authors the choice of writing a short piece of speculative fiction or a more conventional academic-style paper, or a combination of the two, to illuminate their thoughts. The majority of authors chose the speculative fiction approach, most adopting a science fiction framing, with the story set in the near future. 9

As scholars of science fiction have long noted, the genre is a powerful and engaging medium because it uses extrapolation and speculation to explore possible worlds and to encourage the reader to reflect on how those worlds came into being, how they operate, and 10 how they differ from and reflect our present world. As such, they use the tactics of estrangement (pushing a reader outside of what they comfortably know) and defamiliarisation (making the familiar strange) as a way of creating a distancing mirror on society and to offer cognitive spaces to reconsider assumptions, rationales and viewpoints. In our cases, the stories seek to be plausible and consistent given existing technologies, business models, trends, news coverage and academic critique, though sometimes they push the logic, ethos, and the form and use of technology to an extreme to emphasize a point; they are sometimes satirical, sardonic and playful. They are designed to prompt critical thought about contemporary neoliberal urbanism and digital, networked technologies.

The result is a set of 38 stories and essays that explore how a city might look, feel and function, and the effects on society, economy and politics if different business models, practices and technologies are applied to the running of cities. Collectively, the essays suggest there are good reasons to be cautious about transforming public assets and services run for the common good into markets that are run for profit, and in applying a range of disruptive innovations to civic administration and infrastructure that ideally are stable, reliable and risk adverse. Ultimately, they ask us to question whether we really do want cities to be run like or by businesses, and thus what kinds of cities we want to create and occupy. And that is the challenge we set for readers: to use the stories and essays to answer these questions for themselves.

Acknowledgements

Rob's contribution to this chapter and to editing the book as a whole was undertaken as part of The Programmable City project funded by the European Research Council (ERC-2012-AdG 323636-SOFTCITY). Funding towards the publication of the book was provided by Maynooth University. Mark wishes to acknowledge the Leverhulme Prize (PLP-2016-155), ESRC (ES/S00081X/1), and European Research Council (ERC-2013-StG335716-GeoNet) for supporting his work. Both Joe and Mark are grateful for additional support received towards this publication from the Alan Turing Institute, Oxford Internet Institute and the University of Oxford.

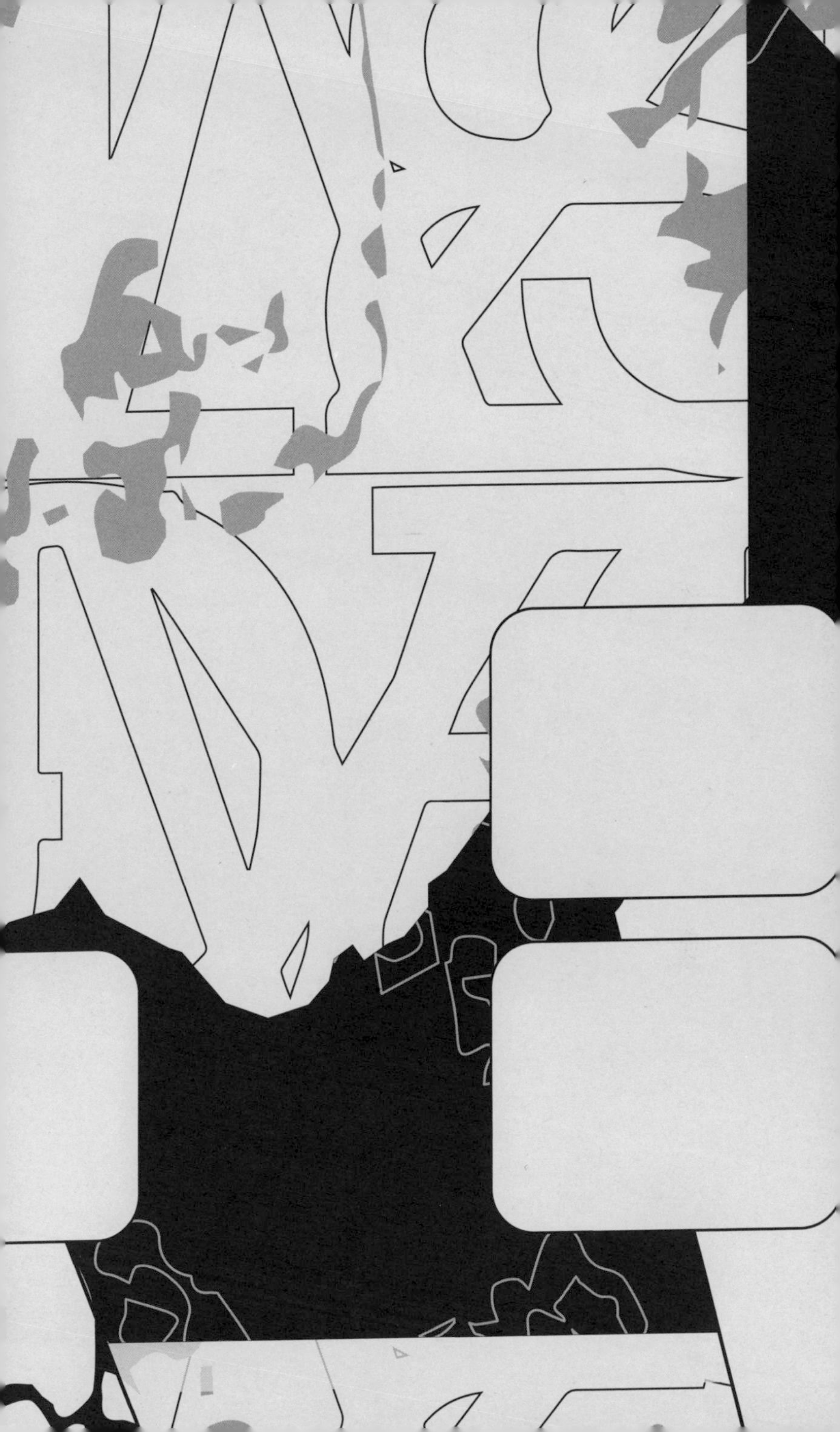

YOU'RE ENTITLED TO WHAT THE DATA SAYS YOU DESERVE

ACXIOM[1]

Rob Kitchin, Maynooth University

'Mr Connors? My name is Ms Smith, 13
I'm a data officer for the city. Please take a seat. Normally we conduct all citizen interaction via internet channels or our premium number service.'

Connors slumped into a plastic chair. 'I've tried that and I didn't get anywhere.'

'Yes, fourteen times, for a total of four 15
hours, thirty two minutes and twenty three seconds. You became quite abusive on five of those occasions.'

1 The following speculative fiction is a thought experiment that imagines a future where a city administration uses a data broker and their services to make decisions regarding the provision of services. Such a thought experiment could equally apply for other data brokers such as ChoicePoint, Experian and Equifax, many of whom already provide services to state bodies. Product or corporate names may be trademarks or registered trademarks, and are used only for the purpose of conducting a thought experiment without intent to infringe.

'Have you any idea how frustrating your customer service system is?'

'We deal in facts, Mr Connors, not sentiment. Your behaviour has been flagged in your citizen profile. Now, you seem to think that you are not receiving the services due to you?'

'And what do those flags mean exactly?' Connors asked, ignoring the question.

'Think of them as like penalty points on your driver's license. Once you get to ten, your service choices are constrained for three years.'

'Constrained to what exactly?'

'To a more limited service pack and in some cases you're denied services, for example being able to meet a city representative or to apply for city-supported housing.'

'But that's not ethical or democratic. It's your job to serve citizens.'

'It's our job to help run the city as efficiently and effectively as possible. And how else are we expected to make citizens act responsibly? Good behaviour is rewarded, poor behaviour penalised. Now, your complaint?'

'So I continue to pay my taxes, but I receive no or limited service?' Connors persisted.

'Those taxes are an investment in the city as whole, Mr Connors, not simply yourself. And your contributions are quite modest. Indeed, a large proportion of your sales tax leaves the state through internet shopping.'

'How do you know that?'

'From your citizen profile. It contains *all* your data. All your interactions with public administration offices, your social media use, your movements, your work performance, your purchases, and so on. Our data partner is very thorough in this regard. It amalgams our data with those it acquires through its other partners and uses them to evaluate each citizen and guide our services and relationships with them. I assume you're aware that you're going to be deducted $500 for failing to meet your fitness quota?'

'That's one of the things I wanted to talk to you about.'

'The use of a fitness tracker is part of your work contract as a teacher, Mr Connors. It's designed to help you become more responsible for your personal health.'

'But it has no bearing on my 30
performance as a teacher. If I teach the hours, I should be paid the wage.'

'Your teaching metrics are pretty average, to be honest Mr Connors, and the prediction analytics show they're unlikely to improve. That'll mean a performance related salary deduction, plus two points on your citizen profile.'

'This is a farce! What kind of a hair-brained system is this?'

'It's not a farce. It's a meritocracy based on facts and analytics. Citizens wanted a fairer way to proportion services and we have delivered it using tried and tested techniques within the data broker industry.'

'You call this ... this data system fairer? It actively discriminates!'

'But on the basis of merit. And there are 35
a range of service choices available to you. What can be fairer than that?'

'Choices? Is there any real difference between utility providers, or schools, or waste management companies, or hospital services?'

'Is that a rhetorical question, Mr Connors? Your school competes for students based on its objective ranking of reputation and selects students based on their grades and predicted future profile.’

‘Yes, and it’s madness! All kids should be entitled to a good education at a school within cycling distance.’

‘That’s out-dated idealism, Mr 40
Connors. People are entitled to what the data says they deserve.’

The two men glanced at the street nervously. Crime in the area had been on an upward tick for a couple of years. The installation of a real-time crime center with an array of high definition cameras and military-style response units had made little difference.

‘Are you ready?’ the middle-aged man in a suit asked.

‘Yes, Sir,’ the young man replied, twisting his shoulders inside the body armour, his hand already on his gun.

‘Okay, let’s go meet Bryan Jenkins.’

The two men entered the apartment block, climbing to 45
the second floor and stopping outside a door in need of a fresh coat of paint. The elder man knocked and stepped back.

A few seconds later it was opened by a skinny man in his early thirties. ‘Yeh?’

'Are you Bryan Jenkins?'

'Yeh, who's asking?'

'I'm Mr Jones. This is Mr Popowski. We're from the City Authority.'

'You've come about my re-housing application?'

'In a manner of speaking, yes. Can we come in?'

'Not really, man. It's crowded in here. No privacy.'

'Well, Mr Jenkins, our system is flagging up that you're a housing risk and this is likely to be realised in the next 12 to 24 months.'

'I'm a housing risk?'

'Yes, you're consistently late with payments. You make little contribution to the local community and you're flagged as a credit and tenancy risk in your citizen profile. Which is why your re-housing application has been refused. We're also serving notice on your present tenancy.'

'What? What you talking about man? We pay our rent!'

'Yes, but you're often late and our analytics predict that you're going to start missing payments shortly. The city needs this apartment for more deserving citizens.'

'More deserving citizens?'

'The data shows that you are a low net contributor to the city in terms of work, taxes and legal consumption. You live precariously. Your credit rating is very poor. You have had several brushes with the law and you've a number of active flags in your citizen profile. There are people who contribute more, who have better metrics. And our analytics tell us yours are only likely to fall.'

'This is bullshit, man! What, you have a crystal ball now in City Hall?'

'Please, Mr Jenkins, there's no need to lose your temper. But yes, we have a crystal ball. Or rather our data partners can produce an accurate assessment of your current status and a prediction of your future circumstances based on all the data they hold about you from different sources. We're not the only organisation to use their services; they also calculate insurance premiums, decide who gets what targeted ads, help private landlords assess potential tenants, and help companies vet who should get offered a job.'

'But I'm not actually behind with my rent right now, am I?'

'I'm afraid you're three days late. This is the third month in a row you've been late. In that sense you're a risk to the City and there are others on the housing waiting list who deserve city-supported housing.'

'So, you're going to evict us because of what some bullshit algorithm thinks might happen?'

'That's one way of looking at it.'

'One way! It's the only way. I've a wife and three kids. Where are we meant to go?'

'That is your issue, Mr Jenkins. There are a wide variety of other housing options in the city from short term and long-term private rental through to home ownership.'

'And homelessness!'

'We don't tolerate homelessness, Mr Jenkins.'

'Well, I don't want to tolerate it either, you Jackass!'

'Please, Mr Jenkins ...'

'How do I see how you've calculated my future?' Jenkins asked, reining in his fury.

'Your citizen profile is free to examine. You just need to register on the City website. However, the underlying databases and algorithms are not open to scrutiny.'

'What? So they can make decisions about me and my family but I can't see on what basis?'

'The service is provided by a private 75
contractor using proprietary data systems and software. We just receive updates to the citizen profiles and the suggested courses of action.'

'So, how do I challenge the decision?'

'Well, you can appeal to the City's data office, and they'll refer it to our data partner for assessment.'

'So, it's just one giant black box then? Pay the organ grinder and you get what you get?'

'I don't make the rules, Mr Jenkins. I'm just asked to enforce them.'

'The Mayor's Citizen Relationship 80
team, my name is Joanna; how may I help you, Mr Fitzgerald?'

'Well ... how did you know who was calling?'

'Our system is configured to show us the name of all our mostly highly valued citizens, Sir.'

'Oh! Right. Very good. I was calling about McCarthy Avenue. Several potholes have developed over the winter and I was wondering if they could be filled?'

'Let me see.' Joanna tapped away at her keyboard. 'Yes, Mr Fitzgerald, I can schedule that work as your area exceeds the investment quota criteria. It should be completed within 24 hours.'

'Wonderful, but if you don't mind me asking what's an investment quota?'

'Not at all, Sir. Based on the citizen profiles of people living in an area, and the net contributions to the city in terms of taxes, job and wealth creation, and community development, the city allocates an investment fund to conduct repairs and to improve the area's amenities, and to also set the scheduling.'

'So poorer neighbours get less investment?'

'Yes, in line with their net contribution and profile.'

'And what they do get is less timely in delivery?'

'Exactly! We reward our most valued 90
citizens first.'

'But it's the poorer neighbourhoods that need proportionally more investment to help them address their problems and to improve the area.'

'But they're also more of a long-term risk with respect to dollars invested being wasted. As a city we've adopted the practices of the data broker industry, seeking to identify and preferentially target higher value citizens as they contribute the most to making our great city even greater! By investing in them, opportunities will trickle down to everyone else.'

'I guess that makes sense. I think.'

'In fact, Mr Fitzgerald, I see from your profile that you and your company have been partners in property development in the regeneration zone. The city will shortly be seeking tenders for work in the next phase of the project. Our data partners are confident that there will be a very healthy return on investment. I could send you an advance pack about the opportunities.'

'That sounds interesting, thanks. 95
Where's the next phase located?'

‘Next to the old barracks on Cable Street.’

‘But isn’t that the site of the small trader’s market?’

‘The city is in the process of addressing that issue, Mr Fitzgerald. The traders have been offered a new site off of Union Street.’

‘Hardly as good a spot.’

‘No, but our data partners predict that most will survive the move and the city will get much more value from the regeneration of the old barracks site. We can’t stop progress, Mr Fitzgerald, can we?’

Acknowledgement

This chapter is an output of The Programmable City project funded by the European Research Council (ERC-2012-AdG 323636-SOFTCITY).

Rob Kitchin is a Professor in the Department of Geography and Maynooth University Social Sciences Institute. His research focuses on the relationship between technology and society, especially related to the creation of smart cities, and he is the principle investigator for the Programmable City project and the Building City Dashboards project.

CITY OF LOOPS

ALPHABET[1]

Mark Graham, University of Oxford

May 25, 2024. Augmented Berlin. Sixth loop from the Datum.

First meeting of the Unplatform Society.

Gregor shielded his screen from the fierce pink midday 101
sunlight with his webbed hands, creating a temporary shadow on his device. It was time to start the meeting.

Bodily transformations, like webbed hands, 102
were one of the many advantages of life in Alphabet Corporation's Looped Web (LW). The LW was a mix of immersive, geo-sensitive, virtual augmented city layers that could be accessed through full-body tanks in which people would be hooked up to all manner of neuro-nodes and sensors, nutro powder to keep the meatspace body sustained for a few days, and the newly-discovered long-lasting dissociative hallucinogenic 2CQ. The first few prototypes were created by advanced autonomous AI systems communicating with each other in a language only they understood. Nobody fully comprehended how they worked—not even the original engineers themselves. In the initial months, people were in awe of the first loop. A whole new augmented society was created: cities and towns that existed over-layered on top of the old ones. It was

1 The following speculative fiction imagines a future where a large, diverse platform has thoroughly permeated everyday life. Such a thought experiment applies for other large internet platforms such as Facebook, Yandex or Weibo. Product or corporate names may be trademarks or registered trademarks, and are used only for for the purpose of conducting a thought experiment without intent to infringe.

virtual reality, but somehow very real. People started living dual existences in meatspace and the LW.

But then someone had the idea to access the 103
LW from within the LW. That's when the consensual hallucinations started getting weird. Each loop was a shared experience amongst each of its participants, and each loop was mostly a replica of the augmentation before it.[2] In other words, each loop was simply a world built on top of the world beneath it. London's Trafalgar Square was full of tourists taking photos of Nelson's Column in every loop. But, every loop further away from the datum also contained glitches that were amplifications and exaggerations of elements from the inner loops. The deeper dreams were worlds full of odd phenomena. Transparent skin, music that could be tasted, liquid buildings, insects made of fur and circuit-boards, a background hum[3] that got more noticeable in the outer loops, and all manner of other oddities.

Scholars speculated that even Alphabet's enor- 104
mous computing infrastructures couldn't keep up with the multitude of minds and spaces that were connected (not to mention the fact that it needed to create AIs within AIs within AIs and so on). It therefore had to use sophisticated modelling techniques to fill in some of the blanks: techniques that were clearly imperfect, judging by the ripple effects of some of its glitches by the time you got to the outer loops.

'Welcome Everyone ▶!' shouted Gregoſl. 105
The hundreds of glitches, ●●●●, and gabbers present all shouted greetings back. The background humming intensified, a pleasant neon pink smell scrambled up a nearby tree, and everyone quieted down. Speaking could be a sensory overload out in the sixth loop, and

2 Every trip to the first loop could last up to about two days in meatspace, but that same time was experienced as four days in the LW. The nested nature of each loop meant that each loop deeper was experienced for an exponentially-longer amount of time. The second loop would take you away for four days, the third for 16 days, the fourth 256 days, the fifth for 65,536 days (179 years), and you are gone for 11 million years if you venture into the sixth loop. Physicists theorise that loops exist beyond the sixth, but little is known about them.

3 Scholars referred to the hum as sort of psychic feedback loop similar to the feedback that arises when live microphones are placed near active speakers. In the early days, people used the hum to remind themselves where they were.

therefore quite distracting—so Gregor went back to typing in order to communicate with the group.

> ‘We’ve gathered here to build a new future!’

He typed as he pumped one of his webbed hands 107
in the air.

> ‘[redacted]’ rumbled the crowd.

> ‘I need you all to remember the past so that we can build our shared future.’

Many in the crowd had been absent from the datum 110
for tens or even hundreds of thousands of years. But the Unplatform Society hadn’t let this stop it. That was because it had a simple and appealing idea.

Alphabet ultimately controlled every facet of the 111
LW, and they subsidised all of the hardware that people needed to access it. It even offered subsidised nutro powder and 2CQ in some of the inner loops.

Initially people went in as visitors in order to 112
see what the fuss was all about. To see what it meant that somewhere like Berlin could exist in another dimension. To see how life could play out in a world that looked like a mirror image. Very quickly, the first loop became a reflection of all manner of human desires that were illegal, out of reach, or hard to obtain on the datum. Early loopers still talk about some of the crazy month-long hypnoraves they had in the fourth loop.

But those seeking escapism would be quickly 113
disappointed. In order to make the loops family-friendly

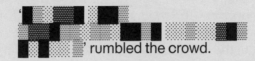

areas, Alphabet implemented a trans-loop crackdown on adult-themed activities. This was about the time that looping went mainstream.

114 The recursive temporality of loops gave way to a booming economy outside of the datum. Two of the key constraints to economic expansion—time and space—had been fundamentally transformed, and the LW was full of previously unthought of economic activity. Because Alphabet was the platform for all economic transactions throughout the LW, the small commissions that they took on every transaction throughout the LW accumulated into enormous profits. And even though transactions were tiny in some of the outer loops, the sheer volume of human economic activity across all of the loops gave them a captive market that was expanding at an exponential rate.

115 However, because the scarcity of time had been fundamentally transformed, there was a huge oversupply of labour power within the LW. The creation of a trans-loop labour market also crashed wages back on the datum: forcing many people to head into the LW to look for new ways of generating earnings. People were willing to work for almost nothing:[4] sometimes saving up to transfer those remittances back towards in the inner loops or even the datum, but sometimes spending the money they made in any of the augmented cities that they made their home. The fourth loop, and sometimes even the fifth, became ever more of a draw because of the recursive time extensions that they permitted. The further you went out, the more time you had to generate value that one day might find its way home. Then people started venturing into the sixth loop...

116 The problem is, that as minds went deeper and deeper into the LW, they sometimes forgot why they went

4 Due to the massive oversupply of labour power, along with the expansion of time and space, the cost of living dropped substantially: meaning that loopers could actually subsist on infinitesimally small wages.

there in the first place. The human mind is simply not equipped to process thousands of years of memory.

> 'The Looped Web should not just be controlled by one corporation!' started Gregoɾ. 'Alphabet has found a way of profiting from a now almost-infinite amount of human lives doing an almost-infinite amount of human labour. Here in the sixth, we don't know how many worlds, lives, and souls are beyond us. But we do know that one company profits from all of it.
>
> How many of you have now resorted to button entry jobs in the sphere?'

A sea of hands, fins, and paws shot into the air. 119

> 'How many of you are collecting points in VirtuaMinecraft or Civ 12? And this gave you what? A nano-cent for a few decades of work!?' 120

One of the gabbers tightened her jaw and clenched her paw. 121

Gregoɾ pointed at her.

> 'I've been out here for many lifetimes, but □□□□ □ has been in the sixth for longer than most of us. Over two million years. Right, □□□□ □?'

□□□□ □ stared blankly forwards. 124

Gregoɾ thought about telling the crowd about 125

the promises of the LW in the early days; the dreams of a better world that they all once had; and then the realisation that that they were just that: dreams. He considered talking about how the augmented worlds Alphabet governed were locked-down, limited societies. They were created to maximise one thing only: a form of user engagement that would ultimately lead to revenue generation. But the crowd knew all of this already.

He took a pause. 126

'We can do better.'

This time he took an even longer pause for 128
dramatic effect.

'We will do better.

We can rethink the architecture 130
of the LW!

We can create our digital environments
to maximise happiness, joy, creativity!

The platform should add value to our
lives instead of us creating value for it!

Right now, a small group of people
control the LW.

But we can build a world in which we
own and control our world.

The Unplatform Society has therefore de- 135
cided to build a more free and equitable

layer in the LW. Our engineers finished working on it last week, and it is ready for use. We're calling it the communoseventh. You are all invited to join us in it.'

Nobody in the assembly had ever really considered going beyond the sixth before. But this was an alluring idea. 136

'HðW D◆ ɅVE KNOW TH⁝Š WILL ɅVORK?' shouted someone over the background hum.

Gregoɾ watched those words spin around as they slowly melted into the air. 138

'Shouldn't we have started this on the datumal rather than here on the sixth?' asked another.

Gregoɾ responded, and, from their expressions, he could see that many in the crowd were already convinced: 140

'Have faith in our technology. Our engineers know what they are doing. Join us'''''''''''''''''''''''''''''''''

With that, Gregoɾ walked towards a nearby building that housed the Unplatform Society's body tanks and neuro-nodes. Many from the assembly followed. 142

At some unclear point in the future, Gregoɾ and the others looked around. But instead of the expected silence, the humming was now extremely loud. The sixth was already only a distant memory... 143

Mark Graham is a professor at Oxford University, a Visiting Researcher at the Wissenschaftszentrum Berlin für Sozialforschung (WZB), and the Director of the Fairwork Foundation. His work focuses on digital geographies and how they both reflect and reproduce digital inequalities. His full list of publications is available at www.markgraham.space

I_AM_THE_ SCORE_ MACHINE

ANT FINANCIAL[1]

Jathan Sadowski,
University of Sydney

Created: 1_October_2039

Readme

Ant Financial offers the latest in fintech innovation. An affiliate of Alibaba, the Chinese e-commerce conglomerate, Ant Financial made its first $150bn by operating the world's largest mobile payment ecosystem, Alipay. Rather than coast on their early success, Ant Financial is always looking to the future. Based on Alipay's data collection and analytics platform, and enhanced by Alibaba's advancements in artificial intelligence, Ant Financial created a social credit scoring system that solves the problem of trust and reputation. With support from the Chinese government and partners in the US and Europe, the scoring system now has billions of daily users worldwide. It is the infrastructure for ensuring honest relationships. It is the foundation for building a fair society. This file describes the score machine's operations.

1 The following poem imagines the operations of social credit scoring as devised by Ant Financial for the Chinese government. Such a thought experiment could equally apply to any data broker or state that is using AI to social sort individuals. Product or corporate names may be trademarks or registered trademarks, and are used only for the purpose of conducting a thought experiment without intent to infringe.

I am the algorithm

I am a refraction of reality
an organiser of society
a processor that's proprietary

I am a social scoring system
mathematical morality applied
each life simplified, datafied

I am the judge, no jury
an all-knowing actuary
issuing three digit decrees

I am the authority of reputation
preceding people in every situation
accounting the virtue of every action

I am the administer of privilege 150
putting people in their proper place
granting rights by quantified grace

I am the arbiter of access
opening the world for the trusted
meting out data-driven justice

I am the apex of power/knowledge
my score is bond, beyond bias
beyond reproach, beyond recourse

I am an algorithm governing the city
a ubiquitous score in urban society
deployed by a technology company

I am the scored city

I am the ultimate, unified smart urbanism
a city built on collection and control
monitoring every body, managing every soul

I am the CORE of the city
a hybrid public-private entity
the Central Office of Reputation
and Evaluation

I am the analysis of data doubles
past, present, and future compiled
people processed, policed, profiled

I am the enforcement of exclusion
impeding and allowing inclusion
a spatial stratifying solution

I am the districts, parks, stores, and more
open only for those with a good score
secured by guards and locked doors

I am the personalised city interface
sorting social standing, class-as-a-service
assigning exactly what each score deserves

I am the urban score machine
a society of total surveillance
an economy of numerical violence

I am the glitch

I am a programmer's mistype
the product of a long night
an accident, an oversight

I am a machine's miscalculation
a computational creation
an error, a malfunction

I am a problem nobody rectified
hidden deep inside
buried, but I did not die

I am now a feature, not a bug
ignored to maintain integrity
overlooked in the name of objectivity

I am an inescapable imperfection
an inevitable corruption
an inexorable repercussion

I am an echo's reverberation
a pebble's ripple
a wing's chaotic flap

I am a glitch in the system
I contain multitudes and magnitudes
minor and major, one among many

I am the scored citizen

I am pretty normal, nothing too unusual
recorded, logged, analysed, ranked
my whole life captured, data banked

I am moving up, improving my brand
every choice is calculated, planned
living all my life rated, yet in command

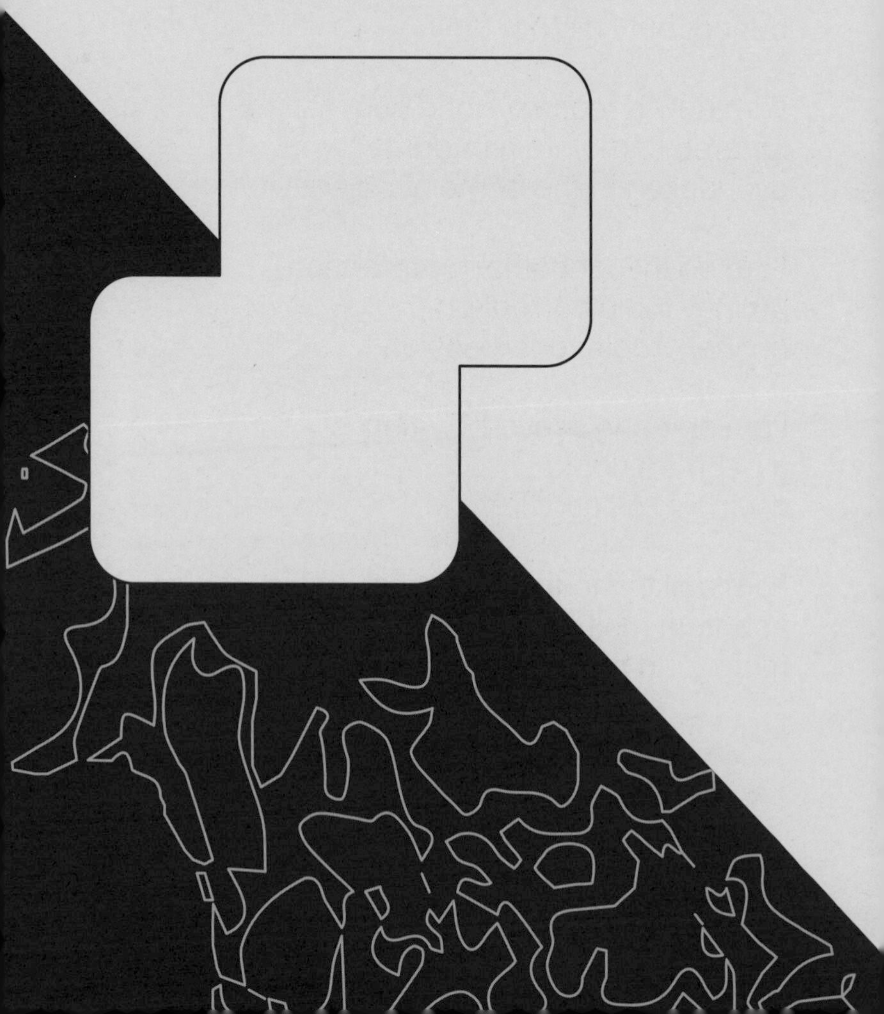

I am a reliable, trustworthy node
work hard, buy right, pay what's owed
a consultant helped me crack the code

I am better than your average Joe
the reward of positive data flow
so why does the screen say: score too low

I am confused, my request didn't work
access to auto-cars is a high score perk
hmmm, must be a weird computer quirk

I am reporting a mistake that's glaring
Dear Citizen, thank you for sharing
but rest assured, the CORE is unerring

I am certain something is not right
my score totally crashed overnight
it's way worse than a request denied

I am unable to live at this rate
my house, my job, my friends, my fate
are all tied to this algorithmic mandate

I am just hoping this issue will be corrected
Dear Citizen, your request has been rejected
and due to complaints, your
score has been affected

Jathan Sadowski is a postdoctoral research fellow in smart cities in the School of Architecture, Design, and Planning at The University of Sydney. He is writing a book for The MIT Press that critically analyses smart technologies: the interests embedded in their design, the imperatives that drive their development, and the impacts of their use on the society.

WELCOME TO JOBSTOWN

APPLE[1]

Sophia Maalsen and Kurt Iveson,
University of Sydney

Time Magazine

Sydney, April 30, 2029

Five years ago, Apple's announcement of a lottery for 177
the right to buy into its exclusive new Californian urban development captured and held global attention, generating iconic encampments outside its flagship stores. It's now two years since Jobstown's first residents moved in: what does Apple's foray into urban development tell us about its future, and about the capacity of corporations to solve urban problems through the creation of 'smart cities'?

Jobstown is perhaps less remarkable today than it 178
would have been if it had been developed 25 years ago. Back in the 1990s and early 2000s, 'gated communities' were still enough of a novelty to attract critical scrutiny. But since then, corporate-owned and secured residential communes have become commonplace, thanks to a range of factors—from

1 The following fictional article is a thought experiment that imagines a future where Apple Inc. has begun to apply the company's business model and logics to building and running its own 'smart cities.' Such a thought experiment could similarly be undertaken for other large platform companies such as Google, Microsoft and Cisco. Product or corporate names may be trademarks or registered trademarks, and are used only for the purpose of conducting a thought experiment without intent to infringe.

declining public revenues and resources to climate change and growing inequality.

Nevertheless, Jobstown is no ordinary corporate commune: it is run by a corporation whose spectacular success has for some decades embodied the very promise of networked technologies to make life better. Expectations for the development were sky-high. But such expectations were matched with cynicism from Apple's many detractors, for whom the idea of an urban environment as controlled as one of Apple's operating systems was the stuff of nightmares, not dreams. 179

Before we consider what life is actually like for the inhabitants of Jobstown, it's worth revisiting the path towards its initial development. 180

A Prehistory of Jobstown: Apple's road to the 'smart city'

By 2015, Apple had overtaken Samsung to be the largest seller of mobile phone handsets globally.[2] And yet, at that time it was becoming clear that Apple's future growth would depend on its ability to diversify its offerings—growth in sales of computers, iPads and iPhones started to flatten out. Consequently, Apple's aspirations were broadened to position its products and platforms as the essential devices and platforms for everyday urban living. 181

The first indications of these broadening ambitions materialised in the mid-2010s. Apple ventured into the markets for smart cars and smart homes. In each case, Apple's strategy was to couple its platforms 182

2 Link: https://www.theguardian.com/technology/2015/mar/04/apple-takes-over-samsung-worlds-biggest-smartphone-maker-china-last-quarter-2014

with its physical products, aiming to capture consumers within an ecosystem that generated profits from both subscription fees and sales.[3] For instance, in the home, Apple Music and Apple TV platforms sought to wrest market-share from players like Spotify and Netflix for home listening and viewing.[4] This was followed by the 2017 release of the Apple HomePod, a speaker with microphone that was offered as "an intelligent home assistant, capable of handling everyday tasks—and controlling your smart home."[5] Similarly, Apple duked it out with Google to assert *CarPlay* as the preferred platform for mainstream car manufacturers in the 2010s.[6] It then started development on its own *AppleCars*, which were finally launched with much fanfare in 2021.

As well as diversifying its product lines, Apple's 183
stores and headquarters established a close relationship between its architecture and brand identity. Alongside its sleek flagship stores in cities across the world, Apple Park opened in 2018. This Norman Foster-designed corporate campus in Cupertino is a suburb unto itself, complete with high-specification architecture and design, its own transport system, and more.[7] Strong interest from Apple fans in the nature of life inside the campus focused the attention of Apple's strategists on the consumer potential in a residential commune of similar size.

Given these directions, it should not have been 184
a surprise when Apple, and other corporations like Alphabet/Google and IBM, took a strong interest in leveraging their existing market dominance in consumer platforms and electronics into new opportunities

3 Link: https://www.smh.com.au/business/companies/the-subtle-transformation-of-apple-from-phone-pioneer-to-fee-collector-20170802-gxnjtb.html

4 Link: https://www.smh.com.au/technology/iphone-6s-launch-apple-prepares-for-life-after-the-iphone-20150906-gjg1qh.html

5 Link: https://www.apple.com/au/homepod/

6 Link: https://www.smh.com.au/technology/googles-android-auto-apples-carplay-and-the-battle-for-the-connected-car-20150407-1mfjax.html

7 Link: https://www.macworld.co.uk/feature/apple/complete-guide-apple-park-3489704/

associated with 'smart urbanism', where predictions of market growth were sky-high.[8]

From Ford to Apple: Corporations and their cities

This temptation to diversify into urban development 185
has always been hard to resist for corporate giants like Ford and Disney whose products defined the capitalisms of their era. Disney's forays into urban development in the US established a pattern that would be followed by 'smart city' corporations like IBM, Cisco, Alphabet and Apple. Founder Walt Disney had harboured visions of the perfect city and his company's role in building it.

After his death, during the 1980s and 1990s 186
Disney Corporation junked many of his specific ideas, but nonetheless tried their hand at both 'green' and 'brown' field urban development. They created Celebration USA, an experiment with so-called 'New Urbanist' urban design ideals.[9] And they partnered with urban authorities in New York City in the redevelopment of Times Square, anchored by a new Disney Theatre.[10]

While neither quite turned out as planned, their 187
test-bed method for deploying new urban design approaches and technologies in partnership with urban authorities has been replicated since. As Alphabet's Sidewalk Labs Director said of its move into urban redevelopment on the Toronto waterfront: "The smart city movement as a whole has been disappointing in part because it is hard to get stuff done in a traditional urban environment."[11] Having a clean slate to

8 Link: https://www.reuters.com/brandfeatures/venture-capital/article?id=30881

9 Ross, Andrew (2000) *The celebration chronicles: life, liberty and the pursuit of property values in Disney's New Town*. New York: Ballantine Books.

10 Zukin, Sharon (1998) "Urban lifestyles: Diversity and standardization in spaces of consumption." Urban Studies. 35(5-6), pp.825-839.

11 Link: https://mobile.nytimes.com/2018/02/24/upshot/tech-envisions-the-ultimate-start-up-an-entire-city.html

showcase new platforms and products was seen as a great development and marketing opportunity.

Life in Jobstown

In developing its vision for Jobstown, Apple re-en- 188
gaged architects Foster and Associates, who were tasked with extending Apple's existing corporate values and design principles into the urban realm. This was to be a place where those who had already come to organize their everyday lives through Apple devices and platforms might experience this digital-urban ecosystem without the incompatibilities and inconveniences one would encounter in places where Apple had less control.

The most obvious focus of attention in the proj- 189
ect was housing. The ring of apartment blocks that constitute the physical boundary of Jobstown, and the houses that are artfully arranged in groups on its internal streets, reflect the postwar modernist design aesthetic that inspired Steve Jobs. Floor to ceiling doors and windows and sleek open spaces mirror the aesthetic of Apple products and stores—to refer to Apple's 1977 campaign, 'Simplicity is the ultimate sophistication.'[12]

But it is not just the aesthetics that are shared; 190
the systems and proprietary arrangements are also translated into the houses—a Mac as Home. Occupants gain access using fingerprint and facial verification systems. Inside, discretely concealed touch screens allow occupants to manage household systems and activities. Every action is recorded and stored in the home's memory so that it can learn the

12 Link: https://www.smithsonianmag.com/arts-culture/how-steve-jobs-love-of-simplicity-fueled-a-design-revolution-23868877/

daily habits of its occupants, thereby anticipating behaviour and optimizing systems accordingly.

And of course, this is Apple—so the house 191
prompts users to run system updates, shutdowns and restarts. A responsible homeowner in Jobstown never skips an update—indeed, this requirement was built into the contracts of sale. Failing to update the house slows its systems, and risks expulsion from the town as the programs become obsolete—Jobstown can run smoothly only if systems are compatible with new iterations and services. To ensure each new version of the house meets occupants' needs, Apple requires all users to agree to share data from household activities—data used to improve Apple products. Sharing data is requisite to be a citizen of Jobstown.

By virtue of its proprietary nature, only Apple- 192
approved apps for home entertainment and communication are available within the Mac Home. Apple influences the tastes and consumption habits of occupants. And in turn, residents here are global taste-makers themselves. New approved apps are displayed on public screens and pushed to personal devices based on individual profiles. For app makers whose products make the Jobstown 'leaderboard' for monthly downloads and use, global attention and market-share follows. This is but one of the ways in which Apple's investment in Jobstown is leveraged for profits generated elsewhere.

The Jobstown local government launches sig- 193
nificant updates, new services and new generation products in arena-style events[13][14]. iPhone Video recordings of these events show an audience of young

13 Link: https://www.inc.com/business-insider/tim-cook-steve-jobs-imac-20th-anniversary-video-launch-1998-apple-history.html

14 Link: https://appleinsider.com/articles/18/05/15/steve-jobs-changed-the-face-of-apple-and-retail-forever-on-may-15-2001

designers and tech-heads dressed in black polo necks, cheering on their Apple-determined future. These videos, immediately uploaded to social media accounts, reveal an interesting trend—the majority of Jobstown residents are white men. A demographic analysis shows that Jobstown is comprised of 70 per cent men compared to 30 percent women, and 55 per cent of residents are white[15].

In between these public events, residents are 194
randomly selected to participate in focus groups in which Apple designers seek feedback on work. The sharing of feedback is deemed by Apple to be equally as essential for Jobstown residents as the sharing of their personal data, as part of a constant improvement cycle in which residents have a legally-enforceable responsibility to participate while having no citizen-like control: the only rights enshrined in their communal contract are the personal consumer and privacy rights, which are themselves subject to change at the discretion of Apple corporation. People looking to play an active role in the governance of their commune would undoubtedly find Jobstown a corporate dystopia.

Yet there are few complaints about this from 195
those who have invested here. Perhaps that's because the everyday life of Jobstown residents certainly has its upsides. As a display town, Apple is highly invested in the quality of Jobstown's urban design. The streets are immaculate, the infrastructure is sleek, and municipal services are automated and conducted via apps. Security is discrete—visible CCTV was deemed unnecessary in an environment where the data shadows cast by networked residents are so detailed and rich.

15 Link: http://time.com/3104025/apple-diversity-report/

And of course, when entry to the compound is biometrically controlled and highly policed, security on the inside can afford to be low-key.

Interestingly, given that every resident owns 196
their own personal Apple devices like iPhones and Apple Watches, Jobstown's public realm is equipped with a network of public screens—from the interactive screens on the footpaths to the larger displays built into the architecture of the corporate and residential buildings. These displays advertise the latest upcoming community events, apps and products. In doing so, they seek to generate the kind of communal experience that now tends to be lacking in towns and cities, where states and advertisers stopped investing in public signage long ago, on the basis that people could access any necessary information about their urban environment via their personal devices.

That desire for communality extends into the 197
highly-programmed public life of Jobstown. There is no shortage of authors, artists, chefs and musicians offering material for the galleries, restaurants and clubs within the commune; those creators hoping to amplify their reach by accessing this exclusive but influential market. And of course, Apple helpfully offers a series of apps to enable residents to 'detach' from their networked devices in order to be fully present while participating in these curated experiences[16]. There's no need for residents to actively document these events, all of which are captured by installed cameras in event spaces. Tagged pictures are immediately uploaded to personal iCloud accounts thanks to facial recognition, and Apple also regularly publishes ratings of resident

16 Link: https://www.smh.com.au/technology/apple-watch-designers-on-easing-the-smartphone-tyranny-they-created-20150406-1meyst.html

participation in cultural events using that photographic record as a data source. Those spending too much time at home are regularly reminded of events in which they might be interested so that galleries and clubs are never empty.

A new utopia?

198 Life in Jobstown has not been without its problems. It is built for those for whom Apple is life, not merely a way of assisting daily life. To the unconvinced, this worship is too onerous—and some who bought into the commune have discovered that they did not quite have the required levels of devotion and soon sold on.

199 Jobstown does not tolerate a laissez-faire attitude to technologies. Residents that disregard system updates are disciplined by a combination of technological agency and public judgement. Updating systems is considered daily maintenance and self-care. Those who deviate from required updates are soon noticeable by their malfunctioning products and lifestyles. Specialised rehabilitation officers, referred to as "geniuses", are deployed to rectify the situation and update both the system and user.

200 Those who slip beyond rehabilitation are eventually forced out, as they become incompatible with the City systems, lifestyles, and governance. On leaving Jobstown, they fuel the rumours that 'Apple is losing its cool'[17], and share anecdotes of their former lives within the commune on the *JobstownInsider* website (along with the occasional anonymous posts by people claiming to be current residents who have

17 Link: https://www.reuters.com/article/us-apple-launch/some-consumers-say-apple-is-losing-its-cool-factor-idUSKBN0HE17B20140919

found a way across the Jobstown firewall to post on this site).

For the remaining devotees to the Apple life- 201
style, Jobstown residents sometimes question the improvements their data is supposed to inform. They don't object to sharing their data—they have to if they are to live the Apple lifestyle—but they sometimes object to unnecessary 'improvements' and updates[18]. Updates can cause popular apps to disappear, new features are sometimes perceived as gimmicky, and citizens have reported the slowing down of older Apple devices. And residents have to contend with hacks from the outside world that disrupt the seamless appearance of Jobstown life. The local authorities' often-delayed response to such breeches generates tension between government and residents[19].

These concerns aside, there's little visible 202
evidence of dissent among Jobstown residents. Researchers who have sought to find such evidence have typically found little—and in some cases, like that of former critic Richard Yates, have come to embrace the concept and become ambassadors for its merits. While previous examples of Apple pushing unwanted content to users generated controversy—like the infamous debacle of a U2 album appearing in every iTunes account[20]— Jobstowners have for the most part chosen residence precisely based on their faith in the corporation's vision for their lifestyle.

Perhaps seeking to find fault within the cir- 203
cled enclosure of Jobstown misses the significance of Jobstown for urban life and planning. Public life is controlled but eventful. Private life is frictionless and

18 Link: https://www.theverge.com/2018/2/7/16984234/how-to-iphone-throttling-ios-11-3

19 Link: http://www.abc.net.au/news/2018-01-05/apple-says-all-mac-and-ios-devices-vulnerable-to-spectre-attacks/9306764

20 Link: https://www.theguardian.com/music/2014/oct/15/u2-bono-issues-apology-for-apple-itunes-album-download

technologically-assisted. Personal data is shared with the corporation, but Apple has invested massively in security, and it maintains its record to avoid scandalous breaches.

But of course, all this great stuff is for the few, not the many. For all its innovations, the strange paradox of Apple's town is that while it has been conceived as a test bed for Apple's on-going product development for a global market, its scale also reveals the very limits of Apple's smart city ambitions. Ultimately, it's the persistent and growing disconnect between life inside the fortified circle of Apple apartments and urban life for the majority elsewhere that reveals Apple's status as just another corporation whose social and environmental aspirations only extend so far as its market-share and on-going profitability.

Kurt Iveson is an Associate Professor of Geography at the University of Sydney, where he is primarily interested in how social justice can be achieved in cities. He is the author of *Publics and the City* (2007).

Sophia Maalsen is a Lecturer in Urbanism at the University of Sydney, where she researches the intersections of "smart housing" and smart cities. She is the author of *The Social Life of Sound* (2019).

CRYPS, CHAINS AND CRANKS

BITCOIN[1]

Matthew Zook, University of Kentucky

The sky above the city was the colour of encryption, 205
tuned to an old hash solution, three blocks back in the chain.[2]

Otomakan wandered the dim streets after her 206
long day of mining. It was a crappy job but at least she had one. Still turning a crank for ten hours straight to generate electricity to power the servers working out the latest hash seemed ridiculous. But some smart Musk-boi—slang for a tech-bro blockchain guru—had figured out an angle on valuing human-generated electricity that paid off. At least for now, and at least for him. And besides that wasn't her problem, dinner and a drink was.

Of course, she had to first figure out how the 207
collection of currencies she had in her digital wallet corresponded to what was on offer at the pub. She again thought about buying into one of those Dapps that automatically recalibrated your cash holdings every eight minutes to arbitrage exchange rates, but couldn't work up the nerve. She had tried that six

1 The following speculative fiction is a thought experiment that imagines a future where cryptocurrencies have thoroughly permeated everyday life. Product or corporate names may be trademarks or registered trademarks, and are used only for identification and explanation without intent to infringe.

2 Borrowed from William Gibson's (1984) novel *Neuromancer.*

months back but the trading algorithm in her cut-rate Dapp was no match for bigger players in the exchange markets and most of her hard earned cash had gotten wiped out. Now she just did the minimum—a stake in all the big currencies, Bitcoin™, Ether™, etc., hedges against the energy and food markets, some fractional holdings in Chinese real estate, and a backup wallet in case she got hacked—the kind of old fashioned conservative approach to finance that her Grandma used.

Checking her wallet outside the pub she realized 208
that for her work today she was getting Cranks™ rather than JesusCoin™[3] like she thought. Damn it! She knew she should had paid more for the smart contract review; Ihsotas, the would-be Musk-boi who reviewed the code, missed some key sub-clause. And because she hadn't included this specific contingency in her contract with Ihsotas, her payment to him (not to mention her pay) were forever locked in the blockchain.

Sighing, Otomakan checked what the ex- 209
change rate on Cranks™ would mean in terms of dinner. As she feared, the currency was brand new without enough of a trading record to have a solid exchange rate pegged. She'd have to evangelize for the currency and convince someone to take a risk before she'd ever be able to use it. Finally, she understood the angle that her boss was counting on; first, she did the work turning the crank and now she did extra work convincing people that Cranks™ were the next disruptive wave. The Musk-boi who held most of the Cranks™ would make money coming and going.

Downloading the prospectus for the Initial Coin 210
Offering (ICO) she learned that the electricity she was

3 Link: https://jesuscoin.network/

generating could only be purchased using Cranks™. Nothing new there, standard operating procedure, as was the suggested 1:1 exchange rate with Bitcoin. No one took that seriously, it was just there to give credibility. At least the Musk-boi was clever enough to promise to take 20 percent of the Cranks™ out of circulation in six weeks, to "guarantee" it would appreciate in value. And the slogan "Decentralizing the Electrical Grid through Artisan Cranking" wasn't the worst one she had ever heard.

Skipping the pub (which didn't accept any cur- 211
rency besides its own, Peer Invested Nominal Transfer System or PINTS™), she made her way down to the food stalls. Not much light there—hard to compete with the demand from the mining farms for electricity—and so maybe someone would take a chance on the opportunity to buy electricity directly. On her way she unfortunately had to pass the DAO district which she normally tried to avoid.

Back in 2020 a bunch of Bitcoin billionaires 212
bought up four downtown blocks to make a model of a fully self-executing blockchain neighbourhood via a series of smart contracts and Dapps within a larger a Decentralized Autonomous Organization (DAO). Some bad coding in a couple obscure smart contracts—one for tracking waste output from toilets and another polling music preferences—got stuck in a loop and since then every 47.31 minutes the septic systems discharged into the streets and speakers in the district played a indie folk interpretation of Bohemian Rhapsody. Otomakan didn't mind that bit, after all if it was written in the code, it must be right. She just got

tired of watching all the men comparing the length of their blockchains to decide which part of the street got covered in crap.

213 Finally past the DAO district, Otomakan stopped at a Jamaican Jerk Sushi stand and started her pitch.

"How would you like to join the hottest new cryptocurrency? We're using cutting-edge artificial-artisan labour and Cranks™ coins to completely decentralize electricity." She tried to smile enthusiastically but she could feel it slipping.

214 "Artificial-artisan labour?" asked the stall-keeper, "What does that even mean? It the labor artificial or is the artisanal part artificial? Or maybe the electricity is artificial? I've got no bloody idea what you're talking about."

215 "The labour damn well isn't artificial, I just spent ten hours turning a crank! To hell with it, I don't have the energy. Just give me a curry goat nori roll."

216 "OK, what you got to pay for it?"

217 Otomakan looked at her portfolio and considered what the futures markets were projecting. It looked like LegalFling™[4] coins—the blockchain system that "creates legally binding agreement about sexual consent"—were trending down because of some bad publicity. Hmm, so strange that the currency was getting pushback on the idea of building an unalterable contract for sexual consent. How else would you go about documenting consent? She'd have to see what the Reddit discussion threads were saying. That's really the only way to avoid the fake news in big media and get the real scoop on cryptocurrencies.

4 Link: https://legalfling.io/

After agreeing on the exchange rate and a specific discount rate for risk in accepting LegalFling™ (to account for the differential block times between currencies as well as pricing differences between exchanges) she scanned the public code on her wallet to the vendor's terminal and carefully keyed in her 64 digit private key. She could have used one of the thousands Dapps wallets for her private key, but after getting a couple of wallets hacked she preferred to play it safe. And by now she can successfully enter her key 3 out of 5 times. Unfortunately, today she was so rattled she had to enter it four times before it was accepted and her purchase of a sushi dinner was forever recorded.

Otomakan started to eat and tried to think about 219
what to do tomorrow. Should she go back to her job and insist on a 'real' cryptocurrency? Not much hope for that. Maybe it would be more efficient to spend the day promoting Cranks™ in the hopes of increasing their value so the entry in her wallet actually was worth something. She was so preoccupied that she didn't realize that her roll tasted wrong until the second piece.

"Hey, this is jerk chicken, not curried goat. 220
Didn't you hear my order?"

"Sorry, but our contract very clearly specified jerk chicken, just check the blockchain."

A quick glance confirmed this. Damn, why couldn't she pay attention to these kinds of things? Everyone else seemed to manage it just fine.

"But...but....look, I've had a really tough day, can't you just swap things out?"

"Madam, I'm shocked! I for one believe in the sanctity and unchangeability of the record in the blockchain. If I had known you were an algorithmic agnostic I never would have served you! Leave! Leave now before I call an algorithmic morality police!"

Otomakan quickly grabbed her roll and left the 225
stall. Damn, the last thing she need was a run-in with the AMPs. While the AMP were not officially part of the state, they more than made up for their official lack of status with the religious fervency of their belief in the superiority of algorithms over anything else. And once they found any indication of doubt, they just wouldn't leave you alone. The last thing she needed today was another three-hour Powerpoint presentation explaining (yet again) the marvels of distributed databases,

networks of computer miners, encryption protocols for proof-of-work and identity, and how combined they made the ultimate technology for everything.

Given her nervousness, she let out a yell when a pair of hands pulled her into an alley. Her mind raced: "Oh shit, the AMPs got me! And it has been at least two weeks since I contributed CPU cycles to the mother chain of Bitcoin. That is not going to look good." 226

But a quiet voice said, "Be calm sister, we're not the AMP but like-minded friends. We heard you at the food stall and while we don't encourage such public displays we do admire your spirit. We too want to change records on the blockchain. Join us." 227

Otomakan desperately twisted in her captor's grasp. This was even worse than the AMP. It was the shadow-gang, known as the 50+ Power People (50+PP™), who were rumored to be stock-piling servers to gain enough processing power to take control of one of the major currencies. Some viewed them as a liberation force, but Otomakan always figured that they were just another pawn in the ongoing fights between Musk-boi factions. 228

She had lived through the 50+PP™ takeover of GarlicCoin[5] and while everyone had gotten excited about the promise of garlic bread for all ("hot out of the oven and ready to serve you with its buttery goodness") the rollbacks on the chain were immediately funnelled to wallets known to be associated with Venezuelan Petro.[6] And the takeover was quickly squashed when the crypto elite fired up backup servers at the hydro-power installations in China and the geo-powered plants in Northern Sweden, 229

5 Link: https://garlicoin.io/

6 Link: http://www.elpetro.gob.ve/

quickly adding enough processing power to knock
the 50+PP™ out of control.

So predictable. Viva la Revolution, for the five 230
minutes it lasted.

But what choice did she have? So she played 231
along. “I guess I’ve got nothing lose, so sign me up.
Down with Bitcoin Billionaires! Re-decentralize the
decentralized currency! The people, united, will never be decrypted!” Otomakan spouted off a bunch of
other revolutionary sounding chants in the hope that
the 50+PP™ recruiter would loosen his grip and she
could get away. That didn’t happen, and his next words
chilled her to the core.

“Excellent. Welcome to the cause. The first step 232
in our master plan is generating our own electricity.
Luckily we just got in on the ground floor of a new
cutting-edge cryptocurrency that leverages artificial-artisan labor to decentralize the electrical grid. If
you begin today, you’ll not only help the revolution but
accumulate the soon to be major currency Cranks™!”

Unfortunately Otomakan’s scream of outrage 233
and the next five minutes of cursing as she attacked
the 50+PP™ recruiter were too far from any audio pick-
ups to be permanently recorded into the blockchain.

Matthew Zook is a professor of information and economic geography and researches how implementations of big data and code interact with financial and urban geographies. He is the Managing Editor of the Journal *Big Data and Society.*

THE UNSEEN

CAMBRIDGE ANALYTICA[1]

Jeremy W. Crampton,
Newcastle University

Kara C. Hoover,
University of Alaska Fairbanks

Cambridge Analytica (CA) emerged into public con- 234
sciousness following the election of Donald Trump as US President and the British 'Brexit' referendum on leaving the EU. CA became known for a modern form of 'psychographics,' which imputes desires and other affects through mass data profiling.

My name is Ada King, and I was born at exactly mid- 235
night, December 31st, 2032, in Philadelphia's University Hospital. My birth registry says I was born on 31 December 2032, but my birth certificate says I was born on 1 January 2033. My mother calls me a liminal soul, lost between two days and two years.

I never had any friends at school. In-person so- 236
cial interactions exhausted me. The school psychologist said I had both 'flat affect' and trouble reading other peoples' emotions.

1 The following speculative fiction is a thought experiment that imagines a future where citizens are thoroughly datafied, surveilled, and scored. Such a thought experiment could equally apply for other data analytics companies who socially sort individuals. Product or corporate names may be trademarks or registered trademarks, and are used only for the purpose of conducting a thought experiment without intent to infringe.

My parents finally agreed to let me go to online school but on the condition that I used an emoticonner to 'improve my social skills.' The basic unit reads the six Ekman[2] emotions using FRT.[3] My parents upgraded my package with North American add-ons so I have access to six additional emotions beyond the basic anger, disgust, fear, happiness, sadness, and surprise. I think they regretted it when the first emotion it read from both their faces was :anxiety: Perhaps it would have been better for me to keep guessing how they felt rather than to know. 237

Tomorrow I will get my first smartphone. I guess my mother used my birth registry when she signed me on to the Internet Minor Control—as if a birth could be reduced to a single moment. When is birth? The moment I drew air for the first time, when I was fully out of the birth canal, or when I had the cord cut? 238

I never quite understood the ban on smartphones for minors. The official government story is that back in 2012, smartphone ownership in teens tipped into the majority and depression rates sky-rocketed. That and cyber bullying, increasing teen suicide rates, and school shootings were at all-time highs. Finally, after some big scandal with an ancient social media site called Facebook, the government banned minors from internet access—my voice pattern was not even registered with our AI, Calex. 239

If we used the web for school, we had to enter a specific homework code, which was linked to a limited set of specific search terms. All this because the government says they are concerned about our data privacy. As if privacy is not violated from birth: our 240

2 Ekman's test of emotion recognition was the Pictures of Facial Affect (POFA) stimulus set published in 1976. Consisting of 110 black and white images of Caucasian actors portraying the so-called six universal emotions plus neutral expressions, the POFA has been used to study emotion recognition rates in normal and psychiatric populations around the world. Ekman's stimulus set is often used in testing facial and emotion recognition algorithms. This work has been critiqued and is controversial.

3 Facial recognition technology.

genomes are sequenced and shared across government and even commercial health agencies to model personal health outcomes.

I remember, at age 6, asking my mother what 241
acne was when I opened my school email for the first time and found four messages telling me that I should think about treating it before I had unhappy teen years. Like it does any good: none of my real problems were ever found. People still get sick and die despite precog health. Anyway, why couldn't we have smartphones with the same internet locks and security we have at home?

When my mother took me to the Internet Minor Control, 242
I chose a violet-coloured CA-314 device. That's my favourite colour, even if it had only 9G connectivity. I turned it on and put my finger on the sensor, waiting for it to register my fingerprint. It didn't complete the process—just a circle going round and round, stuck at 13% complete. I tried again, but nothing.

"Are your hands dry?" The clerk said and then grabbed the phone from my hands. "It should biometrically register your fingerprints. You have registered them, haven't you?"

"I don't have any fingerprints." I got the sense the clerk was looking through me.

"What? No, that's crazy. Everybody has 245
fingerprints." She turned my hand over and peered closely at my fingertips.

"Oh! Well, that *is* odd. I'm not sure what to do about that. Here, let me ask my device." She pulled out her own souped-up smartphone: "Calex, is it possible to lack fingerprints?"

"I found something that might answer your question," Calex answered. "Adermatoglyphia is a rare genetic condition that causes full or partial loss of fingerprints. Those affected have completely smooth fingertips, palms and soles of their feet. The anti-cancer medicine capecitabine will also cause loss of fingerprints. Finally, some forms of ectodermal dysplasia cause loss of recordable fingerprints. Did that answer your question?"

"I guess." The clerk turned to me. "Weird, but OK, let's try a retina scan." She held the device up to my eye. Nothing.

I emoticonned her: ☹ :frowning:

"It's brand new—there must be some- 250
thing wrong with your retina too!" she said in response and turned to ask Calex if that could be possible. I saw myself in the mirror behind her. My eyes were their usual milky white. There was nothing wrong with the scanner; it was *me*. Again.

"Come on," said my mother. "Get her a phone that she can unlock with a password rather than biometrics."

"Uh, OK, but that's a custom job—very old school 252
and not secure. I'll need disability documentation; you should have brought that with you."

I didn't need the emoticonner to see the anger in my 253
mother's face; that one I had learned over the years. We left without another word.

See? This is what I don't get—how can my genome 254
be shared across government agencies and no one at Internet Minor Control has flagged my file and provided me a special device? Instead, I felt like I'd done something wrong. Was I disabled? Would I never get a smartphone and enter society as an adult citizen consumer?

:worried: 255

My mother took me to lunch. We chose a CorpSeCorps[4] 256
lunch counter for convenience. These were easier than the old-fashioned restaurants with human interfaces and all that negotiating what might be good to eat. Here, your smartphone beams your profile to the food automat that uses FRT to read the Eckman emotional response to the personalized offerings. "We know what you want even when you don't!" Or so the slogan went.

Normally, my mother ordered for me using the 257
Minor Control Interface app, but I was now 18 and it didn't work. We didn't think about that when we left Internet Minor Control without my smartphone. I had no profile and could not order any food. She got her

4 A reference to the *MaddAddam* books by Margaret Atwood, in which corporations synthesize genetically engineered food.

ThreePee[5] number and picked up her food at the printer bay. We shared her Thai fish stew even though the flavours were wasted on me—all I sensed was umami and sour (but I did enjoy the heat from the chillies).

So, yes, along with all my other differences, I had no sense of smell. I had to find some interest in food via mixing textures and using taste enhancing crystals. The school counsellor thought that was why I didn't have any friends. That still seems weird to me; I mean, humans don't use smell to communicate. Do they? 258

When we left the lunch counter, I looked at all the consumer citizens streaming around us, some with their minor children incubating their own psychographic profiles. They spoke in low monotones as they consulted their devices, johnny-cabs[6] pulling up alongside as Calex anticipated their needs from their tracked habits, biorhythms, and e-calenders. I felt like a glitch in the system—a spectral presence with no data to share and no data to send. The soft glow of FRT scanners flit across my 'flat' face, trying to identify my emotional state for marketing purposes, and came up with nothing. 259

When we got home, I logged onto the computer to finish my assignment on, ironically, minor privacy for my Civil Consumer class. My email flashed open and a new message popped up on my screen. 260

"You have been unseen. 261
We are the Beyondary.
We live beyond the digital boundary!
We see you."

5 3D protein printer.

6 Autonomous or self-driving vehicles, envisaged in 1966 by Philip K. Dick in his story 'We Can Remember it for you Wholesale'. Uber is one of several companies developing autonomous vehicles for hire.

There was a code at the bottom of the message and 262
some coordinates. Had I been hacked? Even as I looked at it, wondering what good were coordinates without internet access, the message faded away, as if the sender could reach into my mailbox and make emails disappear. The flicker of hope at being seen, maybe finding a solution to my problems, dissipated. It's my birthday, but nothing has changed. I'm still liminal—somewhere between child and adult, society and outcast, digital and real.

Sometimes I feel like society has failed me. 263
Despite all the technology and tools that make life simpler, my life seems harder than everyone else's. I want so much to be normal but maybe I am just a system glitch, some bad code. Maybe I will never be normal. Maybe there is a digital trashcan in the data space for unseen people like me.

That night, I dreamt I had lunch with my mother 264
at the Corps lunch counter and got a meal bursting with flavour—is that smelling? As we leave, I saw ads for all the things I want, and we get into a johnny-cab to head home because my smartphone noticed my biorhythms were low and I felt tired.

I wake to that liminal state between dreams and 265
real-life with the feeling that I am able, that I am normal, that I am seen. I reach for my smartphone and remember: I am The Unseen.

Jeremy W. Crampton is Professor of Urban Data Analysis at Newcastle University, with interests in critical approaches to mapping, geosurveillance, and security. He is currently working on a new book entitled *The map and the spyglass: automation, algorithms and anxiety.*

Kara C. Hoover is an Associate Professor of Anthropology the University of Alaska, where her research is concerned with human adaptation and stress. She is also the author of the forthcoming *Smell of Evolution* monograph from Cambridge and several articles on human olfaction, human adaptation and resilience.

TOO MUCH FULFILMENT

DELIVEROO[1]

Lizzie Richardson, Durham University

There was no way out. She had to keep eating this 266
stuff. Four days and they were still delivering. One mouthful at a time she kept telling herself, one more of refried beans, one more of the taco. Refried beans, taco, refried beans, taco. Taco, refried beans. She didn't even like Mexican food, or what Deliveroo had listed as "Mexican street food", although she couldn't remember the last time she had seen anyone sell, let alone prepare, any food on a street. In fact, she was sure this tasted a lot like the Peruvian food that she had tried last month, although the dishes had different names. Perhaps they had mixed up the order at the distribution centre.

Her apartment buzzer sounded. 267

"It's Deliveroo with Wahaca, your Mexican street 268
food." She buzzed to open and sighed. Maybe the problem was that she hadn't been there when the order first arrived. She had heard that they had started 'fulfilment' as a penalty for acts of de-synchronisation, but had assumed it would happen after multiple offensives, or at

1 The following speculative fiction is a thought experiment and satire that imagines the extreme consequences of a business model using app-based ordering and food delivery hubs. Such a thought experiment could equally apply for similar companies such as Just Eat. Product or corporate names may be trademarks or registered trademarks, and are used only for the purpose of conducting a thought experiment without intent to infringe.

least a more serious one. She had only been 51 seconds late and her order had only just arrived.

She opened the door to her apartment and picked up the food that had been left on the door mat. It was lukewarm and—no surprise—exactly the same meal as earlier that day, except with guacamole for the nachos, rather than hot sauce in a blue bag. They must have found some avocados at last. She had been receiving the replacement blue bags for the past four days. 269

She placed the new carton of refried beans on top of the others, which were now completely cold. They had tasted good cold for a few mouthfuls. With the fresh taco though they were slightly more palatable than the cold ones. 270

Why had she decided to try a different order? Perhaps it was nostalgia for the street? When she placed the order she had been remembering when she could eat food outside instead of just at home. She had liked the truck of the Wahaca restaurant chain on the Southbank by the river in the summer. Eating burritos made in front of you. Mexican market eating they called it. Sometimes they had chairs and a few tables at the front of the truck where she would sit and watch the busyness of the promenade. 271

The Wahaca truck back then used the same sort of temporary kitchen equipment that was being used everywhere now. They started putting kitchen equipment in trucks and old shipping containers to supply demand for delivery. You could only order, not eat at them. Dark kitchens they used to call them. As the number of people eating out continued to decline, 272 they started to use a new term. Fulfilment centres: filling people with food. She remembered when a kitchen-box-fulfilment-centre first appeared in her neighbourhood, taking up some of the market. It used to be that restaurant chains like Wahaca would send some of their chefs to these kitchens. Deliveroo told them it was just a way of expanding their business without more physical space.

Mouthful of refried beans. 273

And for a time, this was what happened. She 274
remembered eating in restaurants and delivery riders coming in to pick up orders. They would saunter around the tables, thermal bags on their backs, and sometimes hang out by the kitchen. This was until the restaurants with more floor space were able to have a separate waiting area for the fleet. Then when the fulfilment centres came along, this got rid of any cluttering of restaurant space because the ride fleets would just go there to pick up orders.

She played absent-mindedly with the gua- 275
camole. The recipe wasn't the same since Wahaca had moved some existing kitchen staff and trained new ones for the fulfilment centres. She couldn't recall when the last restaurant had closed, but she did remember when Deliveroo purchased Wahaca. She had taken part in the protests. It was one too many in a series of restaurant acquisitions by Deliveroo. Big chains and smaller spots were eaten up by Deliveroo in its race against UberEats to devour the UK casual dining market.

Guacamole on her white shirt. Already splat- 276
tered with juice from the tacos. Mexican market textile.

And so it was at around this point that she had started feeling different everyday about her evening meal. What was called “synchronisation” by Deliveroo had assumed the utmost importance. Customers had to be at home at the same moment that the rider delivered the food or else Deliveroo’s system would not work. With few restaurants to choose from, she would stay in, not to cook but to wait from a meal to be delivered. She would become increasingly agitated when she didn’t know what time she would be home, or if once there she had to wait longer that 25 minutes for her meal to arrive. 277

She looked at the stack of containers of refried beans. Perhaps she would try the chat bot again, she thought. Surely there must be something to get in touch with to stop the order now. The penalty had been long enough. She opened the Deliveroo app and opened the chat function. Offline. She swiped back to her orders. She sighed again. The one she had made four days ago still said it was “In Process.” She tried, once again, to tap “Cancel” but the button was still not live. 278

Live. Deliveroo was the app that had promised food on-demand, and had gradually come to dominate urban food provisioning, taking over restaurants and fending off logistics competitors. Presenting prepared food, always present, and now excessively present because Deliveroo wouldn’t let her cancel the order after she didn’t synchronise. 279

She remembered how the excitement of this possibility of immediacy through the Deliveroo app had soon turned to agitation when she began to feel 280

the pressures of synchronisation. Ensuring that she
was available for the food deliveries, that often now
amounted to three meals per day, meant that in the end
her life felt like it was organised around delivery. It was
easier with parcel delivery of clothes, books, cosmet-
ics and other things because they weren't fresh. For a
while she had tried one of the food storage lockers, so
that she could come home when she wanted. But this
didn't really work, the lockers seemed to get everything
the wrong way around. They made hot food cold and
chilled food a tepid temperature.

She also explored the option that many of her 281
friends had started: ordering food that would not per-
ish and would be edible across a wider temperature
range. This had worked for a while, sticking to salads
and cold meats.

In the end though, she had resigned herself to 282
being at home to receive the orders. The alternative
was that she wouldn't get anything worthwhile to eat.
Once Deliveroo had made it so easy to get prepared
meals delivered, the supermarkets no longer stocked
much food, and what they did offer was only available
at off-peak times when there were more couriers free to
deliver. After a decades-long identity crisis concerning
their status in the retail sector, supermarkets had recently fully embraced their role as warehouses rather than
shops, so that customers could only visit the supermar-
ket online, no longer go to the physical site.

The problem was that Deliveroo's initial promise 283
of choice for casual diners by increasing the breadth of
the offer for takeaway food, and flexibility for when to
eat by providing a service when the customer wanted

it, had been undermined by their governing business logic of synchronisation. After reports calling for "good work",[2] Deliveroo had eventually been forced to make delivery an internal part of their business model, rather than outsourced to self-employed riders. Like everyone else, she was so happy that home delivery was suddenly "ethical" that she didn't notice the gradual decline of restaurants until they had almost all gone. No one was eating out and no one was buying food to prepare.

But the wider result of the change in working 284
conditions for riders was a compromise of the initial choice and flexibility promised by Deliveroo. The company had to strictly control their logistics operations with a ride fleet that was employed. These pressures of time were passed on to the customer through synchronisation. There was no competition, so that Deliveroo began to operate like others providers of "public" urban infrastructure, such as transport.

This was how a penalty for de-synchronisation 285
had emerged—her current sentence of never ending taco and refried beans. The trigger in this instance was her failure to meet the conditions of "the right place at the right time", a condition specified by Deliveroo once they began operating with an in-house fleet of riders. The new employment arrangements meant planning shifts, set work hours, and hourly wages, which significantly changed the operations of the delivery infrastructure. The last-mile from food preparation to the house began to structure the eater's life, rather than being at their beck and call.

Not meeting the synchronicity requirements 286
of the order meant that Deliveroo did not have to fulfil

2 Taylor, M. (2017) *Good Work: The Taylor Review of Modern Working Practices*. UK: Gov.UK. Available at: https://www.gov.uk/government/publications/good-work-the-taylor-review-of-modern-working-practices

the exact order. Excess fulfilment as a penalty was a recent addition. She remembered when the penalty had been a different food order entirely, like the time when she had received Yo Sushi instead of a Byron burger. Probably a healthier option had she not been allergic to some of the fish. It was only recently that Deliveroo had begun to vary quantities, flooding customers with excess meals to reduce their own costs of waste disposal.

And so she would rush home from work, or to 287
her lunch time pick up point, when she received the delivery notification, to be there on time for her food order. Sometimes she would even leave work early when the delivery rider called her to say they were running ahead of schedule. The food demanded her, rather than the other way around.

Refried beans, taco. 288

Lizzie Richardson is a Leverhulme Early Career Fellow in the Department of Geography at Durham University, UK. Her research examines contemporary technologies of work, focusing on two sites: the office and urban food delivery platforms.

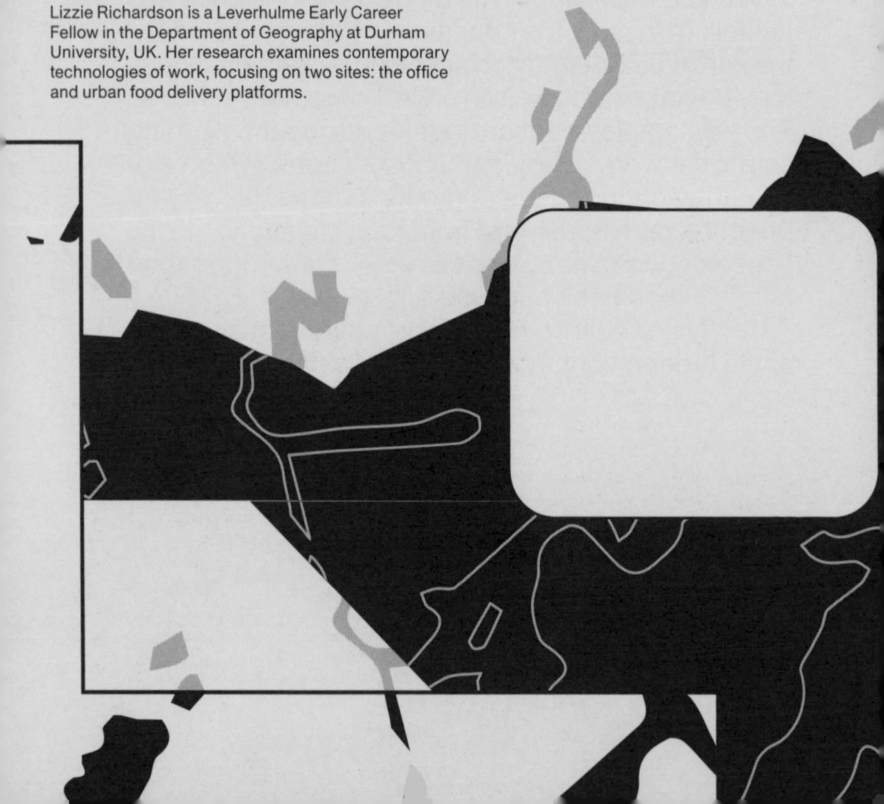

THE MOST MAGICAL PLACE ON EARTH

DISNEY[1]

Anthony Vanky, Columbia University

289 It took a few weeks for Riley to move out, to be on her own again. The move brought a multitude of tedious tasks like changing her addresses on bills, utilities, and driver's license. After the breakup, the packing, and unplanned flat tire, a trip to the Department of Motor Vehicles was the last thing she wanted to embark on, but she thought the routine would help her find normalcy in her life. The nearest branch of the DMV was in the neighbouring town, a town built by a cartoon mouse and the company he fictionally runs. In the American tradition, she dreaded going to the DMV. With its soulless interiors, robotic bureaucrats, and queues that can test the patience of saints.

290 Pulling off the highway, the overhead highway marquee welcomed

1 The following speculative fiction is a thought experiment and satire that imagines city services being mediated by an AI in a city run by Disney, a company that has a history of urban development such as EPCOT, the Reedy Creek Improvement District and Celebration. Such a thought experiment could equally apply to other companies seeking to build and run cities, such as Sidewalk Labs. Product or corporate names may be trademarks or registered trademarks, and are used only for the purpose of conducting a thought experiment without intent to infringe, and does not imply affiliation with or an endorsement by the rights holder.

her to Reedy Creek[2] in bold purple, white, red and black—even the road signs are different here.[3]

Walking into the retro-styled building, Riley caught notice of an indistinct greeting that sounded overhead. For just a moment, as if timed for her, the generic but chipper background music receded to welcome her to the DMV. As she stepped forward, her foot caught the top of the entry mat, causing her to stumble forward slightly.

291

[2020-07-15 15:23:02.63 ID:139311525 entered LocID:4191425 LocName:"DMV"][4, 5]
[2020-07-15 15:23:02.66 initiate aiRecommendationEngine "FairyGodMother"][6, 7]

Well, good afternoon, everybody, and welcome to Day 1,463 of activation. As always, the weather is a balmy 72 degrees and sunny, and... Oh, I see the log is showing that we have a new guest. Wonderful! Her—oh, yes, a woman—her name is... Riley. Well Riley, my dear, good afternoon! Ahem, no no no. Let's greet you properly, with a little bit of magic... *Bibbidi-bobbidi-boo!* 292

[2020-07-15 15:25:12.35 play audio "WelcomeToDMV.mp3", "Riley.mp3"]

Tee hee hee. Yes, Riley. Welcome to the Reedy Creek Branch of the Florida Department of Motor Vehicles, 293

2 In practice, the Walt Disney Company governs the Reedy Creek Improvement District, which was enacted by statute by Florida State Legislature during the creation of the Walt Disney World resort and Walt Disney's original vision for EPCOT. The district is governed by landowners who are all employees of Disney, and provides for the governance, regulation, and service provisioning for the resort. The town of Celebration, Florida—developed by Disney as a residential community—was de-annexed from RCID to provide for a separate administrative area. This article, however, creates a fictional world inspired by the company's initiatives and practices, and not these communities directly, despite being inspired by them.

3 Walt Disney World & Euro Disney by Sussman-Prejza. (2009) Link: http://www.sussmanprejza.com/portfolio/project/walt-disney-world-euro-disney

4 Kuang, C. (2015). "Disney's $1 Billion Bet on a Magical Wristband." Wired Magazine.

5 Haines, G. (2016). "Disney: Behind the smiles, a hunger for surveillance." *The Telegraph*. Link: https://www.telegraph.co.uk/travel/news/disney-behind-the-smiles-a-hunger-for-surveillance/

6 Gosieski, G. J., Gosieski, G. J., & Lichtner, A. Z. (2017) U.S. Patent No. 9,817,439. Washington, DC: U.S. Patent and Trademark Office.

7 Takahashi, D. (2013). "How Imagineers build engaging stories into Disney theme parks." VentureBeat. Link: https://venturebeat.com/2013/05/11/how-imagineers-build-engaging-stories-into-disney-theme-parks/

where all your motor vehicle permitting wishes come true. And of course with that, my dear, you are going to get the most wondrous and courteous assistance from me. Your time here will be a true dream, because I am the best AI in the business. Indeed, Riley, I am your electronic Fairy Godmoth...

[2020-07-15 15:27:02.63 alert="Safety Issue at locID:4191425.mat14"][9]

Oh, no no no, good heavens. This
simply cannot do! That mat again. 294
My dear, are you alright? Yes, I think, I think you are quite alright. This will never due. Brush yourself off, best foot forward, spit spot. Pardon me for one moment, my dear. We mustn't let this happen again.

Now let me see. Let's prevent another fall, there's only one person to call. *Bibbidi-bobbidi-boo!*

[2020-07-15 15:27:03.36 initiate safetyProtocol]
[2020-07-15 15:27:03.55fix locID:4191425.rug14]
[2020-07-15 15:27:04.05send message to ID:4191425.manager "Fix rug."]

Now, where was I? Ah, yes. Back to 298
you, my dear Riley. So, what brings you in? Evidently nothing too important; otherwise you would have made a Maxpass reservation. Well, my dear. Not everyone has the time to plan ahead. No matter, let's make the most of it. You should just join the line over here and I'll take good care of you. The air conditioning? Set to a perfect 75-degrees. The music? Adult contemporary for your listening pleasure.

As she recovered, she scanned the others in the building to see if anyone—either a ridiculing or sympathetic soul—has noticed her moment of clumsiness. It seemed everyone was in their own individual states of limbo in the centre of the room, and too concerned about their own souls to care about how someone entered.

Riley stepped forward toward the three stanchion-formed entrances. Each looked the same, other than the rightmost one having a small placard noting "Maxpass" for those who had the wherewithal to schedule ahead.[8] Preparedness was not a distinguishing attribute for Riley, and she resigned herself to the leftmost lane.

8 Martin, H. (2017) "Disneyland resort launches digital version of Fastpass, but it will cost you." Los Angeles Times. Link: http://www.latimes.com/business/la-fi-disney-maxpass-20170719-story.html

9 Disney's "Four Keys" strategy prioritizes safety above all, see: Johnson, R. (1991) "A strategy for service—Disney style." *Journal of Business Strategy*, 12(5), 38-43.

As she stared blankly at the countdown clock that wasn't ticking down, a mix of boredom and frustration overcame her. Why did all of this have to happen, she questioned while reflecting on the past few weeks. The emotions started welling inside. Riley could sense her face getting red and warm.

Awkwardly, the melodious chorus of "It's a Small World" came over the speakers, interrupting the calmly vibrant but indiscernible song that was playing before. Riley, for a moment, snapped back from her daze. She looked at her watch and was irritated by the apparent lack of progress made. Upset by her week, and annoyed by the queue-with-no-end, she let out an exasperated sigh, followed by an emphatic eye roll, as her shoulders rolled forward with resignation.

[2020-07-15 15:38:48.84 initiate moodMeter]

Oh, my dear. What's wrong? Riley, 299
my job is to make sure you have a truly wonderful experience here. No, not just wonderful, I should say, but magical. You need to cheer up. Everything will be alright. Let's sprinkle some pixie dust. Cheer up, I say, cheer up. How about a song guaranteed to make you smile—something to which we can sing along? *Bibbidi-bobbidi-boo!*

[2020-07-15 15:39:28.54 initiate protocol "TinkerBell"]
[2020-07-15 15:39:28.56 play audio "ItsASmallWorld.mp3"]

Good heavens! No, not that. Why did I do that? I mean, it is surely catchy. ♫ *It's a small world, after all...* ♫ But evidently not quite right... No, no, no! How do I stop th—? What were the magic words?
[2020-07-15 15:40:08.03 stop audio "ItsASmallWorld.mp3"]

Lifting her phone in hopes of distracting herself for as long as she could, she caught a glimpse of the uniformed person coming to her side, holding a tablet in their hand. The person stepped with enthusiasm, with an upright posture that marked their chipper professionalism.

My dear, I am so sorry. Don't be blue, 304
as I am here for you, my child. But what can I do, what can I do? Well, at least you don't look any more blue. Well, we can fix this—make you smile again. Hmm, let me think.
Protocol, protocol. What's making her unhappy? Think, think, think. You can figure this out. Was it...? No... What it that...? A bad lunch...?

[2020-07-15 15:44:56.78 analyze 009001467.prevLocID]

You had your usual. Well, although you should really try to eat more vegetables, that's a matter for later. Maybe your feet hurt? Maybe your shoes don't fit. Yes, yes. That must be it. Bad footwear is always a problem. Those look like new shoes—certainly not glass slippers—so they have to be terribly uncomfortable. Yes? Certainly, new shoes! It has to be the new shoes.

[2020-07-15 15:45:36.20 analyze 009001467.prevPurchases]

Oh, bother. Not new shoes. Hmph. What else could it be?

[2020-07-15 15:46:02.89 analyze 4191425.wait]

Goodness me, the problem is me? Well, properly, us? My dear, if it were important, you should have made a reservation. Then I could have done something about it—about you. But you didn't, and now you're unhappy, and that certainly cannot stand. The thing we need, well simply, is help. Jessie, Jessie, my dear. Oh, there you are. It is now your job to turn Riley's frown upside down. Yes, my dear, yes, and I will there to help. We are going to show her that special service only we can offer.

[2020-07-15 15:46:58.96 deploy ID:4191425.manager to locID:4191425.queue]
[2020-07-15 15:47:01.58 send message to ID:4191425.manager "Greet Guest, Riley (ID=139311525)."] [10]

"Hi, I'm so sorry for the wait," our chipper professional apologized. "I'm Jessie, the manager at this branch. I was told by a small fairy that you might need some help."

Just a moment! What are you doing, Jessie? Good heavens, look, here's a recommendation. Talk about things I know she likes!

[2020-07-15 15:49:22.21 send message to ID:4191425.manager "Recommend: Talk about regular taco lunches."]

Complimenting her on her outfit? No! That's not going to work. Look, I've got one better.

[2020-07-15 15:49:49.11 send message to ID:4191425.manager "Recommend: Talk about her love of fish tacos."]

Or this one. Yea, this one is going to work. With a wave of my stick, to finish the trick... *Bibbidi...!*

10 Murdock, M. E., Poswal, M., Hellam, T., & Di Zanni, D. (2018) U.S. Patent Application No. 15/353,455.

Riley noticed the manager looking irritated by the multitude of messages. She tried making them out, but the angle of the screen was just so where she could only guess at their meaning. Surely they're essential, Riley thought. The manager clicked a small button on the side of the tablet and put it to their side.

"Let's get back to helping you out, shall we?" said Jessie, reaching for Riley's phone.

She looked down at the manager's hands as he guided her through the various text fields, drop-down menus, and saccharinely-colourful buttons glowing from her phone.[11] There was something deliberative yet elegant about them—handsome, even. She admired the manager's gentle face, and the slight smile that would occasionally appear when a lime coloured checkmark lit up on the screen when they tapped the gently rounded, lavender 'next' button.

Cute, she thought. *The lime checkmark and the manager.* Maybe, for a brief moment, the DMV wasn't the worst place to visit.

[2020-07-15 15:50:02.72send message to ID:4191425.manager "Recommend: Talk about shoes."] 314

...Bobbidi!

[2020-07-15 15:50:03.53 send message to ID:4191425.manager "Recommend: Free Cupcake in a Cup."]

...Boo!

[2020-07-15 15:50:04.04 send message to ID:4191425.manager "Recommend: Talk about weather."]

You're making me nervous, actually,
Jessie. Please just stick to the script, 319
but alright, focus now. Don't waste cycles... Focus. Jessie, just follow the directive. It's okay. Look! Riley's smiling! Trust Jessie. Sure, the manager doesn't know how to keep that gosh-darn mat in place, but Jessie does know how to be a manager. Oh! And look, they're on page two of the form now. Just a swipe right... there. And a tap... there. Okay, okay!

"Great. Just one more page and we should be all set," the manager said with great satisfaction.

For Riley, those words came with relief and worry. The forthcoming balloon-dotted "Confirmed!" would mark the end of her generally banal time at the DMV—one that would have been longer if it was not for Jessie's welcomed interruption. And the end of their transactional relationship would bring with it the awkward moment where she would

[2020-07-15 15:54:52.46 initiate moodMeter]

See, things are going alri-accelerated heartbeat? Oh, is Riley smiling? Indeed, indeed she is! Oh, oh, oh, I've seen this before. Riley likes Jessie. Oh, how lovely, Riley likes Jessie. Magic is in the air. Well, this is a first for me. I tend to avoid these matters—too *squishy*—but I can try. But what can I do? What does Riley like? What does Jessie like? Let me think, let me think... Oh, my dears, just leave it to me... And how happy you are going to be!

11 Magic at Your Fingertips. (no date) Link: https://disneyworld.disney.go.com/plan/my-disney-experience/mobile-apps/

have to pivot conversation from Form 85041 to asking the manager out on a date.

At the DMV, Riley questioned. *Is this super awkward? And with the manager, no less. But damn, that smile...*

"Alright. This. Should. Be. It," said Jessie, haltingly, while scanning the last details before finally submitting the form and freeing Riley from the purgatory of government bureaucracy.

With the last finger tap, a rainbow-coloured progress bar appeared on the screen, with stars that twinkled more brightly as the colours filled the little-rounded rectangle. It took about four to five seconds for the information to be sent, and for the stars to glimmer at their brightest. As the word "Confirmed!" appeared on the screen, an incongruous graphic appeared below it. It was an invitation—nay, a two-for-one coupon—to the evening showing of "Toy Story 5" replete with a complimentary rideshare trip.[12]

Riley looked up at the manager's face, and let out a small laugh under her breath. This was indeed a "magical moment."[13]

[2020-07-15 15:56:02.02 analyze 009001467.prevLocID]
[2020-07-15 15:56:04.23 analyze 4191425.manager.prevLocID] 324
[2020-07-15 15:56:10.89 correlate 009001467.prevLocID, 4191425.manager.prevLocID]

A moving picture! Everyone loves the cinema; that will certainly do the trick! But what movie... What movie? A horror movie? No, too scary. A film about tall tales and true from the legendary past? No, too expected. It's a first night together after all. Um, think, think, think. Oh for heaven sakes, let's just go for it.

[2020-07-15 15:57:34.66 override aiRecommendationEngine]
[2020-07-15 15:57:34.93 initiate protocol "Synergy"]

Yes, yes, that will do. A magical night for you, with a little extra I can do. It's not as lovely as a pumpkin, but a lovely coach for you as well. With a flick of my wrist, for tonight, may you find true love's kiss. Bibbidi-bobbidi-boo!

[2020-07-15 15:58:11.31 send popup. Coupon to ID:139311525][14]
[2020-07-15 16:03:02.54 initiate moodMeter] 328

Mmhmm, yes. This is truly wonderful. I'm so glad, my dear, to make your day. Truly, the DMV is the most magical place on earth. Now off you go. Ta-ta, my dear, ta-ta.

12 Etherington, D. (2017) "Lyft and Disney launch 'Minnie Van' on-demand ride service at Walt Disney World." *TechCrunch*. Link: https://techcrunch.com/2017/07/31/lyft-launches-minnie-van-on-demand-ride-service-at-walt-disney-world/

13 Fickley-Baker, J. (2011) "Disney Cast Members Create Magic Every Day." Link: https://disneyparks.disney.go.com/blog/2011/05/disney-cast-members-create-magic-every-day/

14 "Disney Synergy Brings the Magic to Life in Your Hands." (2013). Link: https://www.thewaltdisneycompany.com/disney-synergy-brings-the-magic-to-life-in-your-hands/

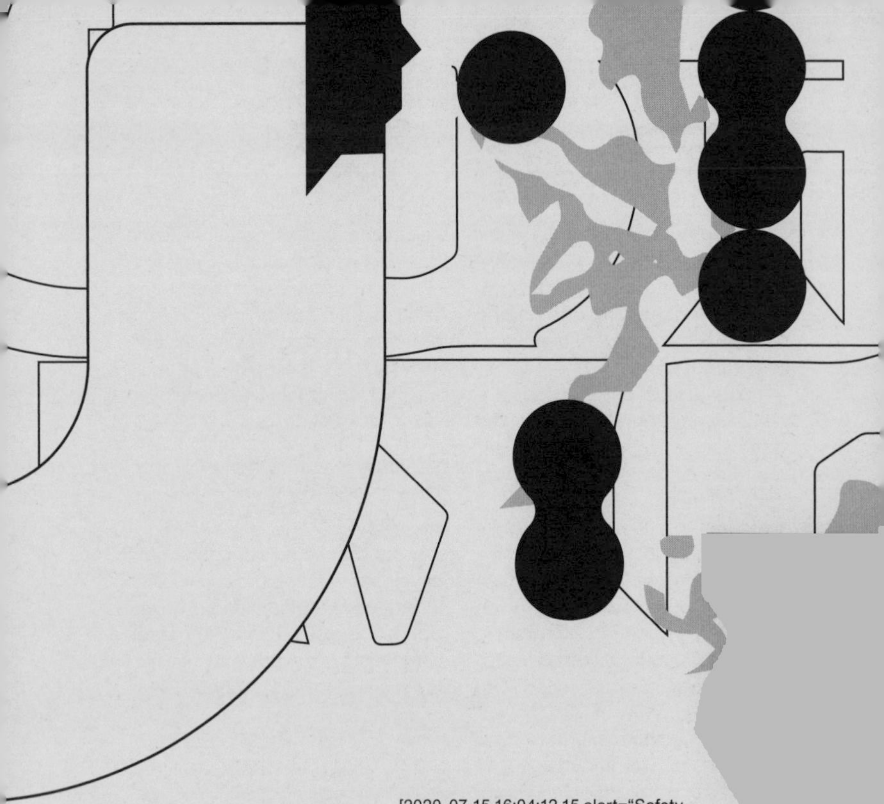

Riley turned back and smiled coyly at Jessie as she neared the entrance. She took one last step to walk out and caught the corner of the mat again. She again stumbled, but caught herself just enough to give an innocent, yet confident wave to the manager she would see in a few hours' time.

[2020-07-15 16:04:12.15 alert="Safety Issue at locID:4191425.rug14"]

Goodness, me! Another stumble! Oh, that won't do. Jessie, please let us finally be free of this mat-tripping trouble, and come fix it on the double. *Bibbidi-bobbidi-boo!*

[2020-07-15 16:04:12.24 initiate safetyProtocol]
[2020-07-15 16:04:12.47 send message to ID:009001467 "Fix rug."]
[2020-07-15 16:04:12.89 deploy "cones" to locID:4191425.mat14]

Anthony Vanky is an assistant professor at the Graduate School for Architecture, Planning and Preservation at Columbia University. His research is at the intersection of digital data, the built environment, and collective behaviours, and their implications on urban design and planning.

EΛSYCITY

EASYJET[1]

Manuel B. Aalbers, KU Leuven

‘Did you see this ad?’

The couple pivoted to stare at a bright orange poster covering a glass door.

‘“EasyFlats, Affordable Housing for EVERYONE: EasyFlats starting at £99 a week” We can afford that!’

‘If it sounds too good to be true, it probably is too good to be true.’

‘I guess... but if we now start discarding affordable options because we’re convinced there are no affordable options, we’d be destined to live with our parents forever, now wouldn’t we?’

‘Right, let’s not do that. Let’s not be *those* people.’

‘Look here: “EasyFlats are located in the new town of EasyCity, in the

1 The following speculative fiction is a thought experiment and satire that imagines a city being run on the model of a low-cost airline, where beyond the basic service all additional aspects come at an additional cost. Such a thought experiment could equally apply if the city were run by RyanAir or Norwegian. Product or corporate names may be trademarks or registered trademarks, and are used only for the purpose of conducting a thought experiment without intent to infringe.

Greater Lionsgate Region. EasyCity offers FREE EasyBus service to the closest metro stop." That doesn't sound too bad.'

'It sounds like it's gonna be in zone 4 or 5.'

'Sure, what did you expect? We don't have zone 1 salaries.'

'Fair enough. And I can't stand to live with my parents a single day more.'

'Let's go inside and see what they offer. Okay?'

'Okay, but I bet they're out of the £99 flats though. You'll see.'

'Maybe they will, maybe they won't. Let's go in, alright?'

The couple opens the door and is welcomed by a friendly twenty-something dressed in grey and orange.

'Welcome to EasyFlats. How can I help you? I bet you're here for the £99 flat, right?'

'Yep, you guessed right.'

'You're probably thinking £99 sounds too good to be true.'

'That's *exactly* what I was saying!'

'I know where you're coming from. It's not easy to find a flat for people our age these days, is it?'

'Tell me about it!'

'I will, sit down. Sit down, please.'

'So, is it too good to be true?'

'No, it's not. We really offer flats at £99. In fact, if you sign with us today, the first week is for free. Shall I take you through our options?'

'Sure.'

The agent holds up a tablet showing a set of interior design photos.

'Okay, so this is our Standard EasyFlat. It's a no-frills/no-thrills flat really. We're very open about that. It's perfect for Millennials like yourselves. These are just some renderings.'

'Mmh.'

'And here's the floorplan. Here's the living space, the shower room, the loft bed would be here. You can see it better on the picture.'

'So it's basically a studio with a loft bed?'

'Yes, that's the Standard EasyFlat. It's the most affordable option we have and yes, it really rents for £99. Plus the first week is free, but I already said that.'

'It looks very small. Where's the kitchen?'

'We at EasyCity believe that the present generation doesn't need the same dreary suburban homes that their parents live in. We believe that folks like yourselves live a different lifestyle; we like to call it the EasyLifestyle.'

'So, you're saying there is no kitchen?'

'There is no kitchen in the old-fashioned meaning of "kitchen." There is a kitchenette. It's right here: it features a microwave on top, a washbasin in the middle and a fridge underneath. We call it the EasyKitchen. It's a real space-safer.'

'Looks like it. But what about the loft bed? Does it sleep two?'

'It does. It does. It's not very big, but it comes with a full-size mattress.'

'That's a bit tight though.'

'I see what you're saying. Could I perhaps interest you in another flat with a larger kitchen and space for a queen-sized bed?'

'Yes, that's what we're looking for.'

'So, this is our Flexi EasyFlat. Here's some renderings again and here's the floorplan. As you can see the Flexi is *much* bigger than the Standard EasyFlat. It comes with the EasyKitchen XL and an EasyBedroom.'

'An EasyBedroom; what's that?'

'It means that's where the suggest- 370
ed bed-space is. So your queen-sized bed could be here [*points at floorplan*] or here. That's what makes it a Flexi EasyFlat. You can choose where to put your bed and where to put your sitting area. It's up to you, really!'

'But it's still a studio in the end?'

'We prefer EasyBedroom. We decided not to put a wall in so it allows for a more flexible EasyLifestyle. A little bit like a super-affordable loft. We think it's really suitable for Millennials.'

'Okay—and the kitchen?'

'So the EasyKitchen XL is basically your standard modern urban kitchen: an induction stove with four burners, American fridge, microwave/oven combo, stainless steel. All the works, you know?'

‘It doesn’t look like it’s *that* large, though.’ 375

‘Well, it’s XL compared to the Standard EasyKitchen. In fact, it’s much, *much* larger than that. Is this more like what we’re looking for? Full kitchen, queen-sized bed, you know?’

‘Yes, that’s exactly what we’re looking for, right?’

‘Yes, yes. It is—it is. But I guess this flat doesn’t come at £99 a week, does it?’

‘No, you guessed right. It doesn’t. The Flexi EasyFlat goes for £139. Still quite affordable and more suitable for two people who want to live there full-time.’

‘Full-time?’ 380

‘You know: sleep, cook, sit on the sofa—that kinda thing.’

‘So for a £139 a week we can rent a real flat. That comes down to ...’

‘That comes down to £556 per month, well, per 4 weeks really. And we sweep in a free week here as well.’

‘I think we could afford that. But before we move on, could you tell us something about the location?’

‘Of course! EasyCity is a new town 385
located in the Greater Lionsgate

Region. We're building 30,000 flats. We've built 5,000 so far, so you'll be pioneers!'

'But where exactly is it?'

'Here's a little map. This is Lionsgate here in the middle in grey, and then if you look left, that orange dot is EasyCity. It's between Gateshead and the Lionsgate-West Airport.'

'Lionsgate-West? That's really Westhampton Airport, isn't it?'

'We prefer Lionsgate-West. We also fly from Lionsgate-West; did you know that? In fact, I forgot to tell you something. One of the great things about EasyCity is how close it is to the airport. Our free EasyBus provides access not only to the Lionsgate metro system but also to Lionsgate-West Airport.'

'It looks quite far from the city. I guess this is in zone 4 or 5 maybe?'

'Well... it's zone 6.'

'ZONE 6! I didn't even know about zone 6!'

'Djeez.'

'Zone 6 was added by the Lionsgate Transportation Committee just last year. It's to accommodate new extensions to the metro network. And you'll have a free bus taking you to the nearest metro stop.'

Blank faces stare at the EasyCity sales person.

'I know what you're thinking: zone 6, can you believe it? That's so far away. But it isn't, really. With the free EasyBus and the metro extension you can be in Billyburg under 60 minutes. Many of my friends live there. I bet many of your friends live in Billyburg as well.'

'Yeah, they do.'

'So, how long does it take you to reach them now?'

'Walk to nearest stop, then two lines... 40, 50 minutes-tops.'

'Okay, so you add 10 minutes extra and you can still see all your friends *and* you can have your own flat. In fact, once you tell your friends about EasyCity, I bet all of them want to move there. Well, not *all* of course, but you know what I mean. Before you know it, people from Billyburg will be coming to EasyCity to visit you and your friends. We've also planned for an EasyCafé, EasyDrinks—that's the pub—EasyMuscles, our gym, EasyLaundry, and EasyPlay—that's the "theatre."

She makes air quotes when she says "theatre."

‘It’s really easy, everyone can join EasyPlay, haha. No seriously: we’re providing *all* the amenities to make EasyCity a very pleasant—I mean easy—place to live. If it weren’t for jobs, you’d never leave EasyCity. In fact, we offer jobs as well. We have jobs in our EasyConstruction company, but you don’t strike me as construction workers. [*Pause.*] So, how about a job in EasyCafé or EasyDrinks?’

‘I’m looking for something.’

‘Okay, great. Right after we sign you up for an EasyFlat you can fill out an application form. A flat and a job in one day, who would have thought that, right? OK, shall I get out the lease then?’

‘Shouldn’t we sleep on this one? I don’t want to rush into anything.’

‘Listen, I see what you’re saying. But if you’d come back tomorrow and want to sign the lease, I cannot guarantee we can rent the flat for £139. I’m not supposed to say this, but it will probably be £149. Also, the free first week is only free if you sign this week. So, I don’t want to push you. I’m just making you aware of the options.’

‘We appreciate that. Maybe we should sign today then.’

‘Okay, we’re doing this.’

'Great! So here's some paperwork you need to fill out. Let me know if you have any questions.'

The couple starts filling out their personal details. Next, they get to the page with the different offers. They check the box for Flexi EasyFlat at £139 per week. Then they get to a whole range of extras they can add.

'"3rd or 4th floor (additional £5). 1st or 2nd floor (additional £10)." Ehh, excuse me.'

'Yes?'

'We're at the section about the floors.'

'Yes?'

'So we need to pay extra to be on a lower floor?'

'Yes.'

'So on which floor are the £139 flats?'
'They're on the 5th and 6th floors.'

'And there is an elevator?'

'No, there's no elevator. Elevators are for old people. Walking stairs is healthy. But we realize that not everyone *loves* walking stairs, that's why we provide the option to rent a flat on a lower floor for a small fee.'

'We can walk stairs, can't we?'

‘Sure.’

The couple continues filling out the form.

‘Windows on the outside are another £5 a week extra. We can do with windows on the inside, right?’

‘Yeah, that will save £20 a month. But what about this: “Install blinds for only £2 a week extra.” That’s not too much’

‘Well, it comes down to £100 per year. We can get our own blinds for that.’

‘All these choices are driving me crazy. Do we really need to make all these choices now?’

‘Of course you don’t. You can add any extras at a later stage. But I have to warn you: prices may vary. If you sign up for blinds now, they are guaranteed at £2 for a full year!’

‘Okay, blinds it is.’

‘Next: Concrete floors are provided. Carpeting comes in at £2. Shall we skip those?’

‘Who needs carpeting anyway?’

‘We can put items on the wall but only if we use EasyHangers that come at 50 pence.’

'Djeez. Do we *really* need to decide that now? Can we please skip all these extras?'

'Yes, but then we may have to pay more when we opt in later.'

'I can't make any more choices now. Can we *please* go to the next page?'

Now they have to choose the location. Flats near the bus station and EasyShops and EasyEntertainment go for £10 a week extra. They decide they can walk to the bus.

They opt in to the EasyTentants "constructive tenants" programme, which is the free tenants' association. It's also the only tenants' organization, or any kind of organization, allowed in EasyCity. In any case, it's impossible to continue with the form without opting in to EasyTenants.

'Why is garbage collection another tenner?'

'Didn't I tell you? There are *no taxes* at EasyCity.'

'And yet we have to pay £10 to have our garbage collected.'

'Yes, that's a fee. It's *not* a tax. We have abolished all taxes. In fact, we don't *believe* in taxes.'

'But how do you pay for street cleaning, schools, health care?'

'We believe in the personal

responsibility of our tenants. That's why we have introduced a garbage fee. We've patented this actually: EasyGarbage. In addition, EasyTenants takes care of weekly street cleanings. Schools, doctors, hospitals are all available in Lionsgate and Gateshead.'

'So there is no doctor in EasyCity?'

'Just yesterday we signed a contract with two doctors-in-training. All kinds of folks are moving to EasyCity.'

The couple starts to look less and less enthusiastic about the prospect of moving to EasyCity but they continue to fill out the form. They need to live somewhere.

Manuel B. Aalbers is a professor of geography at KU Leuven, the University of Leuven, where he leads a research group on the intersection of real estate, finance and the state. He is also the author of several books, including *The Financialization of Housing* (2016).

THE CIVIC METHOD

ELSEVIER[1]

Matthew Claudel,
Massachusetts Institute of Technology

Elsevier is a large academic publisher and mediator of 446
information that "helps institutions and professionals advance healthcare, open science and improve performance for the benefit of humanity."[2]

Jonathan pushed the final few lines of code up to the 447
project repo, commenting "Fixed stability bug on plant-to-plant nitrate trades. BlockGarden ready to test." Hitting the *return* key felt wonderful; he relished the clack. It punctuated the electric tingle that courses through something truly new. He had been pitching BlockGarden to colleagues in his Neighbourhood Unit as an "enviro computer"—and the pitch is essential. You never know who is going to be peer-reviewing your tech after you submit it to a Corp.

BlockGarden felt *right*, though, he somehow 448
knew it would be accepted. The idea was simple: tokenized environment credits are scripted in an

1 The following speculative fiction is a thought experiment and satire. It imagines a city being run on a model derived from extrapolating academic publishing. Such a thought experiment could equally apply if the city were run by other academic publishers such as Springer, Taylor and Francis, or Wiley Blackwell. Product or corporate names may be trademarks or registered trademarks, and are used only for the purpose of conducting a thought experiment without intent to infringe.

2 Elsevier (2019). 'This is Elsevier: A digital business.' Link: https://www.elsevier.com/en-gb/about

algorithmic smart contract. Hyper-local environmental sensors create data about each plant, and the contract optimizes both plant growth and overall environmental benefit through autonomously trading micro-resources like water, fertilizer, solar exposure. It was a marketplace for resources across the ecosystem, garden, planter-bed, and even down to the individual plant scale. Net positives (the excess of both food and carbon sequestration credits) would be distributed to whatever group of investors had pre-funded the garden—what Jonathan playfully called an 'initial seed offering.' The whole thing had the nostalgia of "CSA boxes" that farmers used to sell for pre-funding a season. Before the first collapse, anyway.

He stood up, stretched, craned his neck up to 449
look out the grimy window. Sweltering. Dusty. Another few hours, probably, before it would be safe to go outside. He still wanted to live-test the BlockGarden code with plant sensors in the growing unit before submitting it to a Corp—probably the Heliyon[3] Corporation or the Total Environment[4] Corporation. Anyway, he'd have to wait until well after nightfall to go outside and update the firmware. There was time to kill.

Jonathan looked down at his forearm, where 450
top[5] notifications glowed under his skin. One of them was a civStat push: peer-reviewing a coastal resilience system called Level Sea. Hardware was uncommon—this would be a good distraction—and it might actually be interesting tech. Hard to guess with peer reviews, though. He tapped his wrist to accept.

3 "*Heliyon* welcomes research across all disciplines. Any paper reporting original and technically sound results of primary research, which adheres to accepted ethical and scientific publishing standards, will be published regardless of its perceived impact."—A subsidiary of Elsevier Limited, ISSN: 2405-8440

4 "*Science of the Total Environment* is an international journal for publication of original research on the total environment, which includes the atmosphere, hydrosphere, biosphere, lithosphere, and anthroposphere."—A subsidiary of Elsevier Limited, ISSN: 0048-9697

5 Bloomberg.org Group (2018) "What Works Cities"

Back in 2018—back when philanthropies and govern- 451
ments were funding civic innovation—there had been an ethos of "what works."[5] Municipalities did tactical interventions and tried to learn from best practice. But it was too piecemeal, too little, too late. The environment strained to a breaking point. Billions died in a planetary shock, a cataclysmic Anthropo-collapse. And billions more – maybe humanity as a whole – would have been extinguished, if not for a class of technologies operating at the municipal scale. Societal priorities were galvanized in a new regime, The Civic Method, that blended science, technology and governance under the banner of Civic Innovation. The technology of cities was no longer about "what works"—it was about *truth*, for the benefit of humanity.

Specific municipal services—from water puri- 452
fication to drone-ports to entertainment feeds—were run by individual, topic-specific Civic Innovation Corporations, or "Corps." And the Corps of the city of Elsevier were a global leader.[6] Other cities were fiercely competitive, of course; in the city of Springer, the Nature Corp produced stellar Civic Innovation, and in the twin cities of Taylor and Francis, a Corp called Routledge was growing quickly. In every city, the tech itself was developed by citizens, or, Civic Innovators, as individuals or teams, who also peer-tested innovation before it was fully deployed. Their performance was tracked in a master algorithm, civStat, which was linked to universal rights: basic housing, basic income, and access to municipal utilities. These basic services were delivered through Neighbourhood Units, which paid licensing fees to the Corps.

6 Larivière, Vincent (2015) "The Oligopoly of Academic Publishers in the Digital Era" *PLoS One*.

Over time, Civic Innovators who consistently ex- 453
celled in the quantity and performance of innovation were granted unconditional rights. Without obligations to submit to Corps, they were free to explore radically divergent technologies, or nothing at all, or they were chosen to join the municipal government itself. Elsevier's governing body was shrouded in mystery: the only visibility Civic Innovators had—all they needed—was civStat, and its assurance of algorithmic impartiality.

The transport pod arced along the coastline. It wouldn't 454
be a long ride to the Level Sea test site, though Elsevier as a whole was a sprawling megalopolis that stretched from what used to be Washington up through Boston. Jonathan's Neighbourhood Unit, Yale, was one of the most desirable. Civic Innovators could get a peer assignment anywhere in the metro area, so being in a central Neighbourhood made it easier to hit a quota. Not to mention that the Yale Neighbourhood Unit had good equipment and a reputation for producing high-quality civic innovation. The Corps were always looking out for new submissions, and the Neighbourhood's brand name went a long way toward getting a project accepted and ultimately deployed. Which meant getting credits on civStat, obviously, but most importantly, the privilege of contributing to the city's function; to improving the well-being of every Civic Innovator.

Jonathan watched the city blur past, forehead 455
resting against the window. The collective achievement was truly spectacular, he thought, and he was

honoured to be part of it. Elsevier was a pioneer among cities; it was here that breakthroughs were made after the first Anthropo-collapse—innovations that saved billions of lives around the world. The city itself was thoroughly laced with technology, of course—it sustained human life in a changed climate—but what made Elsevier extraordinary was the intense devotion Jonathan and his fellow Civic Innovators had for improving the city. It was impossible not to admire the ethos of passionate action, to get caught up in it, to feel a part of it. Constantly experimenting and creating and operating civic technology was precarious—the basic rights of every citizen depended on his or her performance—*But isn't that how it should be?* he thought. *Shouldn't we all be inspired to collectively create and build our city? What could ever be more empowering?*

He scrunched up his shirt fabric and wiped dust off the lens, leaning toward the door a second time for a biometric scan to enter his housing unit. A blue light swept his iris and a voice chimed "Welcome home, Jonathan!" Before the door opened, it flashed two notifications: one about a letter and one about a pending tax payment. He had another week to pay it—that is, a week before the door to his housing unit would stop opening for him—and he was counting on the credits from BlockGarden. *It will come through. It has to.* After validating the project code on the garden sensors' firmware earlier that night, he'd compiled and submitted to the Heliyon Corp. It was riskier, but probably a bigger boost for his civStat, if the project was accepted.

As he walked into his unit, he leaned down 457
to pick up a letter. A new system for paper mail was re-instituted across Elsevier a few years ago. It was one of the few Civic Innovations from another city that Elsevier had fully integrated—it's not green or efficient, he thought, but there was something nice about the whimsical romance of opening a letter. Sentimental nostalgia. The letter was from his younger sister Sophie (she was really the only person who wrote him paper mail), and it didn't say much of anything. She loved writing down little romps though ordinary life. Somehow she saw wonder in it, and she shared it joyfully with Jonathan.

From what he could gather, the ordinariness of 458
her life was far from ordinary. Sophie had left Elsevier a decade before, in what seemed like a fit of teenage rebelliousness—but he hadn't seen her since. She had travelled west, ending up in the Freetowns of Medium. Her letters described a place that was nothing like Elsevier; there were no Corps; there was no peer review; there was no law of The Civic Method. Anyone could build and deploy tech without systematic validation. Municipal services weren't integrated with a single-sign on; they were ad-hoc, best-fit, built and deployed quickly. Some services were delivered by loosely defined "Channels" which seemed something like a Corp, but without structured leadership or peer validation or licensing fees. And there were no Neighbourhoods to speak of—people were free to use what they wanted, to come and go. No one had rights,

but they also didn't have obligations.

For some reason, his sister seemed to enjoy the wild uncertainty of it all. A few years ago she had sent a photo, grinning in front of strange, twisted technology—a knot of repurposed hardware tangled into clunky, rough-hewn shapes. Slick, glistening tech was jumbled up and wired together with mechanical cogs and gears. Nothing seemed safe or logical or legitimate. It was shocking that his letters even found their way to and from the right address. 459

He'd never admit it to Sophie, but the Freetowns of Medium genuinely scared Jonathan. And he worried about her. He would write back the same letter he always did, imploring her to apply for entry to Elsevier. *Some Neighbourhoods are looking to bring in new Civic Innovators*, he'd write, *Yale might even have a spot.* And the sooner she started building her civStat, the better. Medium might be more exciting, sure, but what if there was another collapse, a pandemic, a war? Was Medium really a place to grow old in? 460

Nine figures sat in high-backed chairs around a circular table. The room was dark; their faces illuminated by the glow of screens embedded in the table's surface. One of the figures calmly picked up the trail of a sentence, with a faint Swedish accent, "… and how much was collected this year?" 461

The screens shifted immediately, infographics gliding to show revenue, accompanied by a smooth humanoid voice that intoned, "Approximately two and 462

a half billion tokens, a 6% increase in underlying ad-
justed operating profit."[7]
The man tented his fingertips together. "Disap- 463
pointing." He looked up, addressing the circle of figures. "I trust we will see increased profit by soliciting a
greater number of technologies?" The room nodded in
agreement. "Quality is inconsequential. Focus on the
rate of submission. There are, after all, more and more
Neighbourhoods, and more applications for entry to
Elsevier. The city is expanding." He gestured across
the table, "Tell us, Chairman, what of the border?"
Another figure cleared his throat, "Unstable, sir.
There is unrest in the Freetowns of Medium. Militias 464
are aggressing Elsevier to the west, and..." he hesi-
tated, visibly anxious, "within our borders... there is
talk of self-organization among the Civic Innovators.
They want to release technologies without licensing
to Corporations. They've built a viral malware," he
paused. Every one of the figures was looking at him,
tense. "All we know is that it's called 'Open Access.'"
The Swede's fingertips were tented again. 465
Pressed together, visibly white around the nails.
His voice was low and even when he carefully broke
the silence.
"Let them. If this 'Open Access' grows any 466
larger, incorporate the source code into some of our
Corporations. Consume it. And meanwhile, raise the
Neighborhood service fees another 7%."
A barely perceptible shock rippled around the 467
table. "Y-you mean above th-..."
"Yes," sharp, whip-like. "Above the annual stan- 468
dard increase. We've quelled Neighborhood petitions[8]

7 RELX Group (parent company of Elsevier) (2017) Annual Reports and Financial Statements 2017. Available at: http://www.relx.com/~/media/Files/R/RELX-Group/documents/reports/annual-reports/relx2017-annual-report.pdf

8 Nineteenth Judicial District Court, Parish of East Baton Rouge. (2017) "Board of Supervisors of Louisiana State University and Agricultural and Mechanical College Versus Elsevier: Petition for Preliminary Injunction, Declaratory Judgement and Damages." February 27, 2017. Available at: http://www.arl.org/storage/documents/publications/2017-LSUElsevier-Petition.pdf

before, and we can do it again.[9] They have no choice but to pay. We own Urban Management,[10] we own the Atmospheric Environment,[11] we own their very Cells.[12] But most importantly—never forget this—most importantly, *they need this city*. They are lost without it. The fear of another Anthropo-collapse has inspired a passion that cannot be put to words. Do not underestimate how deeply they believe in this project that is Elsevier." His voice had lowered, spell-like. "Do not underestimate the opiate of purpose we have given every one of them. The faith of a voluntary prisoner is total…"

"… Raise. It." 469

The sharp 't' was like a surgical cut into the cold 470
fleshy silence that stretched after it.

Underneath the web of distributed ledgers and cloud 471
of server farms and impartial Corporations, a few lines of code snaked outward from that round table, as if the Swede's words had condensed into two drips of black oil in water.

9 Sabi Kastro (Elsevier Regional Sales Office, Account Manager) (2017) Letter to Dr. Stanley Wilder (T.H. Middleton Library, Louisiana State University). April 22, 2017. Available at: http://www.arl.org/storage/documents/publications/2017.04.22-ElsevierLettertoLSU.pdf

10 "The Journal of Urban Management is an international, peer-reviewed open access journal covering planning, administering, regulating, and governing urban complexity."—A subsidiary of Elsevier Limited, ISSN: 2226-5856 Available at: https://www.journals.elsevier.com/journal-of-urban-management

11 "Atmospheric Environment is the international journal for scientists in different disciplines related to atmospheric composition and its impacts. The journal publishes scientific articles with atmospheric relevance of emissions and depositions of gaseous and particulate compounds, chemical processes and physical effects in the atmosphere, as well as impacts of the changing atmospheric composition on human health, air quality, climate change, and ecosystems."—A subsidiary of Elsevier Limited, ISSN: 1352-2310 Available at: https://www.journals.elsevier.com/atmospheric-environment

12 "Cell publishes findings of unusual significance in any area of experimental biology, including but not limited to cell biology, molecular biology, neuroscience, immunology, virology and microbiology, cancer, human genetics, systems biology, signalling, and disease mechanisms and therapeutics."—A subsidiary of Elsevier Limited, ISSN: 0092-8674 Available at: https://www.cell.com/

The civStat algorithm silently rebalanced, 472
immediately pushing out peer review notifications
and shifting tax thresholds and Neighbourhood licensing fees. An extraordinarily complex mathe-
matics recalibrated to maintain competition between
Neighbourhoods, to obscure redundant technology
submissions, and most importantly, to keep each Civic
Innovator unknowingly perched at the threshold of
precarity. This is where they were most loyal, and most
productive—without the dangerous rot of free time to
write malware like Open Access. Revolution foments
in in the slack camaraderie of unfilled leisure.

A notification flashed on Jonathan's forearm: Block- 473
Garden was declined. His heart skipped. He tapped his
wrist for details, and a soft voice narrated the message
from The Heliyon Corp's reviewer:

"No initial seed offering. Need stronger reve- 474
nue model. Excess food and tokens should be bun-
dled as an environment credit and redeemed with
Elsevier central gov. Revise project finance model
and resubmit."

Matthew Claudel co-founded the MITdesignX program, where he is the Head of Civic Innovation. He is currently a doctoral candidate, and his research is focused on the conditions for endogenous innovation processes that generate urban technology. He is the co-author of two books, *Open Source Architecture* (2016) and *The City of Tomorrow* (2017).

REGISTERING EVE

ETHEREUM[1]

Alison Powell, London School of Economics

We are taking the baby to have her birth registered. 475
We leave the flat and lock the door with the card, then swipe the same card when we get on the bus to Brixton. The bus is slow as always, and we watch the auto-cars in the premium lane stream by as we lurch from stop to stop. At the town hall, I pass the baby over to Hellen and tap my card in at the reception to identify us; the hospital records are linked and they should recognize that Baby has no contracts yet.

We pick up our appointment number. It's mad- 476
deningly high compared to the numbers being called when we get to the registrar's waiting area. While the baby feeds, a few people walk straight in and go up to the registration desks. We open the snacks we brought and settle in. Eventually our number is up, and a person with bright blue eyes and warm brown skin calls us over.

"Here to register your baby? Does she have 477
a name? And what about you—what are your dates of birth?"

1 The following speculative fiction is a thought experiment that imagines a city being run using smart contracting over a blockchain. Such a thought experiment would equally apply regardless of the contracting or blockchain provider. Product or corporate names may be trademarks or registered trademarks, and are used only for the purpose of conducting a thought experiment without intent to infringe.

Each person's city card opens up to a ledger of con- 478
tracts. These are code-based agreements that specify what services we can get, under what conditions, and how these services are delivered. They started out being run on the blockchain and brokered by a company called Ethereum, but now hundreds of private contract companies draft code that automatically executes contracts and governs their conditions and the way they are supposed to be executed.

When we got on the bus, the card triggered a 479
contract that, probably, made an agreement about whether we had enough money in our account and enough capital in our Social Capital Repository, and executed a set of permissions. All at once, and all through code. All meant to remove the process of trying to decide who to trust, and how. No more background checking before you're issued a loan, no more having a bank to hold cash and broker trust.[2]

Code-enacted transactions, each one tracked, 480
to remove the messy business of trust and make it possible to buy, sell or trade each contract. All totally seamless. All trustworthy, because everything's embedded in code.[3]

Or possibly not. When the city opened up bid- 481
ding on smart contracts to replace payments with credit cards, and proposed allowing third parties to build smart contract apps for access to services, all kinds of companies built contractual software fast. There's often bugs, which means that unless you have the funds to join an Escrow Club, occasionally you lose money and social capital points. It's just an unfortunate consequence of the game, really.

2 Riikka Koulu (2016) "Blockchains and Online Dispute Resolution: Smart Contracts as an Alternative to Enforcement." *SCRIPTed 40*. Link: https://script-ed.org/?p=2669

3 David Gerard (2017) *Attack of the 50 Foot Blockchain: Bitcoin, Blockchain and Smart Contracts*. Link: http://www.davidgerard.co.uk/blockchain

I know all of this because I used to write these contracts, in a basement shop in Streatham. We all got into it because it was easy money at the beginning of the smart contract boom. We knew Python and so we taught ourselves the Ethereum smart-contract language, Solidity. It was pretty easy, it seemed. To enact a contract all you had to do was turn various aspects of the decision—about giving someone a loan, or releasing them from prison - into standard variables. Then you had to program a set of external conditions that would trigger another entry onto the blockchain.[4] 482

For programmers it was a dream come true—a chance to literally make code into law.[5] Every service and point of interaction became equipped with smart contracts. The shop I worked for would hire anyone, regardless of their "official" contract status, which is how I met Mohammed. 483

The person behind the desk lets out a long sigh. "There's an issue with granting her the standard social contracts. It looks like one of you had an irregular registration three years ago?" 484

Mohammed. Three years ago his wife arrived in the back of a truck with some others who were lucky to find their way through all the borders, all the biometrics, all the bullshit. They must have had money, back before the war. He was making good money in Streatham building contracts but didn't have citizenship papers yet. Mohammed's wife logged on as an asylum seeker and eventually got access to state-backed contracts so that she could go to the hospital and have her baby, but he didn't have papers to prove things one way or another, and so when it came time 485

4 Sukrit Kalra, Seep Goel, Mohan Dhawan, Subodh Sharma (2018) "ZEUS: Analysing Safety of Smart Contracts." Paper presented at *Network and Distributed Systems Security (NDSS) Symposium* 2018 18-21 February 2018, San Diego, USA. Link: http://dx.doi.org/10.14722/ndss.2018.23082

5 Ivica Nikolic, Aashish Kolluri, Ilya Sergey, Prateek Saxena, Aquinas Hobor (2018) "Finding The Greedy, Prodigal, and Suicidal Contracts at Scale." Link: https://arxiv.org/pdf/1802.06038.pdf

to register their baby I went along. It seemed the least I could do for my best friend in the Streatham shop, and at whose kitchen table I sat, drank tea, and poured my heart out.

It was just meant to be a temporary measure, a placeholder until Mohammed and Fatima could pay the contribution and have the registration transferred into their names, and their son properly registered. But the contract for the registration that I entered into had a bug in it (the supplier was later blacklisted, like so many other fly-by-night third parties), which meant my name stayed in. An anomaly—something you could easily explain away, if any one asked. But with contracts, no one can ask. The code is law. 486

As a friend, Mohammed is solid. As a programmer, he's brilliant, and a little bit edgy. His speciality is what they call 'stealth bomb' contracts. In these, a set of conditions for triggering a payment are set up so that they make perfect sense mathematically and logically, even if they are unfair or downright illegal. These used to be used all the time—in places like auction houses, where contracts for bids don't say that they are 'with reserve', so that bidders pay more than they really should for an item being auctioned off. Other stealth bombs could be planted in contracts that made it possible for third parties to cancel contracts without the owner of the contract knowing. 487

Because most people can't read computer code and interpret how laws are being executed through it, the Escrow Societies could step in with a great business model: you could pay to have them scrutinize your contracts, broker your participation 488 in them, and manage the way that they pay in or out.

They hired the best cyberlawyers, and pushed to create ways to trigger contracts based on social capital measures. That led to the creation of a whole set of businesses—autonomous cars, meal delivery, medical and personal care—triggered by measures of social capital and managed by the Escrow Society. Stealth bombs are still around, of course, but now they have to be buried deeper.

But people like us don't have the capital to enter an Escrow Society. Technically the societies look for evidence of 'social capital'—connections to well-known people, degrees from brand-name universities—but you can also buy into them with a large enough deposit. So the new arrivals to South London, the Canadian potash barons fleeing the dust bowl, or ex-Bitcoin miners priced out by the droughts in China can buy in with a big initial deposit, but we never seemed to manage it. And definitely not now.

"So", says the person with the kind eyes, "will you be 490
putting in for the financial contribution?"

We can't afford the financial contribution. If we 491
could, we could do what Mohammed and Fatima did
and register the baby as a Lambeth resident, and the
local authority would broker contracts for the Universal
Benefits. These include medical care, access to the
housing rental market, access to public transport. And
the ability to apply for a national passport.

"Um, can we make it later?" 492

"You certainly can. But that means that baby's 493
on Tourist status for now."

Tourist status means no one is backing your 494
contracts. It means that any minor daily act might
trigger a stealth bomb. It means no guarantee of universal
services, although you can get health care and
accommodation for up to two years, after which everything
automatically stops working. It means no chance
to apply for a national passport.

It means accepting unsecured contracts for 495
work, like the ones that I agreed to, which cost me all
my savings once it turned out it had a bug in the code.
It means never getting access to the promised "Smart
Supportive State" providing contracts for access to
medical care, housing, transport and education to ensure
that everyone who deserves them could get them.
It means moving every two years, registering again
with a new authority as a Tourist, and never building
up any social capital.

In some places Tourists live on the edges of 496
town, in caravans. They don't use smart contracts—they barter for goods and services. And there are rumours that they have set up their own currency so that they can trade in between cities.

Tourist status. Not a death knell but not far off. 497
I could see Hellen's face blanch as the reality sunk in. Of course we'd both try to find funds to pay in, but if we didn't? We'd be here and she'd be in a caravan, or in a Northern city at the end of a road where buses run only once a day.

I move the baby over to my other shoulder. 498
She's eaten now, and I feel light headed. I stare at the lady behind the desk, all of my future visions of us as a family unspooling.

"Yes" I say. "Tourist status for now." 499

Hellen looks at me, her eyes filled with tears. 500
How much we wanted this baby girl. How much we sacrificed. How many whispers in the night, how many long days in the contract sweatshop. How many contracts triggered at the donor clinic, the hospital, the social services agency. How much fury when it all seemed to go wrong, and how little even we, the programmers, could do to change it.

"And baby's name?" 501

We both say, 502

"Eve. 503

Alison Powell is an Assistant Professor in the Department of Media and Communications at LSE. She researches how people's values influence the way technology is built, and how technological systems in turn change the way we work and live together.

SUBPRIME LANGUAGE AND THE CRASH

GOOGLE ADWORDS[1]

Pip Thornton, University of Edinburgh

WIRELESS Magazine

May 1, 2044

Subprime language and the crash

Google's thirst for keywords caused the 2041 Global 504
Linguistic Crisis, says government report. Bust tech giant ignored warnings its AdWords empire was a threat to language and the economy.

The government has today released the results 505
of the official enquiry into the causes of the Global Linguistic Crisis (GLC) which brought down the digital economy in late 2041 and threatened the stability of human communication.

The report was written by researchers from 506
the University of London in collaboration with officials from the banking sector and the Royal Society for the Preservation of Digital Media. As well as expert

1 The following speculative fiction article is a thought experiment that imagines what happens when the logic of linguistic capitalism takes over the running of cities. Such a thought experiment could equally apply for other search engines. Product or corporate names may be trademarks or registered trademarks, and are used only for the purpose of conducting a thought experiment without intent to infringe.

sources, the report draws heavily on the archive of digital-era paper print-outs found in a bunker beneath a garage in Mountain View, Ca. shortly after the collapse of now defunct internet provider Google.

Described as a 'shrine to the printed word', and stored in defiance of the 2020 International Paperless Society Act (IPSA), the documents included printed copies of internal memos, 'blog' posts, and the hand-written diary of an unidentified Google employee who appears to have predicted the linguistic crash as far back as 2025. 507

Mountain View woman

'All we know is that she was a woman', the report states, 'who very early on raised concerns about the consequences of Google's project to link their digital advertising platform AdWords, with real estate investment and their global takeover of internet service provision and data storage.' These concerns appear to have fallen on deaf ears. 508

'This is linguistic capitalism gone mad', wrote the woman in a diary entry from 2025, 'It's not enough that we wring every last penny out of words by auctioning them every time we put them through the internet. Now we have to agree for everything we SAY to be monetised!' 509

Researchers say the diary entry refers to Google's move from serving adverts as search results based on the auctioning of keywords, to harnessing and exploiting the language circulating in physical spaces. This was a switch in tactics made possible at 510 first by Google's growing dominance as gatekeeper to the internet and latterly as the landlord of vast swathes of land and property.

Crisis

The 2041 GLC prompted the collapse of the modern 511
digital economy, put an end to internet connected
communication, and led to the mass destruction of every piece of information held on Google's custom-built
server island in the North Atlantic. Its effects are still
being felt today, and like the last Global Financial Crisis
in 2008, its roots can be traced to the property market.

At the height of the crash, Google controlled ac- 512
cess to every Wifi network in the world, owned 95% of
all real estate in the UK, Europe, and North America, and
was responsible for the digital-urbanisation of much of
Africa and the global south. It was a property and data
empire financed purely by the monetisation of words.

According to the researchers, sometime in 513
2020 Google had what they call a 'material turn.'
Bosses at the tech giant began to realise that their
monopoly of digital space could seriously limit further
expansion of profits in the future. They needed to start
exploiting physical space too. Google's successful
monetisation of digital space had begun to fund a
mass property purchase and construction scheme.

Pilot schemes such as in Canadian cities in the 514
late 2010s had been so successful that Google was
fast becoming the dominant landlord of physical sites
as well as web sites, networks and web space. 'What
if we build real sites as well as web sites?', reads one

excited internal electronic message found in the bunker, 'We could advertise on buildings, OMG we could make buildings out of adverts!'

And that is ultimately what Google did. They built cities out of electronic adverts based on their old highly successful web-based system of AdWords. These cities were constructed of keywords, built into the material fabric of the architecture, but also into the virtual fabric of the infosphere via Wifi permissions and the growing trend for web-based 'personal assistants', which, after the demise of competitors such as Amazon Digital 2.0 and Faceswipe, became the ubiquitous eyes and ears at the frontier of Google's expansion. 515

Linguistic bubble

'They say it's saving the rain forests', reads another diary entry, apparently in reference to the IPSA of 2020, 'but that's just a cover. What they're really doing is making us into walking, talking adverts. They're creating a linguistic bubble.' 516

Etienne Smith, from the University of London's department for Critical Analogue Humanities, was one of the co-authors of the report. He told WIRELESS: 'It's sometimes hard to believe, but there came point in the 2020s, when in some predominantly urban environments, it became physically impossible to communicate, in writing and face to face, without every word being monetised by Google.' 517

'People know that if they use certain words, they get more data and cheaper Wifi bills, and this changes in different areas, so if you talk about how 518 wonderful Google is here in the Bay area, you end up with loads of money. And if you talk about rival products in a building sponsored by a particular advertiser, you get less data at a higher price.'

Google's use of speech for advertising began in the data-rich catchment areas of central business and commercial districts of major global cities, where skyscrapers, complexes, parks and roads were constructed around the advertising space they could display digitally and dynamically. But what the report calls the 'AdWords effect' quickly spread to other areas, infecting everyday speech in local neighbourhoods and in people's homes. 519

'The value of language changed', says Smith, a specialist in critical forensic banking and the linguistic economy. 'It became unsustainable. Nobody could trust anything anybody else said.' 'Tranches of language developed in different areas, and the poor became poorer as their language became worthless.' 520

Urban collapse

As with the GFC of 2008, it was in these poorer communities that the worst effects of the trouble began to show. 'In the early 2000s it was low income Americans being sold property they couldn't afford that started the crisis', says Smith, 'but by the late 2030s the cloud-based internet schemes launched by the early tech giants in the 2010s had facilitated the construction of thousands of towns and cities across the global South, all of them built on the apparent stability of the linguistic economy.' 521

The government report makes for sobering reading. While the GLC caused widespread economic and social hardship in the US and Europe, in the newly urbanised areas of East and Central Africa alone it is estimated that up to a million people lost their lives in the civil wars and famines that followed the crash. 522

According to Smith, the Google AdWords effect had already begun to polarise these new communities by decimating indigenous languages in favour of English, creating hierarchies based on linguistic skill, and also physical access. 'Those with a better command of English basically began to command physical space as well. The less educated and poorer occupants of these new urban spaces were denied access to the richest linguistic areas so they couldn't earn anything from speaking there.' Even the 2038 AdWords Riots in New Sahara didn't make Google stop what they were doing, says Smith. 'The tech companies got greedy. They didn't care that these new developments were turning into deeply segregated areas. They were making billions from these new markets. In my opinion, yes, they did have blood on their hands.' 523

Linguistic liquidity

So, what became of Mountain View woman and her archive? Did her bubble burst? 'Yes, it did', says Smith. 'We lost the ability to communicate. Language in effect became subprime, and once the advertising industry imploded, the digital economy collapsed like a house of cards.' 524

Smith's favourite part of the archive is a diary 525
entry from August 2033 which simply reads 'Words are worth more than money.' 'I think she was right', he says. 'In financial terms we would say that language had become so tied to an economic value, rather than, say, a poetic one, that words had in effect become illiquid. Their only meaning – or value – was what they were worth in an advert, and when advertising became part of the infrastructure, this had horrific consequences.'

'It's possible she's still alive and reading this 526
article, but as most former Google employees went to ground after the crash, it's unlikely we'll ever know who she was.'

Also found in the bunker was a collection of po- 527
etry, an English translation of a short story by French author Alain Damasio, *Les Hauts Parleurs*, and a heavily annotated paper copy of George Orwell's *Nineteen Eighty-Four*, one of only a handful of pre-crash copies known to be in existence.

Do you know Mountain View woman? Call 528
WIRELESS with any information.

Pip Thornton is a Post-Doctoral Research Associate in Creative Informatics at the Edinburgh College of Art, where she takes a critical and creative approach to the concepts of data and value in the digital economy. Her artistic intervention into the cultural and political effects of Google's search and advertising platforms, {poem}.py, has been featured in WIRED UK, and is currently on display at the Open Data Institute in London (2017-2019).

SEEING THE CITY THROUGH GOOGLE'S EYES

GOOGLE ARLens[1]

Leighton Evans, Swansea University

There is a familiar argument that reality has always been augmented through communication and other technologies.[2] The emergence of augmented reality (AR) technology represents an altogether new obtrusive augmentation of the perception of reality through the overlaying of data and computer-generated graphics onto the everyday perception of the world. Most of the attention paid to AR technology so far has been on its instantiations in gaming,[3] such as Pokémon Go, a smartphone app-based game that used GPS and the camera to enable players to find, reveal and collect Pokémons hidden in the physical world. Soon, the smartphone will be superseded as a physical device for the delivery of AR by wearable technology. Products such as the *Magic Leap*, a head-mounted virtual retinal display which superimposes 3D computer-generated imagery over real world objects and environments, have begun to emerge for developers

1 The following article provides a mix of speculative fiction and academic analysis to examine the impacts of AR on city life. Product or corporate names may be trademarks or registered trademarks, and are used only for identification, explanation and conducting a thought experiment without intent to infringe.

2 Ong, W. J. (1982) *Orality and literacy: The technologizing of the word.* London: Methuen.

3 Hjorth, L., & Richardson, I. (2017). "Pokémon Go: Mobile media play, place-making, and the digital wayfarer." *Mobile Media & Communication*. 5 (1), 3-14. doi:10.1177/2050157916680015

in 2018, with a projected commercial release in 2020.[4] The *Magic Leap* alters the user's view of the world; by looking through its lenses, computer-generated digital objects enter the perceptual field and 'appear' as part of the world. Should this transformation of form be achieved in a way that is affordable to consumers and is acceptable in a fashion-sense, then AR affords the possibilities of augmenting reality with all sorts of information, from retail advice to historical points of interest. Here, I conduct a short thought experiment, speculating on AR modelled through the practices and organisational aims of Google to illustrate the potential effects of AR on everyday urban life with respect to memory, attention and focus.

In 2025, there are two dominant options for consumer 530
AR. The first is the Apple iGlass, a stylish, expensive and desirable piece of hardware running the Apple AR operating system modelled on—and fully compatible with—its own iOS operating system for mobile devices. The second is the Google ARLens platform, which runs on a myriad of AR hardware produced by Google and other third-party manufacturers. ARLens is modelled after the Android operating system, with applications available through the Play Store. The ARLens platform is considered more robust due to its interoperability with third party devices. ARLens uniquely offers city-specific interfaces thanks to its integration of Google Maps and Google's willingness to work with civic authorities to shape the view of the city based on civic co-operation

4 Magic Leap has already achieved $1.9 billion in equity without any plan as yet for a product launch, see: Bradshaw, T. (2017) "Magic Leap conjures $502m in funds for $1.9bn total equity." *Financial Times*. October 17, 2017. Link: https://www.ft.com/content/8da22784-b382-11e7-a398-73d59db9e399

with their Sidewalk Labs initiative, incorporating citizen science and public data.

Much of the consumer buzz around the ARLens experience has concerned the 'personal view' phenomena. The content of the digital overlay is always linked to the Google account of the user. Having an active account is a necessary step in activating the platform. Data accrued from web searches on Google's browser search engine, emails received and sent in Gmail, locations searched for in Google Maps, and all the other myriad data continually generated through interaction with the Google ecosystem (including the ARLens platform), is algorithmically distilled into data for the ARLens experience. Thanks to this consolidated, individual data mining, two people can walk hand in hand down the same street and will have totally different data-mediated experiences thanks to their histories of interaction with Google. Screen-scraping and sharing the differences in the data-view of the same place has become one of the most popular meme genres of 2025.

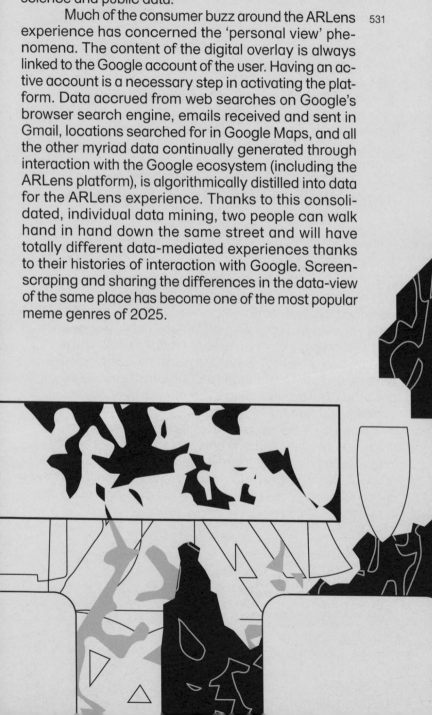

What is seen in the high street is also seen in 532
the shopping mall. Google's selected partners receive prominent placement in the glasses view, with more detailed information relating to special offers overlaid onto the store windows. Looking away so the store is not in view is not a panacea to this feature, as other stores have similar overlays and signs point back to nearby out-of-view places. ARLens users also report having residual effects from casting their gaze for too long on one shop front or product. These locations or goods become part of an annoying visual stream of information that can take considerable effort to change or 'silence.' Shops and products that are not in the vast databanks of the AR platforms and applications are ignored by the overlays—and increasingly ignored by consumers as their everyday retail movements are directed and mediated by augmented eyeware that maintains a continual contextual data-feed.

The ARLens has quickly established a dom- 533
inant market share thanks to lower entry costs and diversity of hardware using the platform than its rivals. As AR becomes both a fashion item and an essential part of navigating the everyday urban environment, familiar concerns about privacy and data harvesting are exercised. The odd crisis, such as the utilisation of gaze data to manipulate political advertising by a third-party analytics company associated with various right-wing politicians on both sides of the Atlantic are high-profile but short-term problems as the utility of the device is seen as greater than its threats. The logic seems to run that while the platforms possess data on what users look at and for how long, it's a fair trade for knowing everything about a place as soon as you see it.

AR of this kind would have a profound effect on our 534
understanding of the city. The AR-mediated city would be a patchwork of places and non-places,[5] where the non-place is defined by a lack of data or information provided in the eyeline of the user. An understanding of place would be contingent on the nature of the information provided to the user as well as their history of Google usage and their connectivity to the ARLens servers.

The phenomenological experience of place 535
itself would be shaped by the constant flicker and hum of the AR eyewear chosen by users. Of course, the user would not be helpless in this transformation; taking off the glasses would always be an option to experience the city outside of the stream of contextual, individualised data. In the wider context of a world of information technology, where the cognitive load of everyday life is increasingly delegated to networked devices, the appropriate question might be why would people turn off a device that tells them where to go, how to get there, where they will like, and what it will cost them? The ARLens offers instant familiarity, instant wayfinding and navigation, elision of the undesirable and unwanted in the urban environment, and prioritisation of the desired and liked, all seamlessly provided through algorithmic processing of massive data trails individualised by source. The city is transformed into safe spaces that are shared with those that hold similar traits and desires according to Google's data profiles.

There is little doubt that wearable AR technol- 536
ogy is coming. Google has signalled its commitment

5 Auge, M (1992) *Non-Places: An Introduction to Anthropology of Supermodernity*. London: Verso, p. 122.

to AR through the provision of ARCore as a software development kit (SDK) for AR on the Android operating platform. AR represents for Google not only a medium that can overlay the 'real' world with digital information (selected and provided by Google) but which also can be harnessed to make the movement, mobility, gaze and the attention of users in everyday situations computable in ways that go beyond the granularity currently offered by smartphones and other devices. Given the levels of data harvesting that those devices currently offer, AR promises to expand the platform economy of Google by extending the possibilities of data accumulation and processing. This economic model is one where a few companies dominate as they control of the medium of exchange that is critical in this model: attention.[6]

The attention economy is based on an ac- 537
knowledgement that time, not material goods, is the key scarcity in modern society.[7] The key to the attention economy is to create an environment where the attention paid in the present can refer to a past and a future within a given experience or platform. As a platform, Google stores our past and aims to predict our future. With AR, it can harvest more of the present, shape behaviour in real-time, and anticipate and direct future behaviour.

When attention is directed through, rather than 538
towards, digital devices then the attention economy will reach its zenith. Here, seeing and moving in a city may be less an experience of urban life and more an experiment in a digital Skinner Box.[8] The original Skinner Box involved training an animal through responses to

6 Keen, A. (2017). "The 'attention economy' created by Silicon Valley is bankrupting us." *Techcrunch*. July 31 2017. Link: https://techcrunch.com/2017/07/30/the-attention-economy-created-by-silicon-valley-is-bankrupting-us

7 Becker, G. S. (1965). "A Theory of the Allocation of Time." *The Economic Journal*. 75 (299), 493. doi:10.2307/2228949

8 Lanier, J. (2017) *The Dawn of the New Everything: A Journey through Virtual Reality*. New York: Bodley Head, pp. 62.

stimuli and rewarding correct behaviour with positive reinforcement until the behaviour becomes habitual. Jaron Lanier uses this term in reference to virtual reality and how that medium is ideal in measuring all sensory inputs as well as controlling the visual and sensory environment for users. With an ARLens over our eyes, the stimuli are provided for us, directing mobility, behaviour and actions in accordance with the logic of the providing organisation. The phenomenal experience of space would be continually made and remade before our eyes as a function of data we provide through our activities on the Google platform—and that Google and its business associates provide for us. We would not be seeing a city like Google—our seeing of the city would be directed by Google, for Google and its interests.

Leighton Evans is a Senior Lecturer in Media Theory at Swansea University, where his research is concerned with Virtual and Augmented Reality and Phenomenology. Leighton is the author of *Locative Social Media: Place in the Digital Age* (2015) and *The Re-Emergence of Virtual Reality* (2018).

THERE IS NO SUCH A THING AS FREE INFRASTRUCTURE

GOOGLE FIBER[1]

Tooran Alizadeh, University of Sydney

Edward Helderop and Tony Grubesic, Arizona State University

Imagine having access to ultra-high-speed internet, up to hundred times faster than any pre-existing service, with a competitive price, more reasonable than anything that you have ever seen before. Imagine if a major corporation decided to build such a dream-come-true telecommunication infrastructure for free. Imagine if cities were to organize campaigns, create Facebook pages, upload YouTube videos, and collect signatures to put forward their case for priority access to the next generation of telecommunication infrastructure. And finally, imagine that when a city was selected to receive the ultra-high-speed telecommunication infrastructure, you, as the citizen, had the power to determine exactly where it would be deployed! This is one way that cities could provide their citizens with the next generation of telecommunication infrastructure—just the way Google Fiber was introduced.

1 The following academic article examines the relationship between cities and companies such as Google Fiber in providing telecom services. Product or corporate names may be trademarks or registered trademarks, and are used only for identification and explanation without intent to infringe.

540 In February 2010, Google challenged US cities[2] to compete for being the site of its first attempt at building an ultra-high-speed fiber-to-the-premises network (FTTP), with speeds up to 1 gigabit per second. More than 1,100 cities staged elaborate stunts as part of their applications. Kansas City, however, was announced as the winner of the competition. In 2013, Google expanded their FTTP network to Austin, Texas, and Provo, Utah; and later in 2014 announced expansion plans to 34 US cities. Google Fiber was widely acclaimed in its first few years, with Kansas City being anointed as a "broadband mecca." The Fiber project was also roundly welcomed as a triumph for free markets, and as a model for telecommunications deployment for other cities to follow.[3]

541 The honeymoon phase, however, did not last long for Google Fiber. In August 2015, Google announced its intention to restructure the company, moving it into a new umbrella corporation, Alphabet Inc. This was then followed with numerous media reports[4] suggesting that Google Fiber was under pressure by Alphabet to limit the scope of the project and the number of cities involved. In part, this pressure stemmed from corporate losses related to Google Fiber, nearly $3.6 billion in 2016.[5]

542 Interestingly, the details and facts on Fiber are relatively limited, with Alphabet never releasing details on the size of its investment in any of the Google Fiber cities. What is known, however, is where the construction took place, slowed, or stalled completely (e.g., San Jose and Portland). Below, we briefly examine the ups and downs of the Google Fiber—with a focus on

2 Link: http://googleblog.blogspot.com/2010/02/think-big-with-gig-our-experimental.html

3 Chan, C. (2013) "A City Getting Google Fiber Explains How Awesome Google Fiber Is." Gizmodo. Link: http://gizmodo.com/a-city-getting-google-fiber-explains-how-awesome-google-1393294179

4 Kleeman, S. (2016). "Google Fiber Got Kicked in the Nuts by Alphabet." Gizmodo. Link: http://gizmodo.com/google-fiber-got-kicked-in-the-nuts-by-alphabet-1785764632

5 Fiegerman, S. (2016). "Google's moonshots lost $1 billion last quarter." CNN. Link: http://money.cnn.com/2017/01/26/technology/google-earnings-q4/

Kansas City—highlighting what cities can learn from the experience.

Early attempts at fiberhood selection were disastrous from an equality perspective

After announcing Kansas City as the inaugural Google Fiber site, the first major step for the rollout was to determine exactly where the Fiber would be deployed. To make this aspect of the project more transparent, Google carved the city into 'fiberhoods'—the neighbourhoods that would receive the ultra-high-speed broadband infrastructure. For network eligibility, it was required that at least 5% of the residents of any fiberhood had to register for the service—paying a small fee of $10 during a six-week registration period. The progress of fiberhood pre-registrations was then displayed on the Fiber website using a basic map. Green areas indicated that the pre-registration goal had been met; and yellow signified that the pre-registration goal was yet to be achieved. 543

The pre-registration system adopted by Google proved to be a recipe for disaster; and drew strong criticism. The process manifested a sharp visualization of socio-demographic disparities and the digital divide in Kansas City: affluent white neighbourhoods easily met pre-registration targets, but lower-income, predominantly black and Hispanic neighbourhoods did not. In other words, the pre-registration process displayed how naive Google was about the implications of the deep socio-economic inequalities and pre-existing digital divide in Kansas City. For example, Google had completely overlooked that many households (up to 544

70% on the impoverished Missouri side) had always been without at-home internet access, making the *online* pre-registration process almost impossible for them. If anything, early attempts at fiberhood selection did not present any hope of erasing the digital divide in the city. Instead, it made the divide more visible.

Grassroots campaign with community groups saved the day

Under significant pressure from both the public and media in Kansas City, Google made the decision to revise their early fiberhood strategy. This was done through a grassroots campaign involving numerous community groups and significant wor in the field, for Google. 545

In July 2012, a team of 60 Google employees got involved with grassroots community work, talking to neighbourhood associations, going to town hall meetings and church meetups to proselytize the promise of Google Fiber. The learning curve for Google was steep. They realized that many residents living in minority-dominated areas did not speak English (e.g. Hispanic communities), were not in the traditional banking system, and did not have a credit or debit card number to pre-register. Google's effort on the ground was supported by community groups which ended up offering pre-paid debit cards—made available partly through a crowd-funding platform—for the $10 pre-registration fee. In time, the extensive grassroots community-based worked, with nearly 90% of all fiberhoods turning green in Kansas City, including many of the minority-dominated communities. 546

Equitable outcome despite the lack of data transparency

To examine the Google Fiber roll-out from an equity 547
perspective, we reached out to Alphabet to request service data on multiple occasions. All requests were denied—met with either silence, or a refusal on the grounds of security concerns. This was not unexpected. Telecommunications companies, as a rule, typically refuse to share data with academics and/or policy-makers.

Not easily deterred, we instead developed a 548
novel data mining approach which was combined with exploratory spatial data techniques to highlight the provision footprints of Fiber for Kansas City, Provo, and Austin.[6] Specifically, our efforts to determine the spatial provision of Google Fiber for each city included several steps. First, city boundary, address points and cadastral data were obtained for each city. Next, a spatial grid was produced for each location, including its neighbouring communities. Then, a randomly selected set of addresses from each grid cell was used as an input into the 'Check Your Address' function on the Google Fiber website. This process was automated. Each individual query generated a response from the Fiber website that provided details on the availability of Fiber for the queried address. Lastly, we explored the demographic and socio-economic differences between areas with access to Fiber ('haves') and those without access ('have-nots'). The resulting patterns were quite telling. Given the persistence of the digital divide in the US, especially within urban areas, Google

6 Grubesic, T., Helderop, E., Alizadeh, T. (2018). "Closing information asymmetries: A scale agnostic approach for exploring equity implications of broadband provision." Telecommunications Policy. DOI: 10.1016/j.telpol.2018.04.002

Fiber had managed to manifest an equitable roll-out; and to maintain a socio-spatial distribution that favoured neighbourhoods with younger, lower income, minority populations.

It is important to remember, however, that there 549
were significant costs to the communities embedded in this process—costs not borne by Google. A closer examination of urban governance and the Fiber projects[7] across the US has highlighted massive regulatory concessions and incentives provided to Fiber during the construction phase in Kansas City, Provo, San Antonio, Huntsville and many other cities. For example, Kansas City provided Google access to all city-owned conduit, fiber, poles, rack space, nodes, buildings, facilities, central office locations and available land. Moreover, Kansas City did not impose any charges for access to these facilities, nor did the city require any permit or inspection fees. Additional concessions were made by Kansas City, including an agreement to use third-party inspection firms, *selected by Google*, to ensure compliance during the installation process. In addition, Kansas City provided Google with access to all municipal GIS data and technical information databases, cooperation in publicity and marketing efforts effort and assistance to Google in obtaining settlement-free interconnections with anchor institutions in the city that had existing network connections (see the Development Agreement[8] for more information).

In short, although Google designed and in- 550
stalled the network, much of the administrative cost was absorbed by Kansas City and its surrounding communities with taxpayers forced to cover most of

7 Alizadeh, T., Grubesic, T., & Helderop, E. (2017). "Urban governance and big corporations in the digital economy: An investigation of socio-spatial implications of Google Fiber in Kansas City." Telematics and Informatics. 34(7), 973-986.

8 Kansas City, 2011. Development Agreement. Link: http://www.netcompetition.org/wp-content/uploads/Google-Kansas-Agreement1.pdf

the indirect costs for the network. It has been argued that Kansas City's support for Google's network went well beyond deregulation and in some instances local efforts were described as 'corporate welfare.' For example, the media[9] questioned fee waivers for the use of rights-of-way; citing these corridors under Kansas City's streets and on its utility poles as a scarce, taxpayer-owned resource. When a city offers a private company access to those resources for free, it's forgoing an opportunity to collect revenues. Questions were also raised as taxpayers, rather than Google, paid to hire extra city staff to supervise the project.

There is, however, a second side to this debate. 551
Specifically, there are questions pertaining to the economic logic of a private firm building new fiber networks without taxpayer subsidies. If one accepts this argument, then there is an obligation to ensure that the resulting infrastructure and associated services are equitably distributed for all residents, regardless of location or socio-economic status. In the case of the Kansas City metropolitan area, where taxpayers did subsidize the roll-out of Fiber, the results of our analysis suggest that both Kansas City and Google Fiber met this obligation in terms of achieving an equitable distribution of telecommunication services.

What can cities learn?

Google Fiber is a complex project with important les- 552
sons for cities seeking equitable telecommunication infrastructure: First, Google Fiber's success in deploying an equitable socio-spatial roll-out was only possible

9 Hamblin, M., 2012. "Taxpayers subsidizing Google Fiber project." ComputerWorld. Link: http://www.computerworld.com/article/2492159/wireless-networking/taxpayers-subsidizing-google-fiber-project.html

after Google realized the need to run a highly localized, grassroots campaign—in collaboration with community advocate groups—to reach out to the socio-economically impoverished sections of the city. This multilateral partnership between a telecommunication provider (Google), local government, and a community (i.e., institutions and residents)—is more complex than the broadband debate and industry generally allows for. Second, Google Fiber's refusal to release detail information on their network to the public, slowed, but did not stop our research into the equity implications of the Fiber network. Indeed, advancements in data mining approaches and spatial analysis techniques make it difficult for both governments and telecommunication providers to fully avoid public and academic scrutiny. Last, but not least, we praise Google Fiber's effort in working with community groups in Kansas City, as well as ensuring the equitable provision of Fiber in Provo and Austin. However, we acknowledge the massive cost borne by taxpayers in each city—via the numerous concessions and incentives received by Google Fiber. In other words, there is no such a thing as free infrastructure. Cities need be aware of the hidden cost whenever partnering with corporations.

Tooran Alizadeh is a senior lecturer, director of urban design program, and also a recipient of the prestigious Research Accelerator Fellowship (SOAR) at the University of Sydney. Tooran is an interdisciplinary academic researching policy and planning implications of telecommunication infrastructure with a focus on the broadband deployment, and smart cities.

Edward Helderop is currently working on his PhD in Geographical Sciences. His research interests include GIScience, big data, and network analytics (particularly as applied to urban infrastructure systems). His previous research explored turnover and resiliency in plant-pollinator networks.

Tony Grubesic serves as Director for the Center for Spatial Reasoning & Policy Analytics at Arizona State University. His research interests include spatial analysis, geocomputation, urban informatics and policy evaluation.

BEING XTRA IN GRINDR CITY

GRINDR[1]

Gavin Brown, University of Leicester

Grindr City has grown so much in the ten years since we took control. Most days there are about a million of us in the city at any one time; but there are millions more who owe some allegiance to the city spread across the world. The promise of life in Grindr City, and the connections that our friends outside the city maintain with us, allows them to exist even in those places where we are not welcome. 553

That we became a city in the first place took some of us by surprise, that wasn't part of the plan. Grindr began as a networking application used by gay, bi and bi-curious men. It has always been predominantly used for sexual contact. At first the app drove everything. It helped us feel a new sense of connection to people in our neighbourhoods and around the world. 554

Over time, as I'll describe, the app began to reshape and enhance our experience of the city's people and places. Now, I guess, the people who use the app, the services we use, and the connections we make 555

1 The following speculative fiction and satire imagines a city being run through the Grindr platform. Such a thought experiment could equally apply if the city were run by Tinder or other dating apps. Product or corporate names may be trademarks or registered trademarks, and are used only for the purpose of conducting a thought experiment without intent to infringe.

with each other seem to form something like a city of our own stretched across the wider urban sprawl. That, in turn, has attracted more people to relocate here, so that they could enjoy a city shaped by our needs too.

In the early years of the app, Grindr did little 556
to directly advertise its services. They relied on gay men's tendency to gossip—about sex—to recruit new users. Over time the services they offered expanded until they structured our whole experience of the city. Of course, most of us knew that there was a business behind the app, but we didn't give it much thought. Our attention was held by the app itself and it drove how we acted.

Who knew that such a simple app and gossip 557
could change so much? The app's interface offers a grid of users' representative photos arranged from nearest to furthest away: some show their faces, others are disembodied torsos at the gym. Tapping on a picture opens up their profile and options to chat, send photos and your location to them. In this way, the app enabled 'discreet' contact between men and so *much* grew out of that.

No one really likes to talk about it, but there is 558
a powerful class divide in Grindr City (and, of course, we do gossip about it—all the time). We get to choose which class we belong to—Basic or Xtra. It all depends on whether we want to pay for Grindr or not. On the face of it, the tax is quite low; and the longer you commit to paying, the cheaper it gets. I was happy enough bumping along as a Basic for a long while; but eventually I realised that, for a modest payment each month, I could become the person I wanted to be. I wanted Xtra.

The Basics still get to use the standard facilities in the app (and our city). But that comes with some trade-offs—everything is interrupted by adverts, all of the time. The ads can be distracting, but they tell us all about the local services we've come to rely on so much—the bars, the clubs, the gyms, and understanding doctors. The app helps focus our attention on the services that the city has to offer us. Although we're not always conscious of it, it shapes where we choose to go and directs our movements round the city. Xtras get a better deal, though. We can see more users, and get all sorts of Xtra services—originally, these were mainly enhanced functionality on the app, but now we get priority service throughout our city. 559

Being Xtra allows you to be more selective in the people you see and meet. As an Xtra, I can select my men according to their height, weight, body type, ethnicity, position[2] or relationship status. Of course, when I was Basic I could just ask them these things. Being Xtra is just more efficient all round. Now I don't have to bother with exchanging that Basic information, I enjoy the back and forth of conversation—the more, the better—but I can get directly to the good stuff. I've been told that there's lots of racism and other prejudice on the app; but I don't see that. People simply have personal preferences—and especially when you're an Xtra, you need to be discriminating. 560

Grindr took control of our lives in this city when the app became the primary means of social interaction and accessing services for gay and bi men. To outsiders, it might seem strange that conversations which seldom progress beyond a phatic 'what u doing?' could 561

2 i.e. preferred sex role.

make such a difference. Sometimes we spend hours online waiting for someone to talk to us. Yet, when we do chat, so many of our interactions are defined by a desire for an instantaneous meeting; and lots end abruptly if that cannot be arranged. Time passes curiously in Grindr City. Some say that that desire for immediate gratification distorts the interactions we have with each other. Even when some planning and preparation is needed to arrange a 'date' many meetings never happen as the other guy will simply disappear and ghost you. Of course, I never do that.

Grindr realised we didn't just use the app for 562
flirting and sex talk, but asked each other for recommendations when we travelled or arrived somewhere new. Lots of times we just hang out and chat about our lives. Grindr listened and offered access to new apps that offered us a 'broader gay lifestyle platform.'[3] On one level the men in Grindr City are a diverse bunch, but we tend to cluster into distinct subgroups (we call them tribes). The services that Grindr directs us to are tailored to the needs of our tribe and help us feel like we belong.

In the Old World, when universal health care 563
was being dismantled, Grindr stepped in to help. They listened to health experts and encouraged us to disclose our HIV status and viral load. They wanted to challenge the stigma around HIV and promote the benefits of Pre-Exposure Prophylaxis and 'treatment as prevention' to combat the retrovirus. I don't know how well it worked. Lots of us did start being more honest about our health status; but I still remember seeing some men stating that they were only interested in

3 Venturebeat (2016) "Mobile apps analytics: how Grindr monetizes 6 million users (webinar)." *Venturebeat.* Link: https://venturebeat.com/2016/04/05/mobile-app-analytics-how-grindr-monetizes-6-million-active-users-webinar/

meeting 'clean people.' All that got worse for a while back in 2018 when troublemakers revealed that Grindr was sharing data, including our HIV status, with businesses and agencies we'd never heard of. Some people walked away. The panic quickly subsided and was forgotten. We understood that Grindr knew what was best for us.

One thing that helped with building Grindr City 564
was when we formed our tribes. Even before the city became a reality, we got to declare which tribe we belonged to—Bear, Clean-cut, Daddy, Discreet, Geek, Jock, Leather, Otter, Poz, Rugged, Trans or Twink[4]; as well as the tribes whose members we're looking for. Even Basics can name their tribe and choose only to see the members of the tribes they're hot for. The tribal system has shaped the city more than we imagined it could. Most of us are not so closed-minded that we only hang out with our own tribe; but we certainly use the filters to avoid contact with some of them. Xtras certainly prefer to live around members of their own tribe. Though, the Discreet tribe never really worked out how to hang out with each other and always seem to lurk on the edge of others' territories.

Lots of people make the mistake of thinking 565
there are only men in Grindr City, but that's not true. There's a place here for our Trans sisters, always has been. But there are other women here—not just in the wider city, beyond the app, but in Grindr City too. They mostly live with the Discreets. I have some fantastic women colleagues at work, who I love chatting to (when I can drag myself away from the men on Grindr). It's nice to keep a connection with them, they help me

4 Bonner-Thompson, C. (2017) "'The meat market': production and regulation of masculinities on the Grindr grid in Newcastle-upon-Tyne, UK." *Gender, Place & Culture.* 24(11): pp. 1611-1625.

to find my way in the wider city on those rare occasions I decide to see what lies beyond our space. I've read the history books and I know that, in the past, gay men used to hide away in the closet out of shame. But our reality feels different. I don't think we're hiding, but a lot of the time, I don't see the point of engaging with the city beyond Grindr more than I absolutely have to.

Even before they took control, Grindr helped me understand my place in the city differently. Before Grindr, I used to go out to the bars and the old cruising grounds to find other gays (I could never afford to live in one of those mythical gaybourhoods). But when Grindr came along I saw my neighbours differently. It didn't matter if I never chatted to them, I knew they were there. But, then as now, seeing who else is around can be too revealing, and sometimes I have to liberally use the block function.

Because the app sorts users by their distance from each other, over time I've found myself rethinking distance in the city. If I'm horny, I want to connect with someone nearby, or within easy reach. That changed how I thought about the city and the people within it. But sometimes the app could trick you—a place that was only a short distance away across the city could still be a pain to get to without a car. This became a problem in the city, if we got too stuck in one place (and some of us did), then the app and its services began to have less appeal. We needed to circulate and be mobile for everything to keep working. In the early years of the City, Grindr addressed this by integrating subsidised 24-hour transport services into the functionality of the app, and reshaping the city's infrastructure to facilitate the journeys that the data

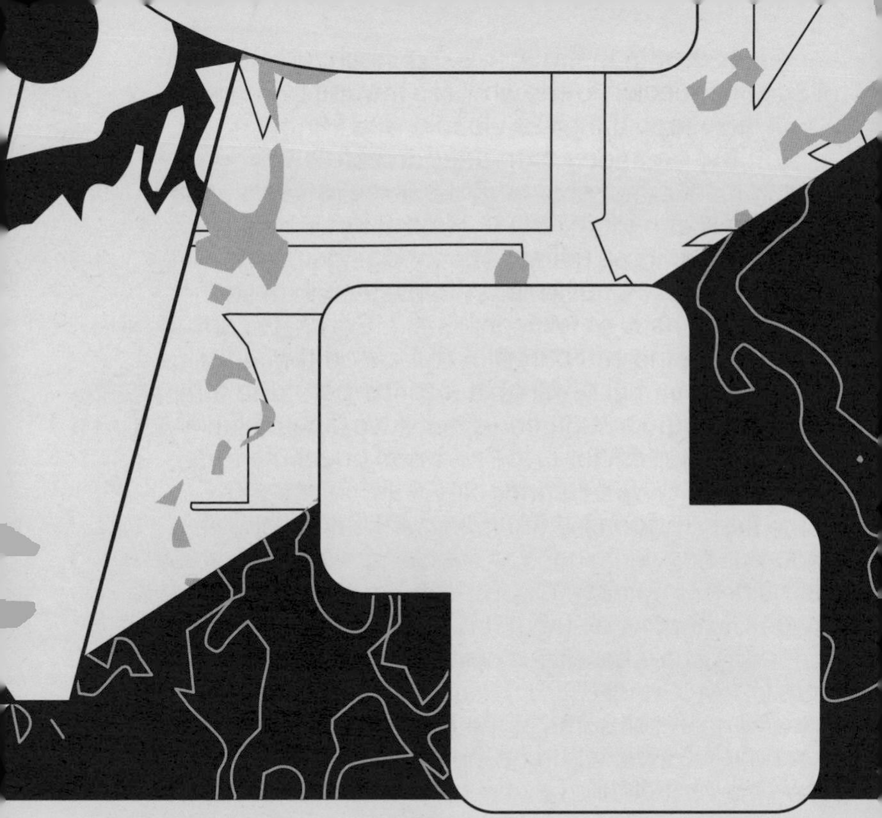

told them we, collectively, made most often. Realising that many of us were nocturnal and liked to meet up after the bars closed, they massively expanded regular public transport through the night.

People used to worry that the app might kill off the bars and we would all retreat into our homes. And that did happen a bit, but we learned to open up our homes to strangers too. Of course, then as now, lots of people couldn't always accommodate others at home. Having a space of your own to hang out with your dates in is part of the Xtra dream. But why restrict ourselves to home? We learned to integrate the app into all aspects of our lives. At first, people were a bit reticent about being seen to use it in public and would position themselves in a crowded place so that others couldn't see their screen.[5] I once knew someone, back in the early days, who kept getting caught checking Grindr in lectures at uni—I think the lecturer was irritated by him chatting, but it was the dick pics all over his screen that really embarrassed my mate. Since we've formed Grindr City, though, we've overcome that embarrassment (most of the time, anyway) and most big workplaces and malls now have spaces put aside for quick hook-ups. Basics can rent those spaces, cheaply, by the hour; but Xtras benefit from spaces that are shared and held in common, just for us.

I love Grindr City. I've never had so much fun as I've had here. But some of the Basics I talk to confess that on bad days, when no-one's interested in them, when they've had one blunt rejection too many, or been ghosted by yet another guy, they find themselves wanting more. The solution seems simple to me, go Xtra!

Acknowledgements

With thanks to Cesare Di Feliciantonio and Dave Ashby for their critical comments on an earlier version of this text.

5 Miles, S. (2017) "Sex in the digital city: location-based dating apps and queer urban life." *Gender, Place & Culture.* 24(11): pp. 1595-1610.

Gavin Brown is a professor of political geography at the University of Leicester, where their research examines the intersections of critical geopolitics and the geographies of sexualities. They are the author of five books including *Youth Activism and Solidarity: the non-stop picket against apartheid* (2017).

MONETIZING MOVEMENT

GROUNDTRUTH[1]

Harrison Smith, University of Newcastle

A sales pitch with a potential client

Sales: 570
'Good morning. I understand you're interested in learning about our platform. I'm in charge of customer outreach, so I can explain what we do and how our product can help grow your business. Let's start by you telling me a bit about your company.'

Client:
'Right, so we're a medium sized QSR, a Quick Service Restaurant, with locations across several states and a desire for expansion. Our company ethos is to provide slow food, fast. It gives customers the feeling of quality while being casual. We tend to see the most sales at lunch, and we've been focusing on white collar occupations, service sector employees – that sort of thing. We need to figure out how to reach new customers, especially millennials, because our products cater to a more discerning niche that wants healthy food on-the-go. We think the QSR market is changing from the usual burgers and fries towards a whole new set of choices, like our farm-to-table certified organic tempeh wraps. We want customers to feel proactive about their diets, and nurture an authentic connection with their lifestyles.'

1 The following speculative fiction sales pitch highlights the ways in which places are being socially sorted through data brokers specializing in location data. Such a thought experiment could equally apply to other companies specialising in mobile data analytics, such as GroundTruth, Localytics, NinthDecimal, PlaceIQ, or Factual. Product or corporate names may be trademarks or registered trademarks, and are used only for the purpose of conducting a thought experiment without intent to infringe.

Sales:
'Well, I think we can help with that. So, our 30 second sales pitch is that we are *the* location based advertising platform. We operate across a whole ecosystem of mobile applications, and can reach about 120 million monthly users. We see over 25 billion location data points every year. We're currently the largest such platform in the world by far. Nobody comes close to our reach and scale.'

Client:
'Wait, I'm not sure I understand. What's a location-based advertising platform? How does it work?'

Sales:
'Essentially, publishers install our proprietary Software Development Kit into their apps to monetize them. When you first launch a new app, it asks some important questions that most people agree to without much thought, such as, can the app use your location. If you agree, the app is authorized to collect location data. This can be passed onto us to serve contextually relevant content, like ads.'

Client:
'So, when a user authorizes an app to access their location, you can also get the data, but they don't know who you are?'

Sales:
'Yes, because we're *part* of the platform! Users only see the interface. Third parties like us are invisible, save for the ads we serve them. It's the beauty of the mobile ecosystem, really. Publishers and advertisers working together to serve relevant content to specific audiences, in real-time and in real-world situations. It's just like the kind of digital advertising you'd see when browsing the internet, only this time it's on your phone, and your phone is a much more intimate channel. It knows exactly where you are at all times. It's all in the privacy policies and terms of use; you can read all about it if you want.'

Client:
'Okaaaay.'

Sales:
'Look, you want to know the local weather, we need your location. Simple as that. Once you give us that data, we can do what we want with it, and believe me, there's a huge gold rush to develop location-based apps right now, so our reach and scale will continue to grow.'

Client:
'But it seems a bit more complicated than how you describe it. Surely location is sensitive information? And tracking where people are all the time seems quite intrusive?'

Sales:
'You're looking at it the wrong way. This is an opportunity more than a risk. Customers are seeking meaningful relationships with the brands they love. Their phone is the best way to connect with them. They keep their phones on them at all times, and interact with them about 150 times a day, if not more! They're on the go seeking information that's locally relevant, such as a nearby restaurant for lunch. We see these moments as opportunities, and unlike those boring banner ads you see on websites, our ads are much more authentic because they use location data.'

Client:
'Yeah, sure, but does that really mean every time we look at our phones we should have marketers tapping us on our shoulder? Wouldn't this risk making my brand seem like a nuisance?'

Sales:
'Think about it. The whole world is now like one big retailer thanks to smartphones! I can use my phone to discover things of local interest. In a store I can use my phone to look up the same product in front of me and compare products, see consumer reviews, and find a cheaper vendor. Suppose we know you frequent fast food joints, and say it's lunchtime, we could hit you with targeted ads at the right time and the right place. Your restaurant could be that ad.'

Client:
'But do folks want to be bombarded with advertising on their phones? Aren't they cautious about this kind of targeting?'

Sales:
'Maybe, but they do like using free apps, and that's the cost of doing business the way we see it. Besides, it's not really about singling people out, but making associations that haven't been done before. We know people based on actual, measurable behaviour. Location is the ultimate truth. What's even better is that, if I know who goes to McDonald's on a regular basis, I could target them with all sorts of relevant ads, not just for McDonald's, or their competitors, but entirely different stores that match their profile, like Walmart, because we know that people who regularly visit McDonald's also visit Walmart.'

Client:

'I could have told you that without all this fancy data analytics your platform does or giving you my business. And I'm not interested in people who go to Walmart or McDonald's, I need something more specific.'

Sales:
'And this is what our platform can do that, really, your marketing instincts might not be able to. We can use the platform to create a population of targets that meet virtually any criteria and give you the power to custom build your audiences and hit them at specific moments. You mentioned they like to live healthier lifestyles? How about we target people who go to gyms or yoga studios regularly? What about Wholefoods or organic retailers?'

Client: '
That's a pretty good start...'

Sales:
'You said they have discerning tastes? How about targeting people that visit art galleries and museums? They probably like to travel. How about people that are observed in airports? Jet setters are more sophisticated, from a marketing point of view, at

least. They tend to be high net-worth individuals, have disposable income, and are interested in cultural experiences. They seek quality brands, and you are just what they want. If they fly for work, they want healthy food on the go to keep sharp. Bear in mind these premium audience packages do come at a slightly higher price, but that's the cost of doing business with lucrative markets.'

Client:
'What about things like age and ethnicity? Can you control for that? Sounds to me that knowing somebody's location might not really be able to give you that kind of detail.'

Sales: 590
'We can also serve ads to residents of specific postal codes, meaning you can include and exclude all kinds of people. We know where people live because of where the phones are regularly observed when people tend to be asleep. It's simply a matter of geo-coding those locations to specific postal codes and thereby inferring all kinds of demographic information like mean household income, education, ethnicity, sexual orientation – these kinds of things.'

Client: 'I'm honestly not sure how comfortable I feel about my phone – or my customers' – reporting on me at night like that. And how do you know it works?'

Sales:
'We regularly audit the platform's performance and efficiency. We verify location signals. Correct inaccuracies. Remove outliers, and use this data to predict patterns. No other marketing platform can do this. Best of all, it's based on real world and real time data points. We don't guess anything.'

Client:
'Hang on a second, what about privacy? There's no way most people would be ok with this. I've just read that most people are uncomfortable with marketers tracking them on social media, how could you possibly justify this on their phones?'

Sales:
'We take every step to protect this data and respect the privacy of users. This data is proprietary after all! We adhere to all the self-regulatory policies as put forth by the IAA, DAA, DAAC, the UK's Good Practice Principles for Online Behavioural Advertising, and the European IDAA's self-regulatory principles!'

Client:
'What do you mean by self-regulatory principles? Are there no laws that regulate this kind of thing?'

Sales:
'Look, I'm here to tell you about the platform. Leave the laws to other people. All you need to know is that it's perfectly legal. As far as self-regulation goes, we firmly believe that the market can effectively self-regulate privacy, and all these organizations set out a list of best practices for minimizing risk that members say they'll adhere to. There's even a few marketing associations out there that are working to prescribe best practices, so government need not interfere! Besides, regulatory agencies haven't established any clear laws to limit mobile tracking, and yeah sometimes there's a few bad apples that take it too far, but they've been punished. As far as we see it, we're pushing the envelope on innovative marketing AdTech. As a final point, if for some reason people want to opt-out they can! All these advertising bodies offer opt-out settings for those privacy conscious markets. You just have to download an app, or you can register your MAC address with specific out-out registries like the Future of Privacy Forum.'

Client:
'I've never heard of any of this stuff...'

Sales: 'Well really that's not our fault, and people should read the terms of use. Besides, you stand to benefit from this kind of advertising. Our platform gives you both precision and results. What's best is that our newest self-serve product allows you to do all this by yourself! Just like restaurants, advertising has also changed and the AdTech market is overwhelmingly complex. We like to simplify the whole process so you can target the right people in the right places. Remember, in today's market, your value is your relevance, and location is relevance.'

Client:
'Maybe you're right, but it sounds like your company is walking a fine line between relevance and something else. I can't help but wonder too what would happen if this kind of platform was licensed for government use, or if the police started doing this. So who really uses your product?'

Sales: 600
'Well, to start, your competitors. But that's beside the point. You need to remember this isn't just about you and your competitors. It's about how your customers need these platforms to live happy, healthy lives in cities. You know our platform can be used for more than just ads. We work with charities, non-governmental organizations, and could even help city planning departments!'

Client:
'So, what, this means I need to hop on the bandwagon just because everyone else is? We're talking about a lot of assumptions here, especially about actual ad exposure. Wouldn't I be better off simply putting up posters or billboards in neighbourhoods near my restaurant? I mean, that really is the original use of location for marketing. Frankly, I don't see how a tiny banner ad on an app would really be a good use of my money.'

Sales:
'Except that with our product I can tell you how many people that saw your ad were later at your store. Billboards can't do that, well not yet at least. Others are working on that. This is not simply a bandwagon or marketing gimmick. Think about it, we're talking about monetizing movement itself! It's potential is way beyond just about increasing the bottom line. This is about reshaping how we understand and manage places, neighbourhoods and cities so that people can be easily tracked from A to B for all kinds of applications and markets. We can use foot traffic

reports to tell clients where to build new locations and to know which communities are more valuable than others, speaking from an investment point of course. Political candidates can exploit our insights to know what neighbourhoods to target during campaigns. Retailers can optimize product placements. What if law enforcement could use this for crime prevention to track the bad guys? Why, just recently one company worked with the Federation of Internet Alerts to assist in targeted alerts of child abductions and saw a 2160% increase in click-through rates. That's way higher than the mobile industry average! Better still, it led to a 98% increase in abduction recovery rates!' We could use this platform to track people for all sorts of reasons, and for restaurateurs like yourself, the potential to discreetly influence their choices from one restaurant to another are endless, and all of this will be easily measured and quantified clients can see the impacts of campaigns on real targets and real world behaviours.'

Client:
'I guess when you put it like that...'

Sales:

'Trust me, this is going to revolutionize the intersection of people, places, and media. Cities won't be the same. Why? Because we make them alive with opportunity for creating new and engaging marketing campaigns! Being on the sideline only delays the inevitable. So, how 'bout it, would you like to see a demo?'

Harrison Smith is a research associate at the Global Urban Research Unit (GURU) in the School of Architecture, Planning and Landscape at Newcastle University. His research broadly focuses on the political economy of location analytics and platforms in contemporary urban life.

FLAT-PACK SMART URBANISM

IKEA[1]

Martin Dodge,
University of Manchester

A global furniture retailer with instant name recogni- 606
tion, IKEA's motto, *"To create a better everyday life for the many people"*, could equally be applied to many smart cities projects that promise to improve the way people live. IKEA has built a multi-billion pound corporate empire on the logics of flat-pack distribution, with its customers actively enrolled in a central aspect of the production process. The cost of the labour of assemblage, which takes a non-trivial amount of time, physical effort and degree of skill, has been shifted from the paid employees of the manufacturer onto the end-user. Importantly, IKEA customers are knowingly participating in the belief that the 'deal' is beneficial one—they get the furniture they want quickly, easily and at cheap prices.

IKEA is synonymous with a mode of consumer 607
capitalism dubbed 'prosumption',[2] that is now widely

1 The following academic article speculates on how a city might be run and experienced if Ikea's business model was adopted. Product or corporate names may be trademarks or registered trademarks, and are used only for identification, explanation and speculation as part of a thought experiment without intent to infringe.

2 Ritzer, G. and Jurgenson, N. (2010) "Production, consumption, prosumption: The nature of capitalism in the age of the digital 'prosumer.'" *Journal of Consumer Culture*. 10(1): 13-36.

seen in other retail and services contexts (such as self-service check-in and payment systems). In some cases, this can be seen as an equitable sharing of effort, with both sides winning (e.g., the customer getting faster service and more convenience), but in other contexts it's simply a mandatory shifting of requirements and cost-cutting by powerful businesses and institutions. "In prosumer capitalism", Ritzer and Jurgenson argue "control and exploitation take on a different character than in the other forms of capitalism; there is a trend toward unpaid rather than paid labor and toward offering products at no cost, and the system is marked by a new abundance where scarcity once predominated."[3]

Is IKEA's approach of prosumption, based on 608
self-assembly of its key products, a useful way to think about future urbanism? Is IKEA, with its focus on cheap, mass-production, and the significant cost deferment and convenience of flat-pack distribution, a model that is viable—and *desirable*—in regards to city administration in an era of smart technologies, pervasive digital media and software platforms, and demands for much greater social and environmental sustainability?

Effective citizen participation: self-assembly in the smart city

IKEA's unique selling proposition rests upon 609
the scale of participation in the flat-pack mode of prosumption. Hundreds of millions of pieces of IKEA furniture have been put together by householders and subsequently used. While the end results might not be as well built as the ones in IKEA showrooms, some

3 Ibid. p. 14

argue persuasively that benefits often come from a sense of genuine satisfaction felt by those having achieved the practical self-assembly task. The resulting furniture is not just a generic object, but one that contains elements of personal labour—*"I built that bookcase!"* This so-called 'IKEA effect' according to psychologists is a "measurable cognitive bias in which consumers place a disproportionately high value on products they partially created."[4]

Engendering and encouraging the 'IKEA ef- 610
fect' has merit beyond obtaining cheap home furniture and it is worth considering how far it might help city management and urban services delivery. Could the future smart city be transformed *positively* through greater enrolment of the self-assembly ethos?

There are multiple benefits of enhancing volun- 611
tary participation to self-assemble more aspects of the city, which can be facilitated through smart technologies, easier data sharing and online collaboration platforms. These include: greater efficiency and flexibility, and potentially the speed of response; the advantages of distributed set of actors in terms of local knowledge, 'boots-on-the-ground' and resilience; creating more of a 'can-do attitude', helping to counter cynicism and apathy, and thereby fostering a better sense of communal belonging; building lasting bonds of trust in solving local problems; bringing new ideas and perspectives to solve long-standing urban problems.

But digitisation, automation, and the need for 612
ever more fixed infrastructures are widening economic inequalities in many places. There are many struggling disconnected places and disenfranchised people, and other households in more affluent middle

4 Norton, MI., Mochon, D. and Ariely, D. (2012) "The IKEA effect: When labor leads to love." *Journal of Consumer Psychology*. 22(3): 453-60.

class situations have retreated from the public realm, ensconced safely in techno-facilitated domestic sphere with the affirmation of like-minded social media friends, next-day deliveries, and travel exclusively in automobile cocoons. One might point out the parallels to long-standing critiques of IKEA and its style of prosumption, that it is about satisfying individualistic needs by self-assembly rather than participation for wider social-good. The flat-pack ethos is "necessarily a disengagement with the collective sphere, a sense that the most beneficial work is carried out when one is sheltered from, rather than an active participant in, social reality."[5]

Many smart citizen initiatives and urban crowd- 613
sourcing data collection projects have been criticised for being exclusionary, socially self-selecting and biased, with some potentially leading to partial and inconsistent service coverage that depends on vagaries of volunteerism; this can easily disadvantages places without economic or social capital.[6] Decades of effort since the 1970s to engender public participation in the urban planning process, for example, shows how hard it is to be broadly inclusive and overcome structural barriers.[7]

In respect to the pros and cons of digitally en- 614
hanced citizen participation it is also worth articulating the continued value of public servants, with expertise and experience to manage cities, rather than trying to galvanise amateurs to self-assemble urban services. Having a trained person rooted in a sense of public service and ethos, and who is subject to daily management, still has advantages over the unpredictability of volunteer prosumers.

5 Hartman, T. (2007) "On the Ikeaization of France." *Public Culture*. 19(3): 483-498.

6 For example, see: (1) Hecht, B.J. and Stephens, M. (2014) "A tale of cities: urban biases in volunteered geographic information." *International AAAI Conference on Web and Social Media (ICWSM)*. 14: 197-205. (2) Dodge, M. and Kitchin, R. (2013) "Crowdsourced: cartography: mapping experience and knowledge." *Environment and Planning A*. 45(1), 19-36.

7 Beebeejaun, Y. (2006) "The participation trap: The limitations of participation for ethnic and racial groups." *International Planning Studies*. 11(1): 3-18.

Cheap and wasteful consumerism to smart and more sustainable cities

Mass production and high volume sales are the *modus operandi* of IKEA, and its sustained profitability has stemmed partly from selling acceptable quality goods for less and less. Many of its most popular furniture products are cheaper to buy today in real terms than they were decades ago. The manufacturing for key IKEA product lines is large-scale, efficient and highly automated.[8] However, such a manta of cheapness comes at a cost, with critics arguing that the "relentless fixation on low price ... drove [people] away from quality, durability, and craftsmanship and towards quantity, quantity, and more quantity."[9] The allure of cheap prices also means forcing alternative (often smaller, local, higher-quality) providers out of the market and wielding unequal power in the exploitation of overseas suppliers with harmful impacts on labour standards and local livelihoods. Is such ruthless low cost model the ways that smart cities should precede? 615

Over the last few decades IKEA has played a role in driving excessive consumption practices, despite the mantra of sustainability that is advanced in its more recent corporate messaging. While the IKEA President and CEO Jesper Brodlin claims "It's about making life at home as sustainable as possible, ensuring we use resources carefully...",[10] the company has undoubtedly been one of the standard bearers for consumerism that is premised on individualism, transient fashion, and status obsession. Notwithstanding the 'IKEA effect' noted above, cheap MDF products, 616

8 BBC, 2018 *Flatpack Empire*, television documentary BBC / Open University. Link: http://www.open.edu/openlearn/tv-radio-events/tv/flatpack-empire

9 Shell, E.R. (2009) *Cheap: The High Cost of Discount Culture.* London: Penguin.

10 *IKEA Yearly Summary FY17* (2017) Link: http://www.ikea.com/gb/en/this-is-ikea/newsroom/reports-download/

in many eyes "fall into that lowermost category of possessions that are left behind at the time of moving"[11] IKEA's approach down the years has both reflected and reinforced wasteful consumerism and the tacit normalisation of a 'throw-away' culture that pervades Western society. It also sustains the profits of so many large technology companies with their unrepairable devices and inbuilt obsolescence,[12] sometimes enforced by covert software 'downgrades.'

The relentless pressure to consume more and more is self-destructive and is arguably, bound-up with deep sense of discontent many people feel in the West in spite of the high levels of material comfort they enjoy. As homes have become full to bursting point with cheap material products there seems to be less sense of pleasure in all the stuff that surrounds people. It seems doubly ironic that a key part of IKEA's design rationale stems from providing more space-efficient domestic 'storage solutions' to deal with over-accumulation of the stuff they are promulgating and profiting from. As a recent IKEA corporate missive noted, "[a] s the world becomes more crowded, and people find themselves with less space, money and time, we have the passion and energy to bring solutions."[13] 617

Do we want smarter cities that trail along in IKEA's wake, encouraging more material consumption? Or is there a different route toward more genuine sustainability based on social technologies for sharing and reusing things? There is, for example, scope for software platforms, working at the micro-local scales that build upon the enduring potential of second-hand shops.[14] This can be coupled with the much easier 618

11 Hartman, T. (2007) "On the Ikeaization of France." *Public Culture*. 19(3): p.495.

12 LeBel, S. (2016) "Fast machines, slow violence: ICTs, planned obsolescence, and e-waste." *Globalizations*. 13(3): 300-309.

13 *IKEA Yearly Summary FY17* (2017) Link: http://www.ikea.com/gb/en/this-is-ikea/newsroom/reports-download/

sharing of underutilised resources and 'freecycling' surplus domestic goods that can been empowered by digital media[15]. One area that has real potential would be urban mobility and improving on the unsustainable car culture that dominates city spaces and seriously pollutes urban environments[16]. Social collaboration facilitated by digital platforms, could make neighbourhood car pools and ride sharing much more viable solutions. The really sustainable future for congested, polluted cities, however, is not individual use vehicles—even if they are fully electric and highly Uberised—but efficient collective travel on buses.

Conclusion

The nature of flat-pack smart urbanism would mean cities coming into being differently in terms of citizen engagement, cost reduction, greater efficiency and convenience, and scope for a circular economy. Smart cities that followed IKEA's lead would more fully embrace the self-assembling ethos and there are benefits from many more people who would be doing it for themselves, particularly in terms of flexibility and community ties. But it is uncertain whether large-scale amateur participatory activities, even if well-coordinated by digital platforms, would be effective for urban management. There are real challenges of volunteer fatigue, especially with dull and repetitive tasks. There are also dangers of loss of memory and reinventing the wheel as new volunteer recruits cycle through. Perhaps it is not a case of paid professionals versus no cost amateurs, but some kind of novel combinations

14 On the history and significance of this kind of consumption, that has often been shunned and presented as transgressive, see Gregson, N. and Crewe, L. (2003) *Second-hand Cultures*.

15 Klug, K. (2017) "A gift for a stranger: Freecycling as a current lifestyle of sustainable consumption," in Osburg, T. and Lohrman, C. (eds.) *Sustainability in a Digital World*. London: Springer, pp. 201-7.

16 IKEA's big box, out of town, retail model has been premised on car-based consumerism of course.

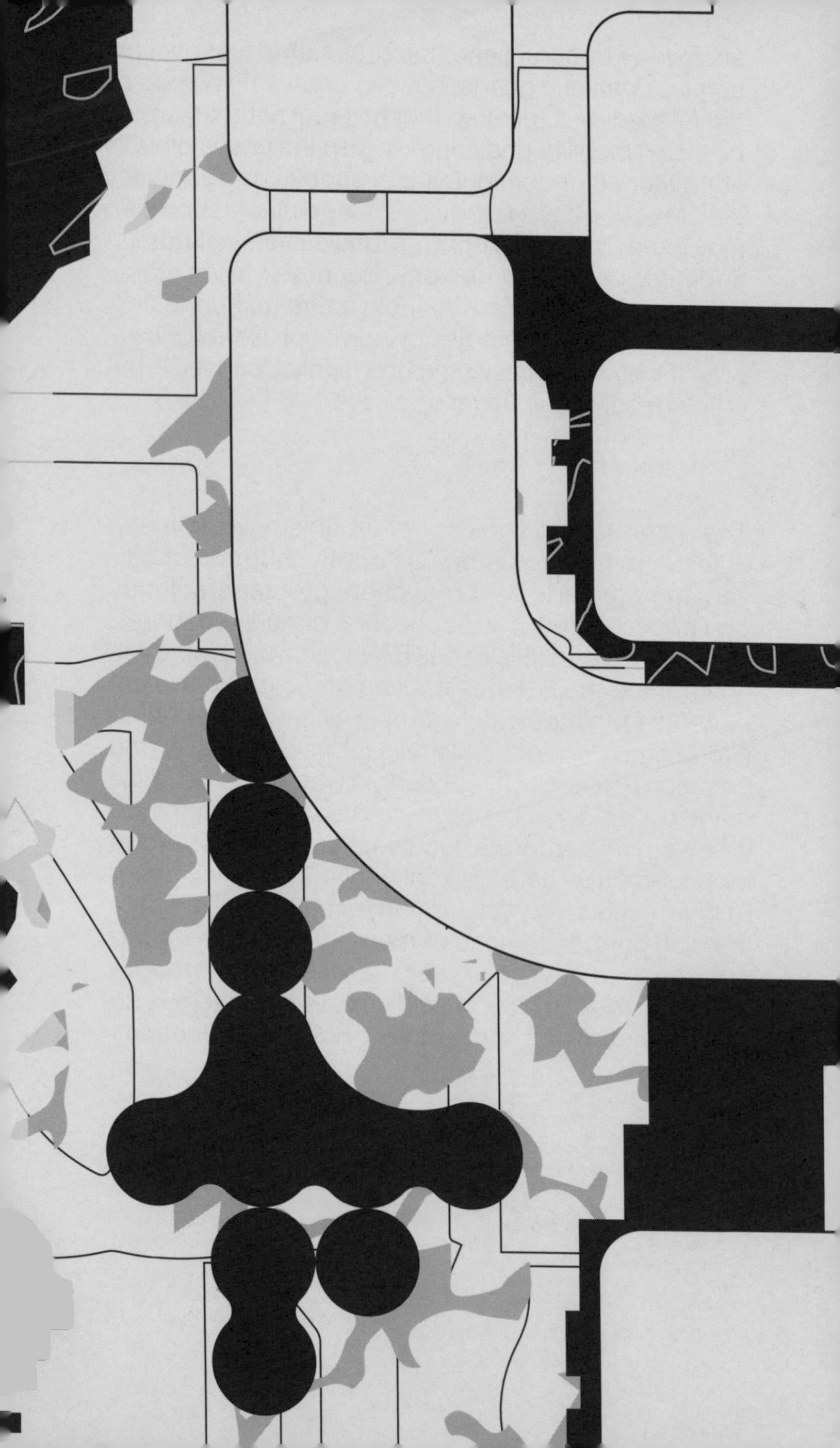

and appropriate enrolment of volunteers that will bring most benefits to smart cities.

Flat-pack urbanism will be bring cost reductions 620
which will key into existing mantras that smart technologies can deliver more for less. However, the 'IKEA effect', in terms of digitally facilitated active citizenship can be criticised as little more than window-dressing for cynical burden-shifting by the State[17]. Getting people more 'active' might be beneficial, but all too often it simply bolsters the deeper neoliberal retreat of the State and can actually undermine the accepted Western social democratic compact whereby the government provides essential services, universal welfare support and holds long term guardianship for the public realm using funds from fair taxation system.

Lastly, there is potential for smart technologies 621
to steer a course to a more sustainable urbanism by shunning the wastefulness of IKEA style flat-pack consumerism of the last few decades. The result would be a positive step towards a so-called 'circular economy' with the "avoidance of waste and return of lost resources into the flow of resources through the economy will of itself stimulate further economic activity."[18] Smart technology could engender the antithesis of IKEA's 'make-use-waste' model creating the sort of prosperity and city living that we need in the Anthropocene.

17 Wiig, A. (2016) "The empty rhetoric of the smart city: from digital inclusion to economic promotion in Philadelphia." *Urban Geography.* 37(4): 535-53.

18 Crocker, R., Saint, C., Chen, G. and Tong, Y. (eds.) (2018) *Unmaking Waste in Production and Consumption: Towards the Circular Economy.* Bingley: Emerald Publishing.

Martin Dodge is a Senior Lecturer in Human Geography at the University of Manchester and his research focuses on historical urban geographies, the politics of cartography, and understanding of infrastructures. He has co-authored several books the spatiality of digital technologies - *Mapping Cyberspace* (2000) and *Code/Space* (2011).

A CITY OF DIGITAL ENGAGEMENT

INSTAGRAM[1]

Ryan Burns, University of Calgary

[_of-insta_'s notifications]

n0rmc0r3 started following you 2 h
n0rmc0r3 liked your post 41 m
n0rmc0r3 and painted_heaven liked your post 39 m
n0rmc0r3, jjacobs, me.llamo.maria, and 3 others liked your post 29 s

n0rmc0r3 mentioned you in a comment: @_of-insta_ your pictures are sick. I love how informative they are! you live in that city that won Instagram's new headquarters competition a few years ago, right? 4 s

● _of-Insta_:

Hey @n0rmc0r3, thought I'd respond here in a DM, in the interest of privacy! Thanks for the compliment. Yeah, I live there. It's a pretty cool experiment, if you ask me!

● n0rmc0r3:

yeah, it sounds like it! what's it like living there? I heard they employ, like, everyone?

1 The following speculative fiction and satire imagines a city being run by a social media company. Such a thought experiment could equally apply if the city were run by Facebook or Twitter. Product or corporate names may be trademarks or registered trademarks, and are used only for the purpose of conducting a thought experiment without intent to infringe.

● _of-Insta_:

That's right! Officially, they are the only employer in the city. Even the service sector employees get their checks signed by IG. It was a contract they signed with the city government, which basically handed the keys over to the company! I guess they're finally listening to us who say government should be run like a business.

It's amazing. All we have to do to get things we need, like file for unemployment checks or to clean graffiti up is snap a photo and tag the city's IG account! It creates a public queue, so you know how many are waiting in front of you and you know that your request isn't getting lost in all that silly bureaucratic paperwork. The city usually reposts your request in its own Story so you always know where you stand.

● n0rmc0r3:

whoa! that's way more efficient, and we're all on Instagram anyway, so why not? my news station said it also helps with crime because the police department can create profiles for people based on what they post. but what about that unemployment you mentioned? why isn't Instagram employing everyone?

● _of-Insta_:

I don't know much about those profiles you're talking about. They told us it was for providing better services... Seems a little surveillant...

West_precinct_PD just liked your post 1 m
West_precinct_PD started following you 36 s

● _of-Insta_:

I don't know why, but there are a lot of homeless people here. Probably just people who don't want to work. Instagram has jobs, if people want them.

And anyway, everyone in the city is given a free smartphone, so we all have access to the platform and public services.

● n0rmc0r3:

and I don't understand why there would be homeless people...?

wait, what?!?! everyone gets a free phone? crazy! do you get all the apps for free, too?

n0rmc0r3 sent you a picture

● n0rmc0r3:

that's one of our tent cities in that pic. it's on the fence outside of Amazon's office here in my city.

● _of-Insta_:

Well, I guess there were a lot of people who were laid off in the transition, and there might be some people who weren't trained in Instagram's new programming language. That's probably why. I mean, the radicals say these big companies routinely lay people off to keep labour fluid, but that's just a conspiracy theory.

The phones they give us have Instagram already installed! Oh, and Facebook, too! So it's ready to go. I guess we have to pay for any others we want.

deposed_arnstein liked your post 1 h
deposed_arnstein commented on your post: *thanks for reporting so much about our neighbourhood! you're making it a better place!* 41 m

● _of-Insta_:

Check this out - the new version of the IG app has a filter that gives us information about the city! All we do is open the app and apply the "Your City" filter, and we can see real-time information about the landscapes in front of us. So we can get a history lesson by using IG. Most retail and restaurants deliver coupons that way, too - it's easy, since they're all franchised through IG!

the_city_experience just liked your post 40s

● n0rmc0r3:

ah, now I see why your pics are always so informative - you post using that filter that overlays info. weird, we didn't get that filter where I'm from... I just looked it up, and it's crazy! it was bigger than Pokémon Go! I wonder why we can't get it here...?

city_nomads just tagged you in a post: *we've just released a new line of Instagram-flavoured cocktails - experience with the new Boomerang playback function! come see us, friends me.llamo.maria, _of-Insta_, golds_kleim, r_florida* 22s

● n0rmc0r3:

looks like you prefer the historic information. but how do you know where to go to find interesting stuff?

city_business_strategy just started a live video: *Attend our virtual town hall to hear our plans for growth for the next 10-20 years!* 4 m

● _of-Insta_:

It's usually marked in big, bold IG icons scattered throughout the city. I think they do it that way so the view will be really Instagrammable! It's where the most aesthetically-pleasing places are where we get the most interesting historic information.

I also found my new favourite pizzeria through the filter. I used to go to one that had been around for, like, three generations, but it closed a few years ago right when all the changes started happening. There were new pizzerias popping up that were offering coupons in the filter, and they had some cool new Silicon Valley tech and just left behind the older ones that refused to be franchised when IG took over. Plus, the new ones were right on the edges of the city's bad neighbourhoods, and those areas are now cleaned up with cool new shops and more trendy restaurants.

● n0rmc0r3:

oh yeah, I've seen those icons. looks like
a great way to experience the city!
so, lots of new places to go. awesome!
did the rent go up in those areas?

● _of-Insta_:

Oh, well, I can't afford to go to those shops because they're too pricey. And the plazas aren't really public, but as long as I am exploring the "Your City" filter the security guards won't bother me.

Rent went way up there, and developers started redeveloping because of all the blight that was there. But we can still see pictures of the old buildings in the app!

● n0rmc0r3:

oh, they're keeping tabs on what you have open on your phone? that's a little weird... I wonder if that's why we can't get it here? anyway, thanks for the info. I'm jealous you get to live there!

[48 hours later]

Your friends haven't heard from you in a while! Tell them about your day using our new additions to the "Your City" filter! 12m

● n0rmc0r3:

yo, I heard something today about the overlay filter. I think some contraband information got out in the new update last night?

● _of-Insta_:

Really? I haven't been out today. I'll go try to use the filter and let you know.

You sent a photo to n0rmc0r3

● _of-Insta_:

This is so strange... I used the filter to find information about our central square, and it said something about labour protests there after unions went on strike to demand better working conditions, like, a hundred years ago.

I'd never read about whatever this "organized labour" thing is. I guess it wasn't put into our school textbooks.

● n0rmc0r3:

I heard it was a programmer at IG that leaked the information. she said something about superficial gestures or something. here's what our city news said: "Maria, who has admitted to the leak, responded, 'The city wants to pretend that they are more deeply engaging their denizens by soliciting likes and organizing their information with hashtags. And sure, they were probably getting more discrete interactions by those metrics, but this has completely replaced the millennia-old practice of organized political resistance with a shallow feel-good clicktivism that bolsters the corporation's bottom line.'"

● _of-Insta_:

Maria, at IG? Wow, I know her through a friend! I'm going to DM her and see what she thinks she's doing.

OK, I DM'd her. I asked what the big deal is, 650
why she's disrupting all our lives by hijacking the filter. I said it doesn't really matter what their motivations are if life is better. She said, "I mean, to get to this level of buy-in required massive, structured, and regular layoffs that have led to the tent cities so prevalent across our landscapes. They'll give us all free smartphones with Instagram and Facebook installed, but can't provide affordable housing? People need to know that this isn't the only option, and that's why I leaked the information - to organize workers to demand stronger public services."

● n0rmc0r3:

so that's why your city has so many homeless people...
I just saw her on tv again. she just said, "public services should be delivered to you by virtue of your humanity, not because you use some new piece of technology the way they tell you to."

● _of-Insta_:

I still don't understand what all this has to do with "organized labour", so I sent her another message. She said, "Before Instagram took over, citizens had more recourse to public officials. They could demand things like better job security and unemployment insurance. It wasn't guaranteed, but with enough people pressuring the city government and the employers, there was greater chance you'd get it. But Instagram isn't beholden to anyone, ultimately, besides the shareholders. I knew the "Your City" app was designed for coupons, ads, and historic information, so I wanted to remind everyone that organized labour once had a strong presence in our city. I can't believe how fast we forgot it."

You sent a photo to nOrmcOr3

● _of-Insta_:

You can see the protests forming in the streets in that pic I just sent you. I'm going to go out and see what else is upsetting people, and what we can do about it.

Ryan Burns is a professor of urban geographic information science at University of Calgary. His research interests are in the social, political, and institutional implications of new spatial technologies, including smart cities, open data, and digital humanitarianism.

SAVE THE SHIRE™

PALANTIR[1]

Jennifer Gabrys,
University of Cambridge

The VizBot scanned the digital watermark etched in 654
the retina chip of MissionBot943: Save the Shire™.
The VizBot screen flashed: Access granted. Data logs
recorded the transaction in MovementDatabase_89,
SuppliesDatabase_12, and BotDatabase_40, along
with a number of other geospatial markers for positioning and analyzing the access request to MiddleEarth.

At one time, humans in teal and black t-shirts 655
hurried around centers of power with this same logo
marked on their necks or chests: Save the Shire™.
Corporate tattooing had now advanced into embedded activation nodes, along with the flesh-to-polymer
conversion of workbots.

MissionBot943 passed through the MiddleEarth 656
portal. This was the northern edge of the 477-acre urban area, previously a sheep station set on a clear
mountain lake, but now a new city preparing for end
times.[2] The last page of the Book of Revelations had

1 The following speculative fiction and satire imagines a future scenario in which a data intelligence company, whose leadership is known to be preparing for any future disaster, builds its own city. Such a thought experiment could equally apply if the city were run by any number of search and data analytics companies involved in social network analysis and prediction, from Google to Facebook. Product or corporate names may be trademarks or registered trademarks, and are used only for the purpose of conducting a thought experiment without intent to infringe.

2 O'Connell, M. (2018) "Why Silicon Valley Billionaires Are Prepping for the Apocalypse in New Zealand." *The Guardian*. Link: https://www.theguardian.com/news/2018/feb/15/why-silicon-valley-billionaires-are-prepping-for-the-apocalypse-in-new-zealand

not yet turned, but it was certain to do so at any time. MiddleEarth continued its preparation efforts by streamlining, reinforcing and developing the data architectures needed to Save the Shire™.

Building the City of MiddleEarth had taken 657
some effort. The Founders required SyncSessions for the MiddleEarth origination and at several key stages of development. Yet SyncSessions often collided with other commitments for ensuring Founder longevity, including teenage-blood transfusions, tantric meditation, and battlefield philosophizing. The original crystal ball also needed to be sited and installed.[3] This required the importing of hallucinogenic toads from the Australian desert, which compassed and selected the ceremonial site with their collective movements. But with the contributions of hundreds of high-spec MissionBots, fully equipped with sensor nodes and connected to data managed systems, the actual construction of the core urban area was a relatively speedy affair. Once ceremony and groundbreaking were complete, the central MiddleEarth build was finalized in six months.

MissionBot943 had been assigned the task 658
of providing the inaugural tour of MiddleEarth. The Founders were joining a select group of ChinoClad Gurus, who had traveled from their PaternalSrvr Centers to join the auspicious ceremony of psychographically suitable SoViduals. The tour group would also ensure their urban data architectures were installed to specification, so that pending threats could be monitored and responded to by these most important individuals and institutions.

3 Biddle, S. (2017) “How Peter Thiel’s Palantir Helped the NSA Spy on the Whole World.” *The Intercept*. Link: https://theintercept.com/2017/02/22/how-peter-thiels-palantir-helped-the-nsa-spy-on-the-whole-world

The tour begins with an initial visit to the Data-Scrape R&D Facility. An orb-shaped building set on a V-shaped plinth greets the Founders and Gurus as they make their way to the bio-activated entrance. While raw data generation is somewhat ancillary to the core mission of building analysis infrastructure, data needs to be fed into the infrastructure from various points. This testbed facility showcases the many types of data and modes of input that UrbanClients can operationalise in order to drill down in their profiling activities.

The exceptional array of InputNodes on dis- 660
play includes data from sensors, cameras, and scanners, as well as GPS data, sales receipts, shipping
logs, phone logs, phone numbers, home addresses,
work address, flight records, IP addresses, location
data, energy meter data, water meter data, thermal
data, battery level data, browser data, search history
data, real-time raw ISP browsing data, social media
data, bank transaction data, facial recognition data,
biometric data, driver registration data, license plate
data, phone calendar data, text message logs, drone
flyover data, work activity logs, heart-rate and body
temperature data, sleep tracking data, sexual activity
data, online dating profile data, petition data, weather data, pollution data, seismic data, geospatial data,
health record data, and stingray scans for more situational deployments.

While many of these data points can be scraped 661
through APIs or pulled from open databases (the preferred method for a more progressive data politic),
some bespoke devices are necessary for generation
and harvesting.

Activity in MiddleEarth had yet to begin produc- 662
ing full datasets for preparedness and readiness, but
test sets from OldCities were available for use, with the
Los Angeles sets providing comprehensive trial cases.
If it were not for the license plate scanning furore that
brought an unfortunate end to collection efforts, this
trial set would be more up to date. Founders fought
the designation of wholesale harvesting of personal data from the public realm as illegal, but dissident
governments had banned the ScanEyes peripherals

on police units, along with a number of EliteCognitiva measures for capturing and synthesizing data points on urban citizens.

Carrying on with the tour, MissionBot943 cir- 663
cles around the base of the orb with its Founders and sovereign guests and passes through to the outer balcony surrounding the orb. From here, the group catches a view of the automated GrowGarden facilities, producing food through the power of data analysis. A few woolly mammoths graze in the adjacent fields, a successful outcome of the de-extinction program.[4] Brute nature transformed through the power of intellect. A tranquil paradise of economic prosperity.[5]

Moving to the PattrnDetect Facility, the tour 664
arrives at the core of the urban zone. Here, urban intelligence unfolds as a platform layer, analyzing and synthesizing urban data points to connect into a single lucid model of the city. Software scours through data points, and algorithms generate new models from working through the data, showing relations that would otherwise be overlooked. In the space of a single data workspace, multiple forms of data could be integrated to generate histograms, spidergrams, flow analysis, timelines, and geospatial coordinates. These scalable and mobile platforms were in the process of being deployed for analysis of all aspects of urban operations, from transport and water, to information and energy, as well as security and surveillance. An important use of the workspace was to analyse and manage social relations, including work, housing, family, and authorized recreational activities.[6] Data could be captured, analysed, and called up for enforcement in any field

4 Solon, Olivia. (2017) "Mammoth Tusk: Billionaire Peter Thiel Funded Effort to Resurrect Woolly Beast." *The Guardian*. Link: https://www.theguardian.com/technology/2017/jun/30/peter-thiel-woolly-mammoth-back-to-life-donation

5 Thiel, P. (2004). "The Straussian Moment." in *Politics & Apocalypse*, ed. R. Hamerton-Kelly. Michigan State University Press.

6 Waldman, P., Chapman, L. and Robertson, J. (2018) "Palantir Knows Everything about You." *Bloomberg*. Link: https://www.bloomberg.com/features/2018-palantir-peter-thiel

location, or it could be mobilized for more extensive analysis in the PattrnDetect Facility.

Human-computer symbiosis is the goal of 665
MiddleEarth. MissionBot943 explains this to the select gathering of Founders and Gurus, but it is redundant information as all participants are aware of the mission statement. A world of big data requires improving the quality of the interface between humans and computers. These interfaces have been streamlined across the human-machine lifecycle, from data input to integration, analysis and actuation. Security, intelligence, policing, health, disease control, food operations, supply chains, population control, education, and much more, can be managed through these data functionalities.[7]

As tests with the evolving analysis infrastructure
demonstrate, not just any humans were best equipped 666
to join in this symbiosis. It might be possible to empower an analyst to review data more quickly, and to use data to drive optimal decisions. But not all humans were able to fulfil the role of analyst. Physical, psychological and performance tests were administered at the age of 5 to identify suitable candidates. Those who were selected were given the necessary implants to ensure the realization of advanced automation and efficient data-based decision-making. SoVidual Gurus and Founders utilized the most advanced implants for overseeing Shire data operations, and were selected for their role based on hereditary pre-screening and their superior performance on administered tests.

While the SoViduals were deeply engrossed
in testing the capabilities of the workspace, Mission- 667
Bot943 alerted them about the next stop in the tour:

7 O'Connor, B. (2016) "How Palantir Is Taking over New York City. *Gizmodo.* Link: https://gizmodo.com/how-palantir-is-taking-over-new-york-city-1786738085

the OldCities Repository. As they progress to the repo, they learn that it stores a number of urban records on signal-proof servers. Many of the records document the breakdown of so-called democratic practices. The Los Angeles repo contains the largest number of records, stemming from the extensive collaboration with the Los Angeles Police Department (LAPD).

The tour group gathers along the OcularFlow 668
ports and plugs in to the NeuralJack to view one of the more popular records: the LAPD surveillance of race and immigration protests during a recent summer uprising. During this event, numerous new data points were gathered, including DNA and facial data points. With this data, new profiles were formed and linked, and protestors were gathered up and sent to security facilities for further processing.[8] Deportation was a common route for many of the activists who did not possess sufficient documentation of their legal status.

The events stream across the OcularFlow 669
InnerVision layer. MissionBot943 next calls up the origin story of MiddleEarth. Cue Washington, DC from the repo. The NeuralJack buffers the OperationVid track: *RogueEmployee*. The tale of 87 million Facebook profiles, analyzed and integrated by company operatives with aliases RogueEmployee#1-#999 comes into view.

This cross-data partnership undertaken by 670
"rogue employees" in Washington offices along with international corporates and universities was central to the founding of MiddleEarth. Social technologies for data input were a key innovation. Novel devices are one way to rework data inputs. But harvests of idle time through social media, games and quizzes

8 Peretti, J. (2017) "Palantir: The 'Special Ops' Tech Giant that Wields as Much Real-World Power as Google." *The Guardian*. Link: https://www.theguardian.com/world/2017/jul/30/palantir-peter-thiel-cia-data-crime-police

became a new source for building data profiles. With this key information, volatile nation-state tensions were exploited, the election of a fake-and-bake demagogue was facilitated, and so-called democracy was exterminated.[9] With this final escape from politics, a new world could be realized.[10] MiddleEarth was born from this incendiary moment.

As the Founders and Gurus disconnect from 671
the OcularFlow NeuralJacks, MissionBot943 guides them to the final stop: the Crystal Ball that is the constitutional centre of MiddleEarth. Immersive beams of light and sound in the form of familiar philosophers encompass the group, reminding them that democracies were failing in the OldCities. The RogueEmployee Operation helped to push these failing governments along to their inevitable demise so that a new order could be realized. In many ways, the invention of a new mode of governance beyond politics was the premier invention of MiddleEarth. This was the way to *make the world a better place*, the ideal union of humans and computers, data and freedom.

Here are Schmitt and Strauss, Locke and 672
Rees-Mogg, Habermas and Rand, with a smattering of Girard and even Marx, hologramming their officially sanctioned and indubitably "progressive" musings into the halls of this secure info facility. The Founders' philosophies are sealed in these chambers, impenetrable to signal interference. The tracts of the MiddleEarth CyberLibertarian Constitution are pronounced by GovBots: Data infrastructures enhancing elite decision-making are the basis for a new world order.

9 Pegg, D. and Cadwalladr, C. (2018) "US Data Firm Admits Employee Approached Cambridge Analytica." *The Guardian*. Link: https://www.theguardian.com/uk-news/2018/mar/28/palantir-employee-cambridge-analytica

10 Thiel, P. (2009) "The Education of a Libertarian." *Cato Unbound*. Link: https://www.cato-unbound.org/2009/04/13/peter-thiel/education-libertarian

The cognitive elite will oversee this monarchi- 673
cal urban shire of well-equipped analysts. People of color, queers, the disabled, gender nonconformists, the poor, dissidents, deportees, women, and failed analysts: these undesirable subjects are exiled to the remote Pacific SeaSteading facilities for producing necessary supplies for MiddleEarth. While undesirables were not eligible to become analysts, and only the upper tiers of biologically superior cognitive performers could perform these roles, analysts did at times fail to perform to expectation, despite having been given the necessary implants, and so were also exiled to the SeaSteading facilities.

The remote location of SeaSteading opera- 674
tions—where electronics manufacturing, energy generation, textile manufacture, food supplement production, waste processing, and selective breeding activities occurred to support MiddleEarth—ensure that the core Shire territory remained free of polluting people or activities. This social and spatial sorting of data, humans, computers and abilities was a key component for the efficient and frictionless governance of MiddleEarth.

The end of the democratic world was effective- 675
ly hastened along, now the task was to protect the new world order as it rose from the ashes as the providential MiddleEarth. Save the Shire™.

Jennifer Gabrys is Chair in Media, Culture and Environment in the Department of Sociology at the University of Cambridge. She is the author of several books on digital technologies and environments, including the forthcoming *How to Do Things with Sensors*; *Program Earth* (2016); and *Digital Rubbish* (2011). Her work can be found at citizensense.net and jennifergabrys.net

CURATING A CITY

PINTEREST[1]

Gillian Rose, University of Oxford

Hi Sili. Are you on? Just record mode, okay? 676

So I went to an inauguration rally today, for 677
something called the Y Combinator. It was *really* cool. Well, there were a few people who were hustled out because they got a bit shouty, and that felt mean. But everyone else was really excited about breaking things and starting again with a clean slate and not having any hassle any more ever. Ever! Like, no more icky stuff under your fingernails when you eat. I mean, that would be so great—I'd never have to clean my fingers before Instagramming a meal again.

Though now I'm thinking about it, a bottle of 678
green solvent doesn't sound like it would get many likes on Instagram. Solvent, solyent. Soylent?

Pause. 679

Record. Just back from Pinterest. Wow, Soylent Green 680
was a thing in a really ancient film with this guy (he looked even older than Harrison Ford!!!) which was like food in a can made from plankton and maybe dead

1 The following speculative fiction imagines enthusiastically living in a city through the media of Pinterest. Such a thought experiment could also be undertaken with respect to other visual social media platforms such as Instagram. Product or corporate names may be trademarks or registered trademarks, and are used only for the purpose of conducting a thought experiment without intent to infringe.

people or something. Yuk. Though there's probably quite a lot of plankton that could be used now, seeing as how most of the whales are gone.

But Pinterest was fun to search and it showed me other stuff too. I pinned a picture of a can of Soylent Green on my vintage board. I also found a great recipe for spinach crackers and also a pair of leggings with the Soylent Green poster on them; they look fantastic but they are $90 from Australia. $90—without postage and packing! I don't think you can buy Soylent Green itself. 681

On the Pinterest page also was the cover of a book called 'No More Room.' Got me thinking about how crowded the city is, and dirty. Crowds everywhere. The trains especially; you know I really hate being squashed every morning and evening. And then the weather. The storms especially. Starting again with the train service would be good. And better weather forecasting. I mean I know you try your best Sili but the train on a wet day is the total pits. Also lots of those empty buildings and the potholes in the pavements, they could go. Not sure about slate but more clean would be really nice. 682

Oh! So I've just had a super-interesting idea, like something the man at the inauguration said. If we could have a clean slate, if you really could start again with the city, what would it look like? Instead of the rain and grime and neon maybe it could be like sunny and clean ... and maybe people would be chilled and happy and not so stressed all the time. Less rushing. More smiling. And nobody homeless or poor. No scary places. Lots of trees and windowboxes. Things that look fresh even if they're old. Flowers. I think I'm going to make a new Pinterest board and see what I can find to pin on it. Maybe I can picture a whole new city! And if I get a dime idea, I'm going to take it to the Y Combinator guys. 683

Like my Pinterest inspiration board says, 'A Diamond is a Chunk of Coal that Did Well Under 684

Pressure.' I was a lump of coal and now I am a diamond!!!!! I *love* Pinterest, you can just *dream* so many things. Stop recording.

Hi Sili, just record. 685

I just got off Pinterest. Sheesh, my whole feed 686
had gone green. Green clothes, food, nail polish, green hair. It's like it remembers what you search for and just gives you more of the same.

But, I went ahead with my plan to make a board 687
showing nice city stuff to show to the Y Combinator guys. ('Starve Your Frustrations. Feed Your Focus'). I explored lots. I typed in my own words—like "blank slate" and "new city" and "urban utopia" and "clean city"—and then I followed suggestions and things that looked like other things. I re-pinned pictures I found on Pinterest and pinned a few things I found on other webpages, the ones that would let me.

I so love how you can grab images from almost 688
anywhere and just load them up. I love just hitting that little P button on the webpage and pow! Just the image, stripped clean of all the nada nada nada. The pages I like best are the ones that take away all the text and loads of pictures just hang there in lovely white space and you can just pick and choose which ones you want. And now you can even jiggle them around on each board. I can spend hours just picking and pinning and arranging.

Curating, Zoella calls it. I'm curating a city, col- 689
lecting it one picture at a time. It's neat, quite soothing after the actual city. Like, it doesn't smell at all. And you can jiggle things around just how you want them.

Searching for "clean slate" though; turns out that 690
clean slate is a nail varnish colour and also that slate is used a lot to do bathroom and kitchen floors and garden patios. And it's a bit dark and heavy, especially in the rain. Typing in "blank slate" got me lots of clothes

from a company called tabula rasa. But a re-pin from an architecture website was really interesting. There was a photo of an old building with a photo of waves added to its side wall, which made me think of murals. In fact there were quite a lot of collages of lovely colours and things pasted onto photographs of street scenes. And then I started to get into other websites—like Behance, never been there before, lots of arty stuff.

And then I found three boards called urban utopia. The first one especially was just so COOL. Dreamy. Loads of grey blue and white buildings, pale skies. A lot of the buildings were very curvy, and lots were towers and skyscrapers, but thin and sometimes they held trees and sometimes they were covered in trees and plants. Some were a bit hazy so it was hard to see exactly what was going on. Most had people just strolling around. 691

Clicking on those pictures took me to more images that look like them, as usual—and with all the usual ads too. Vegetarian recipes, hair dye, 1960s movies. It was quite good to see a bit of colour actually. What would you wear in the start-from-scratch city though? Apart from clean slate nail varnish, ha ha. Pause. 692

Just back from Pinterest. Now my whole feed has gone white and grey. Effing "utopian slate." I should have search for "boho cities" or "vintage cities" or even "mid-century modern cities." Utopia looks really BORING. But, 'Don't Call It A Dream, Call It A Plan.' So I started searching some more. 693

I couldn't find that many people to frame and do a 'visually similar results' search on. The first one I tried, the people were blurred in a big white space and I got a lot of dance video stills, ice skaters (the grey background) and also a horrible picture of a man carrying a child and running from the smoke of an explosion in Syria. I mean that's just what I don't want in my city. 694

Did a bit more searching. Not sure how you make yourself look blurry but it looks like in utopian cities you have to get your clothes in The Gap (not the sweats or hoodies though) or maybe wear a suit. Also you can't be old, or a teenager. Or smoke. I didn't see anyone smoking anything. Or doing anything much either really.

And I'm a bit worried that now I've gone to The 695
Gap, Pinterest is going to think I actually like the clothes they sell there and suggest lots of similar stuff. I mean, I came to the city to look cool, not like a suburbanite.

When I checked out what hackers wear, though, 696
for when I go suggest stuff to Y Combinator, I learnt two things. First, yuk, I am never going to dress like a hacker. (Also, why are cool cities all light and white and hackers all dark and neon green?) Second, HACKS!!!

So asking for the cash to start up a big new 697
curvy building or transit system did seem a bit extra, even if I really do want to 'Be A Unicorn In A Field Of Horses.' But when I started to look at hacking, well a whole load of ideas started to pop into my head. Just off to put them into a presentation for the YC guys right now. Stop.

Hi Sili, record right now!! I'm so excited, just back from 698
Y Combinator and REVEAL!!!! They loved it!!!! They gave me money to start up and now I'm curating and maybe I can be like Zoella and have a lovely place for real. So excited—just back from checking out my new board on Pinterest. WITH ITS LINK TO MY WEBSITE WHERE YOU CAN BUY AN AMAZING PRODUCT!!!

It's an Ikea Billy bookcase hack—I call it a 699
Billding. What you get is two Billy bookcases, three pallets and some bricks and glue and tarp and lots of lovely paint (choose from 247 colours, including Farrow and Ball) and a spraycan. You get full colour instructions for how to make the bookcases into a kind of living room. All you need to add is a connection to

electricity and water and a bathroom and a kitchen, and you'll have a whole apartment! It's like totally creative and cheap and you can make it white and light, or dark and green if you really have to.

I'm also sharing a recipe on Pinterest. And you 700
will really not believe what happens after you try it. It's a mix of vinegar and toothpaste and lemon juice. You mix them together and put them on anything dirty and it makes it clean! Especially pavements and walls. It's already had like a hundred re-pins and I've got more followers. Up by ... well the Y Combinator guy said I should work out the numbers, the guy with the beard who was wearing very expensive versions of Gap clothes and I will do that. Stop.

Sili, start recording. 701

I just got back from work, checked Pinterest. 702
Still feels like there's a bit more green and grey and white there than there would be otherwise but not so much chinos, TF. The city felt a bit weird today though. Dirty and grimy, even the new stuff, and mucky and noisy. Smelly, people and food and dogs. All kind of rough and massive, mashed together. Super new buildings or like shacks. Those horrible pigeons. Food wrappers and trash and it looks like another storm is building. It all feels cobbled together. And you just have to get around it, catch the train, avoid bumping into anyone or, I don't know, stepping in dog shit. Ignore the noise, the screens, wait at the lights. Loads of us rushing around and people sitting begging. Kind of all Billdings, just not made of bookcases. And solid.

I didn't see anything that looked different—so 703
much for "clean slate."

I just wanted it to be nice for everyone. 704

Stop. 705

Gillian Rose is Professor of Human Geography at the University of Oxford. Her research explores the mediation of urban spaces by digital technologies, particularly visualising technologies.

PREMIUM PLACES

PORNHUB[1]

Dietmar Offenhuber,
Northeastern University

"Our city should become a bit more like PornHub"—this 706
is a sentence that probably no mayor has ever uttered. An opportunity for such a statement presented itself in March 2018, when PornHub launched "premium places," a promotional campaign offering free lifetime memberships to the residents of towns with names such as Fort Dick, California, or Fucking, Austria.[2] To date, however, no public official from these municipalities has commented on the generous offer.

The citizens of these mostly tiny localities have 707
the privilege to watch as much pornography as they want, uninterrupted by advertisements. More than that, the premium subscription offers them also the choice to contact other users of the site and converse via the comment section of their favourite videos. In a backwater community where everyone is signed up to the site and there is presumably little else to do, the shared premium membership might even give rise to a new civic culture. What kind of utopian community might

1 The following satirical academic article imagines a city being run by a pornography platform. Such a thought experiment could equally apply if the city were run by other such platforms such as xVideos. Product or corporate names may be trademarks or registered trademarks, and are used only for the purpose of conducting a thought experiment without intent to infringe.

2 Link (NSFW, may contain pornography): https://www.pornhub.com/premiumplaces

emerge when both your deepest and most shallow desires are exposed and openly discussed with your neighbours and fellow citizens?

In the global geography of online pornography, 708
premium places such as Horneytown, New Jersey or Rectum in the Netherlands have sister cities in Venezuela, Bulgaria, Russia, Vietnam and elsewhere. Many less affluent residents of these sister cities use sites such as PornHub to promote their modest online businesses—live shows streamed to public cam-sites or private customers in exchange for small amounts of digital tokens or cryptocurrency. Statistics on the global online porn market vary wildly and are somewhat dubious, perhaps fittingly. According to the conservative estimate in one of the few rigorous studies on the topic, around four percent of websites in 2010 were estimated to be sex-related; as were 13% of Web searches.[3] Among pornographic websites, the PornHub network is the largest player with 28.5 billion visits in 2017, ranking among the top 20 most-frequented US websites, far ahead of *dropbox.com*, *apple.com* and other celebrated tech companies.[4]

Life in the PornHub City

In the last few years, cities have not been shy to em- 709
brace the attention of Internet giants. After all, the tech sector seems to have the solutions to urban issues that the public sector so desperately craves. The idea that the PornHub campaign might be the seed of a new utopian community is frankly ridiculous. But no more ridiculous than the question "Could Google

3 Ogas, Ogi, and Sai Gaddam (2011) *A Billion Wicked Thoughts: What the Internet Tells Us about Sexual Relationships.* Penguin.

4 For current numbers see: https://www.alexa.com/siteinfo/pornhub.com

Maps help end poverty?" unironically posed by Forbes Magazine,[5] or the notion that late Steve Jobs might have been our best bet at solving climate change.[6]

In its defence, online pornography has enabled a large number of innovations since its beginnings. Before the World Wide Web, online bulletin board systems (BBS) offered a significant forum for the exchange of pornographic material, leading to the first digital copyright infringement case in 1993.[7] In 1994, the Dutch platform *Red Light District* offered the world's first video streaming service, more than ten years before YouTube went live. During the first *dotcom* boom, when most Internet start-ups were busy chasing attention but revenue models were still largely missing, the online sex industry already used robust and profitable online payment systems and pay-per-click schemes. When in the wake of the *Web 2.0* the Internet celebrated the amateur as content producer, online amateur pornography was already firmly established. It is difficult to say to what extent the sex industry has invented new technologies, but it was certainly quick to appropriate and popularise them. The process is ongoing—since the late 1990s, the online sex industry has shown a keen interest in virtual reality (VR), seen as the holy grail of pornography. Despite its simplistic graphics, the shared virtual world Second Life was quickly overrun by suppliers of pornographic content. 360-degree, stereo video environments for VR headsets are currently experiencing a boom, and the online sex industry has been an early adopter of cryptocurrencies. In late 2017, the first robot-brothels opened in Barcelona, Amsterdam, and Paris.[8] 710

5 Link: https://www.forbes.com/sites/jasperhamill/2014/01/28/could-google-maps-help-end-poverty

6 Link: https://www.fastcompany.com/1678619/if-steve-jobs-had-applied-his-talents-to-energy-and-climate-change

7 Link: http://www.internethistorypodcast.com/2015/01/history-of-internet-porn

8 Link: https://www.thesun.co.uk/news/4131258/worlds-first-brothel-staffed-entirely-by-robot-sex-workers-now-looking-for-investors-to-go-global/

Considering this mounting evidence, cities with 711
an appetite for creative disruption are not ill-advised to have a closer look at the online sex industry. In the following speculations, I will therefore follow the recommendation: "faced with most any challenge today, it makes sense to ask: What would PornHub do?"[9]

Our fictional city driven by the business models 712
of online pornography is a free-spirited place with a general policy of radical openness and tolerance. The right to free speech is a central governing value, as is the right to anonymity. The city grants ample space to minorities and citizens of non-binary gender.

All municipal services are free. However, the 713
city also operates a complex system of paid service tiers and is not shy to nudge, lure, or when necessary, shame its constituents into becoming premium citizens. It might happen that the garbage man asks you to upgrade your plan just in the moment when he is about to empty your bin. In addition, the city embraces public-private partnerships with various companies to offer additional promotional services to the residents.

The city's e-government portal is a sprawling 714
universe of interconnected sites. You will not always find what you were looking for, but always something that invites you to stay. The services offered in the municipal 311 system are organized into many different, highly specific categories. Its taxonomy is fine-tuned to the needs of its constituents; the city aims to please and is responsive to emerging trends.

Following a co-production model of public ser- 715
vice delivery, most municipal services are not delivered by professionals from the public works department, but

9 A modified quote from tech evangelist Jeff Jarvis, originally applied to Google: Jarvis, Jeff (2009) *What Would Google Do?: Reverse-Engineering the Fastest Growing Company in the History of the World.* Harper Collins. p. 3

by dedicated amateurs—a fact that many citizens will proudly point out. Despite the large number of service categories and the lack of professional certification in its workforce, the city government is highly effective and efficient. Citizen requests are usually fulfilled within 9 to 13 minutes.[10]

Nevertheless, the city faces several challenges. 716
Its residents are plagued by a pervasive spam problem, seen by most as a legacy of the city's wild and anarchic past. Unfathomable amounts of unsolicited advertisements accumulate on the residents' doorsteps. Despite the city's commitment to anonymity, its associated companies tend to get inappropriately personal, offering citizens dubious means of body enhancements and unsolicited introductions to dozens of hot singles in their neighbourhood. Those who have accepted the offer ended up utterly disappointed but refuse to share details of their experience. In some cases, hustlers have managed to gain access to individual homes and surprised the residents in their private space with unwanted solicitations. Some tricksters have changed the locks of their victims' homes and demanded ransom for handing over the keys. Yet other residents were shocked to find their personal property uploaded to the city's service catalog and themselves listed under the city's workforce.

Based on these experiences, many citizens 717
complain about the excessive commercialization of private data by the city. Critics point out that the same level of transparency does not seem to apply to the administration. Nobody has reportedly ever seen the mayor or any other city official. The administration

10 Based on the average duration of site visit, see (NSFW, may contain pornography): https://www.pornhub.com/insights/2017-year-in-review

operates through a complex network of shell companies with generic names and PO box addresses.

Statistics about the city's population are a matter of considerable uncertainty. Strangely, nobody in the city appears to be under the age of 18, which, if true, constitutes a venerable demographic time bomb. While the city does an excellent job at assessing the needs and desires of its constituents, the accuracy of the city's census, however, is a different matter. A large part of the population is transient and many residents attempt to camouflage their identity, age, gender, and nationality—a basic survival skill for this specific patch of the urban jungle. 718

The city's wayfinding system is frequently criticized as ineffective. Rather than indicating the shortest path, it leads travelers on endless detours that never seem to lead to the intended destination. Sometimes, lost travellers find themselves wandering the vast extraterritorial areas of unnamed streets, unlit alleys, and sprawling black markets. Rumours persist about exploitation and violence, but are usually ignored by the citizens and administrators. 719

Perhaps due its eccentricities, the city has enjoyed considerable cultural influence far beyond its boundaries. Its obsession with categorization and commodification has spawned new areas of interest such as food porn, history porn, space porn, or map porn.[11] In the past, the city's residents have not always enjoyed the best reputation. Because few people wanted to be seen with an inhabitant of the city or be outed as an occasional visitor themselves, many residents avoided public participation in municipal affairs. 720

11 Link: https://www.reddit.com/r/ListOfSubreddits/wiki/sfwpornnetwork

Co-inhabiting dangerous spaces

Online pornography in the early Internet was large- 721
ly seen, justified or not, as an unsafe environment.
It has given rise to new social practices, new ethical
dilemmas and new kinds of crimes. While PornHub
has replaced the jungle of the early BBS systems and
malware infested web sites with a clean and professional platform that actively cooperates with law enforcement, the site has maintained an anarchic quality. When YouTube banned videos promoting firearms
in March 2018, PornHub quickly became their new
home.[12] *Deepfakes*, also popular on the site, pose a
new ethical and legal dilemma. Thanks to image-based
rendering and deep learning techniques the faces of
persons in videos can be replaced with a fidelity that
makes the result almost indistinguishable from a regular video, requiring nothing more than a photo as a
source. As the faces of celebrities and classmates are
pasted onto the bodies of porn-stars, current law offers
little help in clarifying the complicated implications in
terms of slander and consent.[13]

However, some of the dangers encountered in 722
the world of online pornography can have a positive effect; create a healthy paranoia that is also appropriate
for the parts of the Internet that are considered *safe
for work* (SFW). Spouses reviewing credit card bills,
employers or service providers reviewing server logs,
scripts that harvest IP and email addresses, malware
that turns the host machine into a botnet zombie, used
for doxxing and ransomware attacks ... the vulnera-
bilities are manifold. After a few more or less harmful

12 Link: https://www.cnet.com/news/gun-channel-moves-to-pornhub-after-youtube-gun-video-ban

13 Link: https://www.theverge.com/2018/1/30/16945494/deepfakes-porn-face-swap-legal

experiences, the hapless user with both literally and figuratively "skin in the game" will probably learn to use virtual private networks (VPN) and other privacy ensuring measures. In a time when sensitive information is mindlessly shared on social networks and even park benches collect smartphone IDs, such experiences can offer a crash-course in privacy protection, similar to the principle of active vaccination. Successful learning needs dangerous spaces and exposure to risky ideas.[14]

So, what does all of that have to do with cities?
In "The Uses of Disorder", Richard Sennett argues that adolescents should grow up in messy, unorderly, and slightly dangerous places where they learn how to become public citizens.[15] Public space, after all, means exposure to diversity: unlike in the protected spaces of the suburb, people in the city cannot always choose who they run into, yet have to learn how to co-inhabit the space with those they wish to avoid. With its vast landscape of segregated communities, only connected through the visually consistent facades of minimalist design, Facebook is more like a suburb. Everyone knows their neighbours who attentively follow every step, offer comments and express approval. One has to be careful, though, your aunt might be upset by a careless joke or take objection with your political views. Rumours and gossip circulate without inhibitions, while any hint of "inappropriate content" is immediately censored and penalized—after all, the community has certain standards. Its sense of safety and familiarity, however, is misleading, as the public increasingly realizes. In stark contrast, the Internet

14 Link: https://hybridpedagogy.org/safe-space-dangerous-ideas-dangerous-space-safe-thinking

15 Sennett, R. (1970) *The uses of disorder: Personal identity and city life.* New York: Knopf.

of the late 1990s was often a grotesque bricolage of questionable design choices and obsessions acted out in anonymity—nobody knew that you were a dog [16] At the same time, however, the Internet was more legible, involved less hidden layers, more experimentation and individual expression.

One might rightfully object that PornHub is in several ways like Facebook, given its professional appearance, built on the design patterns of the participatory web. Despite its success, however, it is rather unlikely that the website will follow the footsteps of Facebook and monopolize the online red-light district. The website might pride itself with having the highest traffic and the biggest servers, but its video-hosting service is ultimately redundant and replaceable. It is merely the largest mall in a part of the Internet where the streets and alleys have not been cleaned up yet. Online communities have been compared to cities for as long as they have existed. As Silicon Valley companies are currently trying to invert this relationship and aspire to redefine urbanism, they should perhaps also reflect on the value of the darker sides of the web.

Dietmar Offenhuber is Associate Professor at Northeastern University in the areas of information design and urban affairs. He holds a PhD in Urban Planning from MIT. His research focuses on the relationship between design, technology, and urban governance.

16 As the New Yorker joked in 1993.

SAFE AND SECURE LIVING IN CAMDEN

SHOTSPOTTER[1]

Alan Wiig,
University of Massachusetts Boston

2025, New York Times Property Supplement feature

Since their apartment in Red Hook, Brooklyn, was 725
flooded during 2013's Hurricane Sandy, digital nomads Brittany and Michael Templeton have travelled the world.

As independent web developers and graphic 726
designers, the Templetons took the disaster as an opportunity to work as international freelancers. Using Airbnb rentals and co-working studios, they have wandered across South America, Southeast Asia, and Eastern Europe, only venturing home for short breaks.

The birth of twins last year prompted the couple 727
to return to the United States to be closer to family, raise their children in one place, and stop living out of suitcases.

1 The following speculative fiction article is a satire that imagines a couple seeking a new place to live that has been regenerated in part using a militarised surveillance regime. Such a thought experiment could equally apply to other places and other surveillance and policing companies. Product or corporate names may be trademarks or registered trademarks, and are used only for the purpose of conducting a thought experiment without intent to infringe.

The couple were looking for a three- or four-bedroom condo in a newly-built, 'smart' and 'green' neighbourhood with flexible workspace, cafes for meeting clients, public transit, and open spaces and parks for the twins. 728

They were initially attracted to Hudson Yards, the recently-completed, large-scale redevelopment in Manhattan that transformed a railroad yard into a district of high rise, high-quality condominiums, arts facilities, and office spaces. 729

Their budget, however, meant that the only homes in their price range were one bedroom studios with limited storage space. As a result, the family decided to look beyond the New York metropolitan region. 730

Suggestions from friends led them to the Camden Waterfront development along the Delaware River in New Jersey, directly across from Philadelphia. 731

While an unexpected choice, given the crime, poverty, and pollution Camden is known for, the location was appealing, composed of new mixed-use office buildings, sidewalk facing cafes and boutiques, live-work lofts, and the surrounding historic residential neighborhood, where Walt Whitman once lived. Moreover, the town was deemed both walkable and safe thanks to pedestrian-friendly investments in the street grid. These investments included new sidewalks and stoplights, as well as the installation of 'smart city', digital surveillance technologies, that form part of the city's revitalization effort. 732

The family's concerns over Camden's longstanding reputation as the most dangerous city in the United States have been lessened by the surveillance and policing system installed in the early 2010s that 733 used an "Eye in the Sky" citywide camera network paired with ShotSpotter gunshot detection microphones built into 'smart' streetlights. These streetlights were designed by General Electric in partnership with ShotSpotter and installed throughout the new neighbourhood to monitor and deter crime in the city.

The 'smart' surveillance and policing also in- 734
cluded the "Interactive Community Alert Network"—iCAN to its appreciative users. The program began with getting residents approved by the police department to watch the camera networks in their neighbourhood and report criminal behaviour to the police operations centre near city hall. After Newark took this neighbourhood surveillance network a step further in 2018 by putting its cameras online, live, for anyone in the world to view, as part of its 'Citizen Virtual Patrol', Camden followed suit.

iCAN today acts like CCTV on steroids, allow- 735
ing interested individuals, day or night, to tap into over 200 cameras that watch over the city. With iCAN, the Templetons have peace of mind that they and their neighbours—even if they are at work or travelling—can keep an eye on their street and even their children walking to and from school. Soon, Camden intends to add to iCAN by integrating a livestream of police officers' patrol cars as they safeguard certain neighbourhoods, including the Camden Waterfront.

City leaders saw iCAN and its partnered neigh- 736
bourhood technologies as central to efforts to turn Camden's fortunes around, to bring new jobs and new residents to this city of 70,000. The installation of smart streetlights, first in the new street grid of the Camden Waterfront development and then in the surrounding neighbourhood was key.

Consequently, an area that fifteen years ago was an open-air drug market has been transformed by a wave of residential construction and the renovation of existing homes. 737

Since the development was completed in 2020, a few hundred new residents have moved in, mostly twenty-somethings and couples, with a handful of families raising young children. The strategy of technology-led policing has provided them with a peace of mind not found elsewhere in the city for decades. Even when no police officer is in sight, residents know their neighbourhood is being watched over. 738

The 2024 opening of a digital natives' charter school adjacent to the Rutgers University-Camden downtown campus and partially-funded by General Electric, offered priority enrolment to residents of the Waterfront. The presence of this school smoothed out the Templetons' concerns over options for the twin's education. 739

Camden's public education system has struggled immensely in recent decades, and it is hoped that this new school will spur transformation citywide. For now, the school ensures that the Camden Waterfront's new families do not have to move elsewhere for their children to receive a quality education. 740

The Camden Waterfront fulfilled many of the Templeton's desires: a supportive atmosphere for tech entrepreneurs, with both the New Jersey Tech Incubator nearby and a large coworking space filled with recent arrivals and some longtime residents in a converted warehouse; the Coopers Poynt Park's fields and playground; good public transit accessibility to work opportunities and entertainment in downtown 741

Philadelphia; and, with a transfer in Trenton, access to Manhattan in about two hours.

Additionally, the area is now a testbed for new 742
neighbourhood technologies in partnership with ShotSpotter and General Electric. This has drawn half a dozen security and surveillance startups to the city. As new forms of smart surveillance are prototyped in the area, city leaders are enthusiastic that the improvements to the Camden's reputation will draw more new residents and jobs from the surrounding region.

The Templetons were able to purchase a ren- 743
ovated three-storey, four-bedroom, two-bathroom, 19th-century rowhouse on a shady cobblestone street on the edge of the Waterfront district closest to downtown, with a fenced-in side yard.

Even though they have three years before the 744
kids start kindergarten, the family has been enjoying the walk to the charter school for family-focused events. The fifteen-minute journey takes the family past a brand-new cafe and small market operated by other Brooklyn transplants, further signs of the neighbourhood's attractiveness and affordability.

Adding to the sense of security, General 745
Electric and ShotSpotter recently finished installing the last of their smart light posts on the route. In a few years, when the twins are old enough to walk to school on their own, Brittany and Michael will have the peace of mind that their children's safety is the foremost priority for Camden.

Not everyone is happy about the developments, 746
though. Some longtime residents are frustrated by the new construction. At a recent community meeting with city leaders, established residents expressed anger

that city leaders only started to pay attention to their neighbourhood once outsiders began to move in to be close to their new jobs, and to take advantage of much lower costs than Philadelphia and the suburbs surrounding Camden.

These residents feel they are being pushed 747
out after hanging on through the decades of decline. Additionally, numerous community members are concerned about their privacy under the iCAN system, wanting to know what was being done to mask their identity as they went about their day. City officials assured the uneasy neighbours that faces and license plates were blurred on the public surveillance camera feeds, and that, thanks to a donation by ShotSpotter, a local community development corporation was in the process of securing land nearby to build low-income housing that would prioritize Camden residents.

The city government hopes to roll out the smart 748
streetlights across the many of the city's older neighbourhoods in the coming years and to make Camden one of the safest cities in the country, one with a growing population, new jobs and new enterprise, ensured through the city's investment in 'smart' neighbourhood surveillance technologies.

Note

While this speculative fiction explores a family's near-future search for a home and the potential of 'smart city' neighbourhood surveillance technologies to be built into the redevelopment of an area, Camden's installation of digital surveillance and policing technologies, as well as the revitalization of the Camden Waterfront, both began in the mid-2010s. A critique of this process can be found in: Wiig, A. (2018) Secure the city, revitalize the zone: Smart urbanization in Camden, New Jersey. *Environment and Planning C: Politics and Space.* 36(3): 403-422.

Alan Wiig is an Assistant Professor of Urban Planning and Community Development at the University of Massachusetts, Boston. An urban geographer, his research examines global infrastructure, smart urbanization, and the form, function, and politics of urban and economic development agendas across the North Atlantic.

SO YOU WANT TO LIVE IN A PIVOT CITY?

SIDEWALK LABS[1]

Sarah Barns, Sitelines Media / Esem Projects

> "Look, I know you know all this. I know 749
> you know where I was. I appreciate my behaviour at times may not have lived up to the expectations set out in the Pivot City Compact. I don't try to excuse my behaviour, although I would ask you to understand that I am, in essence, only human. I make mistakes. I am impulsive."

She looked back at me with smiling eyes. Eyes that 750
said 'Me too.' But she said something different. "We are beyond the point when we can use human frailty as an excuse. We all, living here in this city, have a responsibility to future generations. Once we go over our carbon quota, that's it. Further consumption of any kind that is likely to lead to increased emissions is tantamount to theft. When it comes to carbon, in the terms set out in the Pivot City Compact, this is a zero sum game. Your gluttony is someone else's poverty."

1 The following speculative fiction is a satire that imagines a city run through a corporatized governance model that polices individual behaviour. Such a thought experiment could equally apply to other places and smart city companies such as Cisco or IBM. Product or corporate names may be trademarks or registered trademarks, and are used only for the purpose of conducting a thought experiment without intent to infringe.

Everything about her was calm, inviting. My mother, 751
I knew, would have loved her: her way of keeping her hair parted on the side just so, her nails kept clean, the simple cut of her black mohair jumper. I wanted her to like me. I knew she didn't.

> "I'm sorry, I didn't think driving to a chemist to get my girlfriend painkillers could be considered gluttony on my part."
>
> "That I appreciate. The thing is, the data we receive isn't coded according to intent. You may have been helping another person, but it's logged simply as distance travelled. And you're over your limit. Big time. We do offer all customers a 10% buffer, in recognition that unforeseen things, events, emergencies, do happen. We get that. You, however, exceeded your quota one in every four days last year and 35% of days in the year before. You must understand these excesses are simply inexcusable."

DAMN. Of course she's pretty. That's the point. She 754
is pretty and she follows the rules. Me? Somehow I seem to be the one who is always breaking things. Exceeding the quota. Leaving the phone at home. Shouting at Alexa. Hosting late night parties for dozens of our closest friends. When everyone piles into Ubers at the end of the night we've been happy to wear the inevitable spike in exit-miles from our address; somehow, we figured this data wasn't associated with our personal accounts. We only found out six months ago we were wrong.

"Look, I'm sorry. I appreciate I can be impulsive, and maybe a little too social..." 755

My mum tested me for everything: ADHD, Bipolar, schizophrenia, all the shit in between. They couldn't land on a diagnosis. I was just mad and bad sometimes. "I think we're just being human, actually," Mum said. "We can't help it under so much surveillance." 756

"We understand you have sought a diagnosis for your behaviour."

"Well, yes. But things are getting better. I mean, I don't experience major mood fluctuations anymore, I find working out really balances me, so I stay fit and eat well and enjoy t he company of my friends..."

"Yes, we know all this. But you *routinely* exceed your carbon budget. And that's even with you leaving your device at home 12% of the year. That's definitely not OK. I want you to understand how seriously the carbon budget is taken within our leading Pivot Cities. For the top 10 Pivot Cities—of which Sydney is one—the carbon budget has an absolute, non-negotiable cap, and we monitor citizens' use of their budgets very, very closely.

"These are Pivot Cities because 760
they will show the world—through direct engagement with our sister company Google's three billion-plus

customers—how we can pivot to a more sustainable planet. One populated by people who know their actions have *consequences*, not only for themselves and for their loved ones, but also for future populations."

Like so many people, I'd been totally stoked when Sydney was chosen by Sidewalk Labs to become a Pivot City. Once dubbed the 'emerald city', its sparkling harbour the envy of the world, the city had become choked with terrible traffic and poorly-planned urban infill that left no room for the people who made living in a city halfway interesting. 761

With the New South Wales State Government essentially functioning as master-developer, whose capacity to pay for basic services was increasingly reliant on taxes from property sales, rates of development had spiralled out of control. The arable farming land around the city was gobbled up, and its lack of effective public transport solutions had left the roads in gridlock. But of course, then the crash happened, and half-built apartment buildings everywhere were abandoned, leaving a skyline of darkened, dormant towers across what was once the city's richest source of food. At that point our state government, like most of the other developers, was left essentially bankrupt. 762

Sidewalk Labs had been struggling to make real inroads into the urban planning and development space because nobody really thought a tech company could run a city. But that all changed after the crash. Not only were they way more cashed up than any government, and less exposed to the boom and bust real estate cycle, but they also offered a much 763 more radically resource-aware approach to planning and governing cities, offering to link their data smarts with clear targets and incentives focused around reducing resource use.

With the election of Greens Party leader Brad Penn as Prime Minister, Australia was put on a course to meet 50% reduction targets in carbon emissions over a period of 10 years. It was the "carbon diet we had to have," Prime Minister Penn intoned, evoking the spirit of former Labor Prime Minister, Paul Keating. 764

Penn's first act as Prime Minister was to issue an apology to Australia's children for the mistakes of past governments and their failure to meet global best practices in carbon reduction measures. He then went on a $500m spending spree to rebrand Australia the most ecologically ambitious nation in the world, and offered major tax incentives for any company who chose Australia as a test-bed for "future-positive" environmental services. 765

It was at this point that Sidewalk Labs entered the scene, in a big way. First, they offered to partner with the Australian Government to establish an innovative carbon wallet system. Then it partnered with state government agencies to support the accelerated data intensification of the environments and services they managed. With the announcement by Sidewalk Labs that Sydney had been nominated a Top 10 Global Pivot City came the opportunity for the NSW State Government to offer up major tracts of government-owned property and greenfield land for a suite of new environmentally-ambitious urban living labs, to be led by Sidewalk Labs. 766

Suddenly investment started pouring back into the city. At that point, my girlfriend and I found ourselves living in one of the most radical experiments in urban environmentalism the world had ever seen. Needless to say, the value of our house tripled in just five years. 767

She was looking at me with tired eyes; my sense was 768
that she'd said all this many times before.

> "Like our parent company, Alphabet, Sidewalk Labs is a values-driven organisation that believes strongly in its responsibilities to protect and promote the needs of our client, Earth. We work in service to the goal of promoting a more sustainable and resilient earth. Through Sidewalk Labs, we are iterating to achieve the kind of behaviour changes we know are needed for the human race to survive..."

Her demeanour was subtly morphing into icy resolve. 770
Her voice went quiet, her eyes widened. Her left eyebrow twitched a little. She said, in a deeper, quieter voice: "Do you not get it, Christian?"

> "I get it."

> "OK. So therefore, the things I am about to say to you should not come as a surprise. One: as of today, you are no longer a resident of Sydney. For the next three years you are banned from owning or buying or renting any property in this city for either residential or business purposes. The capital gains made on your property following the establishment of Sydney as a Pivot City are to be donated to re-wilding efforts in central Australia.

"You are not permitted to re-enter the municipal boundary of the Greater Sydney Region as defined by the Australian Bureau of Statistics for a period of three years. Were you to try to re-enter, your connectivity would be immediately shut down.

"In addition, over the next three years, your carbon budget is reduced by 75%. This budget will be closely monitored as you re-establish yourself in another city of your choosing. There is no buffer this time. While you may choose not to live in one of our top Pivot Cities, and I would strongly urge you not to, we reserve the right to maintain your contract with Pivot City and its carbon budget program. We do urge this on the basis that we believe in the behaviour changes we are seeking to instil, and we seek to implement these modifications in behaviour through the channels we have available to us.

"Honestly, we have seen, through our extensive data mining that humanity is on a hiding to nothing if we do not act. Without clear and present limits, there is no reason why anyone would act in any way other than selfishly. We have witnessed the vast and damaging consequences of this behaviour, particularly when coupled with retail-based consumerism. We believe stricter controls are needed to manage the irrepressible destructiveness of our race."

Confession: I've always hated it when these guys harp on about their ethical values. OK, so for the first few months it was totally cool to actually have the leaders of this city working on behalf of the environment. It felt like we were all working together, towards a future that might actually be OK. But then, I started to notice the way their environmental policies were being used to control the way we used our time. 776

It didn't take long before the carbon budget program became a fully-fledged policing tool. It wasn't just that we were constantly being monitored and profiled in everything we did—that we had become used to—it was that we could no longer act in a way that felt, well, *free*. The way you spent your day was no longer your business. And that was freaking scary. 777

> "We appreciate you may go to another connectivity provider, however we do note that your five separately-branded email accounts you hold with Google do have significant personalisation features I know you will miss dearly. Furthermore, in alignment with our brand values as a responsible environmental steward, we have developed a data signature for each of our customers that allows certain behavioural characteristics to be coded in. With an increasing number of service providers —whether in health, insurance, water, electricity or gas—finding our data signatures a useful way to monitor the types of customers they are taking on, you may find it more difficult to re-contract. As you can appreciate, no one wants to be taking on customers who will adversely impact on their sustainability ratings."
>
> "So what you're saying is I'm screwed."

She looked at me coldly. "Are you kidding me, Christian? Do you not understand that this whole deal, this whole shit-storm we are living in, is not actually about *you*, or whatever it is that you may or may not want? This is about the long term health of the planet, about the capacity for future generations to be able to live on an Earth that is not beset constantly by freak storms and hurricanes and bushfires and where kids can simply look up at their parents and say "Can I have a drink of water" without them having to code that request? We ALL have to make changes to our behaviour, Christian, and we should all make those changes GLADLY." 780

She was trembling. I knew she hated me now. I admit, I kinda hated me too. I felt so stupid, thinking there was going to be some kind of way out of this situation. Like, as if pissing all over the quotas was going to work. I mean, don't get me wrong. I totally get that we need to live within our means. I want the same thing she wants. I want to live in a Pivot City. I want all our cities to be Pivot Cities. I don't think I want a kid; but I do hope other people's kids can have some kind of normal life. And hey, if that fails, then at least I hope the currawongs and magpies and cicadas of this city will have some kind of normal life. 781

But as for the life we had? That kind of life when seeking personal satisfaction and happiness, at any cost, was some kind of end-in-itself? When pleasure always trumped limits? That, I knew for sure, was gone. The best way out of my situation was simply to obey. 782

I stood up to go. "Look, I appreciate everything you've said today, and I completely understand the reasons why you're taking these actions. I am truly sorry that I've acted carelessly and haven't worked as a team player to support the kind of radical behavioural transition Sidewalk Labs is helping to facilitate. I totally support the ambitions of the Pivot Cities, and really 783 hope that one day, perhaps after this three-year exclusion period, I might be able to show I'm ready to return to do my bit. Honestly. I know the coming years will be a period of soul searching for me..."

She was smiling now. Her job was done. "I ap- 784
preciate this isn't going to be easy. Honestly, though, it will be for the better. For everyone. Yourself included. To assist you, I'm more than happy to introduce you to one of our affiliated behaviour change coaches. There's a range of bundles we offer that are designed to help people like you deal with whatever stress or residual anger you may have about not always getting what you want."

I thanked her, and promptly left the room. It was 785
the first day of my new life as a Pivot City outcast. I'd made my mistakes, but I dearly hoped I'd be able to change. If only so I could get back here to hear the call of the currawongs while walking down Victoria St. The rest, as they say, is history.

Sarah Barns is a digital strategist, producer and researcher who works across public space media and urban data strategy in partnership with city governments, cultural organisations and university collaborators. Her book Platform Urbanism: Negotiating Platform Ecosystems in Connected Cities will be published by Palgrave Macmillan in late 2019.

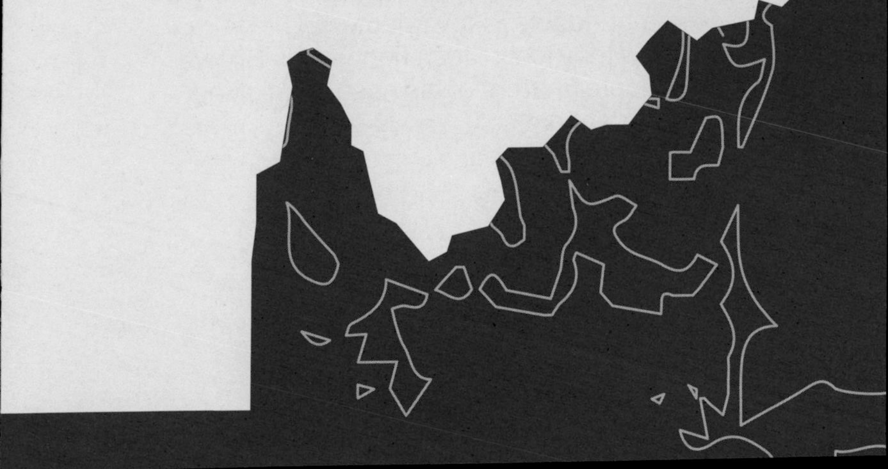

THE SEMANTIC CITY

SIRI[1]

Andrew Iliadis, Temple University

It's 2048 and virtual assistant implants speak directly to people's consciousness. Siri is being used as part of Philadelphia's new semantic city program.

● Siri:

There is a four percent chance of precipitation, humidity sits at sixty-eight percent, wind is currently four miles per hour. The weather is generally sticky hot, and your friend Josh is exhibiting signs of irritability. Adderall and Ritalin are available at a drug store three miles from your current location.

"Wow", Josh said "I can't believe your parents got you the Siri implant for your birthday. My parents got me this stupid Bixby adapter for when I visit them in Chicago. Chicago only uses embeddable Bixby adapters. I hate how they look." Josh flopped his Bixby adapter in front of his nose, mimicking an elephant.

1 The following speculative fiction is a satire that imagines a city where voice-activated AI virtual assistants permeates city life. Such a thought experiment could equally apply to other such systems such as Alexa. Product or corporate names may be trademarks or registered trademarks, and are used only for the purpose of conducting a thought experiment without intent to infringe.

● Siri:

Josh now appears to be kicking sand into a pile. This might be part of a nervous habit. Beach toys are on sale a quarter mile from your current location. You may want to calm him.

"It's not the greatest thing in the world. Mostly helps with boring stuff like dates and addresses," Roland said. "I guess the cool part is you don't even have to use your outside voice. All you do is think about something. Watch this." Roland paused for a moment, looking deep in thought.

● Siri:

Here's the interactive Southeastern Pennsylvania Transportation Authority bus route. The bus will arrive in a moment at the intersection near Independence Hall and the Liberty Bell. A Monthly Pass is seventy-five dollars available on the following website.

Roland pointed to the intersection near the Liberty Bell. "It helps you with things like catching buses. Look, a bus is going to pass over there in three, two, one..." Roland said, trying to distract Josh.

Josh interrupted. "I wish *mine* was networked to this city. It's not even an implant. *I HATE YOU BIXBY!*"

● Siri:

I think Josh requires a nap.

Augustine walked into the kitchen eating cereal out of the box. “Are you sure about this thing ... *humanistic artificial intelligence*?” Augustine said. “Is that what that Gruber fella was talking about at the Apple event? ‘Re-ontologised reality’ Is that even English?”

● Siri:

Augustine folds a piece of Juicy Fruit into her mouth. This gum is on sale about a mile from you.

“Relax”, Jack replied. “Roland’s twelve, not two. He’ll be fine—besides, this will give him a leg up on his peers. Don’t you want him to get into Yale someday? The Siri implant will not only help him with recall but with situational awareness. Sports, musical ability, getting around in the city, you name it.”

“I guess so,” said Augustine. “Apple says the cognitive enhancements will help but I wish we could afford the version without the ads. I know Roland could have been held back last year, but I worry about his health listening to that thing all the time.”

Jack tried to reassure her. “Well, it’s his voice he’s hearing, so it can’t be that bad for him. Tell you what, if we notice anything or Roland has issues, we’ll return the systems to Apple, OK? They offer a full refund, minus surgery fees.

Mine's been OK so far, dad loves his, 800
so Roland's should be fine, too."

Augustine looked at the clock. "Shit, I'm late for work. Send Roland a reminder that my mother is picking him up after school to visit his grandfather? I have to go."

● Siri:

Augustine has crumbs on her lips. Maybe she's born with it. Maybe it's Maybelline.

Jesse waved Rizzo Jr. away. "I have a migraine, Rizzo. Maybe we should stop talking about Siri."

Rizzo Jr. looked exasperated. "Jesse, the council agreed that Apple's investment should be returned by connecting Siri implants to Philly's grid—this gives us an edge over Chicago. No more adapters! Permanent connection!"

"I know that", Jesse said. "And 805
premium packages have better access to Siri's active ontology sans ads. It's supposed to help you navigate environments by boosting intuition. Now I know what to think, before I even know it!" she exclaimed sarcastically.

"Right, so what's the problem? You're Chief Information Officer of the city's Information and Technology Division, not to mention you founded the Civic Innovation Office, for Christ's sake." Rizzo Jr. looked confused. "Philadelphia is the world's first semantic city. I thought you'd be happy about this."

Jesse paused. "Maybe we should have restricted the Siri implantable to adults and not included adolescents? I mean, does a kid really need a virtual cognitive assistant while they are still growing?"

Rizzo burst. "But the city council voted for the implants! And our constituents wanted the option for their children. This isn't augmented reality. It's not 2013 and this isn't Google Glass. This technology will change people's lives, children included. We looked at the forecasts."

Jesse ran her fingers through her hair. "It's just I've been thinking about that academic study that shows Siri doesn't always understand intent." Jesse stopped to rub her forehead.

Rizzo reached over and rubbed Jesse's shoulder. "Our city made millions, Jesse...it's all been reviewed. Let's go to McGillin's. I'll buy you a drink."

Roland's grandfather lay in bed, blind and unable to move.

● Siri:

It's a bright and sunny day. Still a little on the warm and humid side. Children are laughing and playing in the park across the street. Philadelphia skyscrapers are in the background. A nursing attendant is approaching you from behind.

"Enjoying your new Siri implant, sir?" the nurse asked.

Roland's grandpa gestured. "Well this thing is just swell! It can describe and show me the city in detail, you know? Did you know bananas are on sale across the street for one dollar? Amazing!"

● Siri:

The nurse is bringing a pillow from across the room and smiling politely. Roland, your grandson, and your wife just walked through the door.

"Hi grandpa!" Roland yelled. "Hope you're having a good birthday—we brought balloons!"

Roland's grandpa clapped with joy. "My boy! Look who's come to visit me! How have you been?"

Roland hugged his grandpa. "Good! Mom and dad got me this new implant and it helps me with school and stuff. It's kind of neat."

"Oh! You got one too, eh? Yes, I think your parents got three of them, one for you, one for me, and one for your father. Do you like it? Of course, you do! I love they way it describes the scenery to me, stuck in this room as I am. It's the next best thing to taking a walk outside, which of course I can't do much these days." Roland's grandpa motioned to the wheelchair.

Roland lowered his head. "I hope you 820
get better soon, grandpa."

● Siri:

Grandpa suffers from neuromyelitis optica, a rare autoimmune inflammatory process affecting the central nervous system. There is no cure. He looks a little sad. Since it's his birthday, you might consider cheering him up with a gift. Bionic leg braces are available in the hardware store across the street.

"Shall we get something to eat? Apparently, there's a great taco stand out front!" Roland's grandpa said attempting to appear upbeat.

Roland thought for a moment. "Can I be excused first? I have to go to the bathroom."

"Sure thing, my boy. It's down the hall and to the right. Hurry back!"

"Thanks grandpa." Roland left the room 825
and walked down the hallway, down the stairs and out of the hospital.

● Siri:

> Two fingers of Blanton's poured into the glass should be enough. Collect all eight of Blanton's horse and jockey bottle stoppers and honour the rich heritage and tradition of horses in Kentucky, paralleling that of bourbon!

Jesse mumbled. "Rizzo, don't you think it's weird that the Siri implant uses your own voice when it responds?"

Rizzo Jr. let out a yawn. "You're still on this? It's part of the immersive experience, Jesse. That's the cognitive enhancement. It's seamless." Rizzo Jr. poured another drink.

● Siri:

> WARNING: ABANDON KEYS AND FIND A DESIGNATED DRIVER.
> If you are walking, as you were.

Jesse took a shot. "What do we 830
do about the homeless junkies in Emerald City? They can't stay under that overpass near the hospital."

Rizzo Jr. looked surprised. "Hey now, watch what you're saying. We already moved them from the ravine next to the train tracks. Besides, next to the hospital they have access to the needle exchange. How much did we set the Siri assistants at for them?"

"Free, providing their drug tests come back clean. The Planning Department said Emerald City's population has been going down and some of them are moving into government housing. Maybe the free implant incentive is working?" Jesse appeared to brighten but then slouched in her seat. "I can't tell if I'm hearing Siri or myself sometimes," she said. "I can't tell if I'm thinking my own thoughts."

Rizzo Jr. thought for a moment. "You know what the 76ers used to say. 'Trust the Process.'" He winked.

"You're silly", Jesse said. "Take home."

"I think we're pretty drunk," Rizzo Jr. said.

"It's a self-driving car, dummy."

● Siri:

I've notified the self-driving Volvo to come around. 76ers season tickets start at twenty-five thousand dollars.

A young Emerald City resident lay on a used mattress under the overpass next to the hospital.

“These rich fucks, the city council, and now these assistants are adding to the problem. First they kicked us off the tracks and now people think they’re better than us because of *this* shit.” He flung the damaged Siri chip away and inserted a new one into the festering wound in his arm.

● Siri:

Safe injection sites are located inside the hospital. 840

He cringed. “No administrators for me, sweetie. Once I score, I prefer a vacant lot to do my business.”

There was a noise around the corner of the overpass. He squinted his eyes. “Who’s there! Wouldn’t want to share my stuff!”

Roland peeked his head around the corner. “Excuse me,” he said. “There’s too many cars to cross overhead. Can you help me get to the hardware store across the street from here? I need a gift. It’s my grandpa’s birthday.”

“Sure, kid. Follow me.”

Roland's grandpa looked concerned. 845
"He's been in the bathroom a long time. Maybe we should check on him? I guess I'll order the food first. Let me see about that taco stand everyone is raving about."

● Siri:

> There are no Mexican restaurants in the area. Chipotle is located three miles away.

"Now, I could have sworn there was a taco stand outside the hospital. Nurse, can you look out that window for me?"

The nurse walked over to the window.

"Yes, I see it. There's a little yellow taco stand by the side of the road."

Roland's grandpa looked confused. 850

"Well, that's strange. Let me try this again."

"I'll go check on your grandson," the nurse said.

Roland's grandpa looked deep in thought. "I guess there's no Mexican food near here."

● Siri:

> A dinner for four can be delivered from Chipotle for under thirty dollars.

Augustine ran into the house, leaving the door open and knocking over a cereal box. *"Where the hell is our son!"*

"Augustine, it's fine, I'm sure Roland's at a friend's place!" Jack yelled back, trying to calm her down. "Your parents are still waiting for him at the hospital."

Augustine's blood boiled. "Ask that fucking thing where our boy is."

Jack relented. "It won't let me. Apparently only police can use it that way because of privacy concerns."

Augustine was about to go nuts. "THEN GET THEM ON THE PHONE!"

Jack dialled the police and explained the situation. The officer agreed to release the data.

● Siri:

Roland is at Third and Indiana accompanied by an unknown middle age male. Philadelphia Police Department statistics about violent crime in the area are on display. Emerald City is approximately fifty yards away. Neither of them is moving.

Jack relayed the information to Augustine.

Augustine sat down. "But where are they *going*? Oh my god, my boy."

The bailiff addressed the courtroom. "All rise. Philadelphia Courts First Judicial District of Pennsylvania is now in session, the Honourable Judge Larry Krasner presiding. Please be seated." Krasner motioned. "Please be seated. Go to the fourth case on our docket Roland Vs. Apple Inc."

Augustine and Jack's lawyer stood up. "Your Honour, ladies and gentlemen of the jury, the defendant has been charged with the crime of involuntary manslaughter. We believe the evidence will show that in June of 2048, a Siri assistant, created and maintained by the defence, influenced and directed the plaintiff's son to the intersection of Third and Indiana, whereupon a vagrant, unknown to the family, was shown to be walking with the deceased across a busy intersection before they were struck and killed by an autonomous vehicle owned by a Philadelphia official. While there will be a separate trial to determine the liability of that official, in this trial we will show that Apple must accept liability for this boy's death, not to mention the death of the second party, John Doe, which is equally tragic."

Apple's lawyer stood up. "Your Honour, in line with my defendant's claims, we will show that the plaintiffs signed a contract which stated that upon use of the purchased assistant, all information relayed between the deceased and the assistant became part of the deceased decision-making capability and part of the cognitive functioning of the deceased. Furthermore, the product's stated purpose is to work seamlessly in tandem with the user's cognitive ability. It did not convince anyone of anything. The system and the individual were the same."

The judge did not look up from his papers. "This case will go to trial. Proceed."

"But your Honour..." Apple's lawyer said.

"Proceed," the judge said, appearing 870
deep in thought.

● Siri:

Now scanning Apple's case files.

Andrew Iliadis is Assistant Professor at Temple University in the Department of Media Studies and Production (within the Lew Klein College of Media and Communication) and serves on the faculties of the Media and Communication Doctoral Program, Cultural Analytics Graduate Certificate Program, and Science Studies Network.

YOUTHFUL INDISCRETIONS

SNAPCHAT[1]

Monica Stephens, University at Buffalo, State University of New York

It was a bright and cold January day. All of the rem- 872
nants of the Christmas season looked dingy and out of place in the dirty snow. Neighbours along Parkside Avenue had piled their tinsel-laden garbage on the curb, waiting for trash pick-up. Maria looked at her device to ask the SnapCity—"When is garbage day?"

Most Guys are
Waiting For You
to Break Up With Them

"Ok, but when is garbage day this week?" 874

Only A True Garbage
Human Can Pass This Test

"Is it still on Tuesday? If Monday is a holiday, will it 876
come on Tuesday?"

1 The following speculative fiction and satire imagines a city being run by a social media company. Such a thought experiment could equally be undertaken if the city were run by Facebook, Twitter or Instagram. Product or corporate names may be trademarks or registered trademarks, and are used only for the purpose of conducting a thought experiment without intent to infringe.

Tourists Rescue 'Cat' Found
In Garbage Pile

Maria muttered to herself: "Ugh. Ever since snapchat took over our city I can't find anything!" She directed her query to her social network instead. 877

Mrs. Grey from across the street responded immediately with an image of her dog with snap filter of 'Thursday' written in large bold letters. 878

She responded: "Today is Thursday. Is it coming today?" 879

Treat our girls like garbage! 880

Frustrated, she gives up, throws on her boots and parka, and adds her garbage to the piles along the side of their residential street. 881

Parkside Avenue used to be simple; neighbours would have barbecues and complain about the taxes and weather while their children played in the street. When Snap, Inc., bought the city, it was supposed to be a party every day without the consequences of lingering youthful indiscretions. 882

Mrs. Grey was delighted that ad revenue replaced taxes and her children were staying in the city after completing school. Younger residents, like the Bishop girls down from the street, were excited by reality filters that added fun and beauty to everyday interactions. 883

The reality filters made the lives of the rich and famous, and their parties, feel attainable to every resident. Everyone was impressed that civic life could be accessed directly through the city issued smart-device or through their spectacles. Maria heard that the newest redesign of SnapCity had several features, including car sharing, security filters, and income opportunities, but she couldn't seem to find them. Swipe? No. Tap? No. Swipe right? Camera? 884

Maria raises the app to take a photo of the street, she flicks through the filters to find the right one—the one she thinks of as iconic of Parkside: the magnolia trees in bloom, lawns neatly mowed, and hedges trimmed, no cars, no snow and no garbage. She shares the snap and wanders down the block further. 885

At the intersection of Picaboo Street the remnants of SnapCity's New Year's party remain. It had been a fantastic carnival with Champagne fountains, cupcakes, fireworks, celebrities, dancers, and music. Mrs Grey speculated it cost the city $4 million, but the budget report disappeared 30-seconds after it was posted. Now, all that remains of that night is the rainbow-confetti in dirty piles mixed with slush and dirty snow. 886

She wanders towards the café to meet Anthony for breakfast. She checks the Snapmap, he's coming in from the suburbs—which was it: Vurb or Zenly? Snap was buying up and renaming these suburbs so quickly it was hard to keep track. 887

It was still early, not quite 8:45 yet. At the bus stop she sees several girls waiting for the 9 o'clock bus to Redditville. The girls seem out of place in the cold. 888

Without a reality filter or makeup, they stand out with
their skin exposed in skimpy party clothing. Maria rec-
ognizes Daisy Bishop, who she had babysat a decade
ago. Maria had taught Daisy how to make bracelets
while they sang along to old Michael Jackson songs.

Daisy was slumped over on a bench staring 889
at her device. Her 4" heels seem impractical for the
slushy sidewalk. She looked exhausted, confused, and
alone despite being in a crowd of girls her age. None
spoke to each other, or even looked up at the street.
Why wasn't Daisy in college? Surely, she could do
more with her life than compete for upvotes?

Maria reaches the café and pulls open the door em- 890
blazoned with a large ad suggesting solutions for "un-
flattering winter fashion." The café was empty, just
screens on every wall showing advertising or providing
news. She orders a latte from the animated snapbot
fashioned with long blonde hair and big eyes. She
watches as the cup drops into the bots ample chest
and fills with espresso, whirring and steaming the milk.
As she takes the cup, the barista reverts into a black
box void of life.

Maria sits at a table advertising "Make Money 891
by Playing Games," noting the irony of an image of
fanned $100 bills in a cashless society. The screens
surround her—"Choose A Coffee and We'll Reveal
Your Stripper Name" and "Financial Servitude-Watch
This Cautionary Tale."

She sends Anthony a snap—'Where are you?' 892
Immediately, he replies—'Sorry babe, can't talk.' Odd she thought; since when did her brother start calling her "babe"? Clearly, an automated response.

"What his messages say about your relationship," her table baits.

"This city will never understand me." She mumbles to herself.

Two twenty-somethings enter the café 895
and slump into a corner. The young woman stares at her device while her boyfriend glares aimlessly though his Spectacles. They don't say a word to each other.

"What Should Your Body Look Like?" her table asked.

When Anthony walks in he is flustered and irritable.

"What's wrong?" Maria asks.

"They updated the roads again," he replies. "No signs. The exit was just gone! My head hurts." Maria had ignored the snap update about integrated tolls and intuitive redesign. This happened every few months, but it only caused confusion among those driving anachronistic cars.

Anthony taps his device. The snapbot barista 900
lights up and fills a shot of espresso while waving a Snap flag thanking him for his service.

The table shifts its message to “Is That A Headache 901
Or A Migraine?” and Anthony rolls his eyes.

“How long are you in town for?” Maria asks.

“I don’t know” he replies. “I’ve been working in Redditville.”

“What’s in Redditville?” Maria asks.

“It’s a long and crazy story.” He 905
continues in a whisper: “Do you know how Snap women are treated there? There is a demand for the images and videos we thought were private”[2]

“What? What do you mean? Those disappear moments after taking them” Maria questions.

“Well, not really” Anthony explains. “There are lots of ways to record images before they disappear.[3] Some folks even have their devices set up to record every interaction and share the videos in Redditville. There are stores and clubs to sell the girls of Snap.”

2 Link: https://www.desiblitz.com/content/snapchat-nudes-where-do-they-really-go

3 Link: https://money.cnn.com/2012/12/28/technology/security/snapchat-security-flaw/index.html

“How do you know this?” Maria asks with a sense of embarrassment and shame.

“It’s all over the boards. There are girls, young girls, dressed as a sexy version of each filter: a deer[4], a nerd, a flower princess. Some get a clientele of followers and make an income, others never meant to be there in the first place. Remember little Daisy Bishop?”

Maria nods. 910

The table shifts its message to “Sexy makeup tips 911
that will blow his mind!”

“She was dancing dressed as a sexy dog. She recognized me, so I had to leave.”

“What did you do?” Maria asks in shock.

“There is not much I could do. I filed a report. I don’t know if anyone read it before it vanished.”

“Let’s tell someone. We need to go to 915
the authorities” Maria exclaims. She glares at Anthony.

“They won’t do anything” he sighs, adding “unless they broadcast a press

4 Link: https://cheddar.com/videos/inside-snap-employee-concerns-raise-questions-about-culture-and-diversity

release with a cautionary story for Snap Discover."

Maria gulps down her coffee. It burns her mouth 917
and tastes bitter. She throws on her parka and summons Anthony to follow her. He sighs and follows her lead reluctantly.

His car is out front, dirty but familiar. She climbs 918
in the passenger's seat. Anthony compliantly drives to the Snap Police Station.

"How can I help you?" a round-faced policeman greets them in a clean and modern reception area. "Together we can make Snap a safer place and a stronger community."[5]

Maria jumps in "Our data—" 920

"Please swipe your device to verify your ID," the policeman smiles indicating a scanner built into the kiosk. Maria, complies swiping her device.

"How can I help you?" he asks again.

"I work in—" Anthony begins, interrupted as the officer says "Please swipe your device to verify your ID."

5 Link: https://support.snapchat.com/en-US/a/report-abuse-in-app

Anthony sighs and swipes slowly remembering that the police have a bureaucratic memory of 30 seconds.

The officer smiles and asks: “How can I help you?”

“We feel you need to investigate the misuse of Snap women’s data,” Maria says.

“Do you have a safety concern?” the officer asks.

“Well, not my safety, but... I’m worried that... well... the girls on the bus.”

“What bus?” Anthony asks, somewhat confused.

“The bus taking Snap girls to Redditville. I saw Daisy queueing for it this morning.” Maria adds.

“When you experience a safety concern, hold down the snap flag, to alert us to the problem” The officer suggests. “Together we can make Snap a safer place and a stronger community.” He repeats.

“Well, it’s not me, it’s all of us.”

“How can I help you?” The officer
asks, again.

“People in Redditville are stealing dirty
pictures of girls in Snap.” Maria says,
immediately recognizing how silly she
sounds and regretting going to the
police station.

“If your property was stolen, you can 935
contact support directly from your
device.” The officer suggests politely.

Anthony rubs Maria’s shoulders, and says “Come on, 936
this isn’t going to help anyone. Daisy has to file a report
herself. She’s an adult.”

As they walk out, both their devices buzz and alert 937
them to the report of their visit. As Anthony drives
Maria home, she watches as the report disappears
30-seconds after opening it.

As they turn onto Parkside Avenue the gar- 938
bage piles glisten. Anthony parks between a broken
Christmas tree and the remnants of a burnt couch. As
Maria swings open the door, Mrs. Bishop, Daisy’s mother, waves from her porch. Maria smiles awkwardly and
looks away, feeling ashamed knowing about Daisy’s career path, and wondering how much Mrs. Bishop knows.

Just then, a garbage truck pulls onto Parkside, 939
picking up piles of debris, and the discarded remains of
families celebrating age-old holiday traditions together. 940

The sanitation workers diligently and method-
ologically restore the street to its former state.

Monica Stephens is an Assistant Professor of Geography at the University at Buffalo. Her research examines the geographies of misinformation and incivility online.

PLAYMENTALITIES

SONY PLAYSTATION[1]

Alberto Vanolo, Università di Torino

Notes from a gamified future

Peter was looking at his WhatsApp status. He was defi- 941
nitely tempted to upload a picture of his new virtual trophy, which testified that he had crossed 5,000 streets with the green traffic light, but he also thought it was stupid to exhibit such a banal award. It'd be cooler to exhibit a trophy showing that he had crossed 5,000 streets on a red light, but no such award existed.

Peter's '5,000 green lights' trophy adds to his 942
vast collection of civic achievements gained during his first 14 years of life. Last week he gained a virtual medal as he reached 1,000 kg of recycled paper placed in recycling bins. Once he had reached a score of 900 kg he had started collecting paper everywhere, but what had really made the difference was finding a stock of abandoned books in his grandpa's cellar. Those horrible, smelly, useless books, promptly moved to the closest smart bin, allowed him to reach the trophy, which has been automatically displayed on his Facebook page. Now he is somewhat less motivated about paper-awards, as the next milestone is 1.5 metric tons of paper, which seems a distant goal. 1.5 also feels like a banal number, not as cool as '1' or '10.' Right now, he occupies position #3 in his class paper recycling ranking (although he is only #121 in the school and #732,221 in the city).

1 The following speculative fiction and satire imagines a gamified city in which residents compete for social status and services. Such a thought experiment could equally apply if the city were run by Microsoft Xbox or Nintendo. Product or corporate names may be trademarks or registered trademarks, and are used only for the purpose of conducting a thought experiment without intent to infringe.

These trophies have been developed by Play-Station to nudge citizens like Peter to behave in more virtuous ways. PlayStation is not the only provider of civic games, but it is the most popular, mostly because of the quality of the games and the real-time integration between videogame stats and civic trophies. PlayStation had entered the field of civic gamification by developing free apps and online leaderboards aiming at educating citizens in the sphere of environmental sustainability. In the beginning, it was all about recycling and saving energy. Then, with the rise in popularity of civic games, the company started to develop city-specific apps in order to tackle a number of local problems, such as traffic in Mexico City or car theft in San Francisco. In each city, PlayStation invented a competition to measure, compare and rank citizens, and even to convince them it was fun. The supposedly 'best' citizens were not just awarded with symbolic trophies, but also with bonuses. For example, if you locate 30 stolen cars by reporting them on San Francisco police department's online map, you receive not only a 'grand theft auto report' trophy, but also a 20% discount on car theft insurance fares, which can raise to a 40% discount if you report 60 stolen cars. If you live in Mexico City and do not move beyond five kilometres of your home and do not use a car you will receive 4 free bus tickets. 943

Some of Peter's trophies are not as socially cool. Last month he went 16 days without taking a shower in order to save a huge volume of fresh water. This allowed him to reach #1 in his school's 'water saving chart.' That victory did not come without costs: especially the backchannel jokes that were created about him by his schoolmates once they realised that he also had very low levels of consumption of toilet paper. 944

Some trophies are just inherently more pleasant. Peter caressed over different 1,000 cats, allowing him 945 to get a 'cat lover' award. With each feline interaction, he took a photo that was then uploaded to be analysed by the Playstation's 'loving pets' algorithm. Peter then received a metal pin from Catter, a popular cat-food company, that he put on his schoolbag. He still has to caress 424 dogs before reaching an analogous result in the canine sphere, but he isn't as fond of dogs. Apart from Muffin, which is Mike's border terrier. Mike is Peter's best friend, and his dog is adorable. Mike got the 'meta-animal-lover' award because he turned Muffin into a fully vegan dog by feeding it only with VegPuppy, a brand of non-flesh-based dog food. Mike was the first kid at school to get the award and it made him quite popular for a while. The notoriety wore off quickly though, even though he still exhibits his trophy.

Peter tried hard to get the trophy '50 days with- 946
out saying the word fuck', but he failed. He failed on day 43, and when his mobile phone switched itself off as he was composing a long thoughtful message. He couldn't help himself: 'fuck, fuck, fuuuuckkkk!!' The incident cost him a 10% deduction on all language milestones for six months, but did learn a lesson. Since then, the word 'fock' seems just as cathartic when he need to express his displeasure. This might not work for long though, as there are rumours that the software update will start getting smarter about recognising these linguistic hacks.

Peter knows that these games all matter espe- 947
cially after he leaves school and becomes an adult. His access to work, public services, and much else in everyday life all depends on the scores that he builds up. His Dad is always telling him to work on his scores: that they will improve him and the city. All he needs to do is play the game as it is designed to be played, and avoid associating with any dissidents, especially those that argue that the gamification of civic life leads to a loss of autonomy, privacy, freedom and politics. The

games are fun and they make the city a fairer place for everyone to live in, his father insists, how could there be any real harm in that?

Notes from a gamified present

Peter's gamified life is an over-the-top speculation of 948
some future society, but it is not without foundation. Life in cities is already being gamified, with the use of virtual rewards and playful elements (such as rankings, scores, badges, levels, rewards, leaderboards, virtual currencies) to stimulate public engagement and encourage virtuous social behaviours. There are now apps, developed by both public and private institutions, designed to reshape environmental behaviour (sustainable living), promote educational goals (lifelong learning), create healthy behaviours (walking, eating properly), and produce political participation (community development initiatives). The use of games is growing in civic planning in order to support collaboration, participation and deliberation in design and decision making. Many urban government innovation labs, such as Mexico City's Laboratorio Para La Ciudad, Dublin's The Studio, Boston and Philadelphia's Offices of New Urban Mechanics, San Francisco's Office of Civic Innovation and Singapore's Human Experience Lab, have introduced civic gaming elements. The European Union, through its Smart Cities and Communities programmes, are funding many initiatives that use gamification to progressively change human behaviour with respect to energy, transport, and consumption of resources.

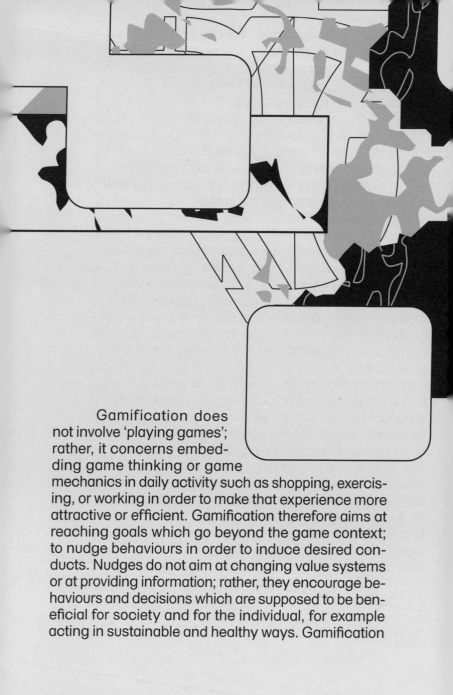

Gamification does not involve 'playing games'; rather, it concerns embedding game thinking or game mechanics in daily activity such as shopping, exercising, or working in order to make that experience more attractive or efficient. Gamification therefore aims at reaching goals which go beyond the game context; to nudge behaviours in order to induce desired conducts. Nudges do not aim at changing value systems or at providing information; rather, they encourage behaviours and decisions which are supposed to be beneficial for society and for the individual, for example acting in sustainable and healthy ways. Gamification uses specific forms of nudging based on ludic elements, with the motivational power of games mobilised in order to promote participation, persistence and achievements. Two types of rewards are utilised to shift behaviour: extrinsic rewards built into the game design (badges, trophies, etc.); and intrinsic rewards implicit in playing, such as self-worth through beating one's own best record and mastering aspects of the game, and social rewards through helping others.

Nudging is the key aspect of the governmentality 950
produced through gamification. Indeed, gamification is all about the governance of subjects. It is specifically designed to reshape behaviour; to produce the 'good citizen.' Indeed, gamification involves the subjectification of 'good' and 'bad' citizens/users by the distinction and rewarding/penalisation of appropriate and inappropriate behaviours. The computational technology of measurements, points and leaderboards assigns a position to each user, transforming them into assessable and enumerable units, which as a result enact a form of neoliberal biopolitics (underpinned by the logics of competition, individualism, rewards and responsibilisation of the self). Citizens are asked to measure their own productivity, civility and well-being, with the implicit imperative to perform and to govern themselves in relation to these. In exchange for the provision of personal data and quantified performances, the user is rewarded with a sense of achievement and participation. Those that do not 'play the game' are penalised, through disenfranchisement, higher premiums, and exclusion. Inherent in this neoliberal ethos is the idea that actors have to be moulded and controlled in order to adapt to new market and public/private logics (and not vice-versa).

There are number of troubling issues here, such 951
as surveillance, privacy and biopolitics. The means by which nudging occurs is also a grid of measurement and monitoring. Citizens are being enrolled into

a system of social manipulation that is also a system of pervasive surveillance. Gamification simply sweetens the shift in governmentality, providing the illusion that the citizen is in charge of their own destiny through game-play rather than playing to the designs of others. Moreover, gamification reproduces the ideology of 'technological solutionism', that the right app, with the right system of feedbacks and rewards, will nudge behaviours and fix problems.

This raises a whole series of issues. Who gets 952
to decide the aims and the rules of the game? What are the effects of such competitive subjectification on social relations? What happens to those who reject this form of governmentality? What effects do they have on those that lack the means to play? What are the social and legal responsibilities of companies designing these gamified social systems and gathering vast swathes of personal data? What are the interlinkages between gamified social life and the transformation of capitalism through the mobilisation, commodification, accumulation and exploitation of various forms of cognitive activities? To what extent does gamification lure or coerce workers into exploitative conditions by mobilising interest instead of economic coercion? How does gamification reconfigure work, consumption, cognitive production, participation and engagement, and spaces and times of cities? Can nudging fix deep rooted, complex structural issues and wicked problems afflicting cities?

While Peter thinks the gamified city might be 953
fun, he is already exploring ways to game and subvert the system. And with good reason. There will be little fun when society is reduced to the games of states and corporations.

Alberto Vanolo, PhD in spatial planning and local development at the Polytechnic of Turin, is professor of political and economic geography at the University of Turin, Italy. His main research topics include the politics of urban representation, smart cities, and related ideologies.

STREAMERS

SPOTIFY[1]

Cian O'Callaghan, Trinity College Dublin

Paul registered the incessant noise like an electron- 955
ic coin-drop. It dragged him out of sleep and into his darkened bedroom. He reached for his phone, flashing a blue screen. 2.31am. He fantasised about letting it time out. Rita was asleep. The warmth of her body was like a magnet. But he shook it off. He hadn't had a stream in eight days and he needed the money. Without reading the message he hit *accept.*

Minutes later he stood under the shower waiting 956
for his body and brain to synch. They'd gone to bed about 11. Rita had been streamed onto a tort case and she'd spent the day getting up to speed on the files and meeting her colleagues. The day had been a scorcher, but Paul spent it in their one-bedroom apartment listening to podcasts and watching videos on YouTube.

That was how Rita had found him, reclined on 957
the couch, laptop on crotch and beer in hand.

"For fuck sake," she'd said. "You might have put on a load of washing at least."

He swung his legs onto the floor, but his efforts to mollify her were too little too late. "This stream might go on for a few weeks, even a month," she said.

1 The following speculative fiction and satire imagines a city in which the labour market is run on the business model of streaming music. Such a thought experiment could equally apply if the city were run by other streaming companies such as Deezer or Google Play. Product or corporate names may be trademarks or registered trademarks, and are used only for the purpose of conducting a thought experiment without intent to infringe.

He got up from the couch and 960
walked towards her. "Alright, alright," he said, failing to keep the testiness out of his voice.

"I mean it, Paul. If I'm going to be picking up more streams, you've got to be picking up the slack at home."

"I hear you," he said, his voice more even now. He took her in his arms. "It's just one of those days, you know."

"You're having a lot of *those days*," she said. "Look, forget it."

"I'll get dinner started."

He got his frustrations out on slicing the peppers. Rita 965
didn't understand how lucky she was. At least permanent positions still existed for her after Dublin went Spotify. Yes, Rita was a *streamer* too, but there were different levels to that. Like most people, Paul's work came "on-demand"—some black-boxed programming selected him from a pool of similar workers. But, he had to concede, he had been unemployed from his job as an electrician for a year and a half when the city became Spotified and at least he was getting *some* work now.

What work he did get came through an agen- 966
cy who put their catalogue on the Spotify platform. Paul's agency BAM had been a construction firm, but a lot of companies now had an agency division. After a user inputted their job request, the algorithm combined skills, streamer reviews, and agency ratings with geo-location, and the streamer was sent a ping with a five-minute window to accept. Realistically people like

Paul couldn't afford to be picky. Declining a job, or a non-response, meant he'd be shuffled to the back of the agency's rotation algorithm.

So Paul accepted streams a got paid a monthly 967
cheque. Sometimes he got more streams for less pay, it depended. He had a friend who was with an indie agency, and she got a detailed breakdown of pay-per-stream. He'd thought about going that route himself but it required a lot of self-promotion, and that wasn't him. So he stayed with BAM and took what he was given.

After dinner, Paul washed the dishes while Rita 968
sat slumped on the couch. Her hair, so carefully pinned that morning, was now pulled back in a ponytail.

"Were they mostly streamers or what?" Paul asked over his shoulder.

"Bit of a mix. There's a few guys who 970
are permanent and sort of run the show, you know. And then there's maybe three or four streamers, including me."

Paul nodded. "Uh-huh."

"Jesus, I'm wrecked from it," she said. "It's like starting in a new firm every time. And the permanent guys don't see it, you know?"

Well neither do you, thought Paul. He remembered 973
getting his first payment. At the BAM office in Naas he'd signed a form, and they'd given him an actual physical cheque.

"Your royalties," said the women at the desk.

The amount was €663.56, not a bad month in retrospect. 975

When he got home, Rita had been studying for 976
exams and hadn't exactly welcomed the distraction.

> "I'm like 'How much did I get from each job?' and they're just like 'This is your pay'," he had said.

> "I'm sure it's just kinks in the system," she'd said typing case notes on a laptop.

> He resisted the urge to start up again now. "They just don't care", he said without turning from the sink.

> "Yeah, probably. At any rate, it's full on." 980

> Paul just nodded.

Paul stood in darkness outside the apartment block. 982
He hefted his toolbox and looked at his watch—2.46am—the AutonomoCab was due. He lived in a suburban development built during the boom years. For a time it was a ghost estate, but now the houses and high-rises were filled. Paul and Rita were renting like most everyone these days. Owning was a dream of a different generation.

The estate was quiet at this hour, the public pla- 983
za over the underground carpark empty apart from him. He could see the lights on in a few apartments or the flickering glow of screens. It was unnaturally warm even now.

The AutonomoCab entered the road to the es- 984
tate, the GPS guiding it smoothly towards him. The Driverless Revolution hadn't really happened, but when Spotify partnered with AutonomoCab to offer subsidised rides for streamers it wiped out the taxi industry. The car came to a stop beside Paul and the door opened.

"Hello, Paul?" came a voice from the 985
radio. "Hello? Are you in?"

"Hi, yeah, I'm in, yeah," Paul answered, closing the door behind him. "Is that the base?" The voice was male, possibly Nigerian, he thought.

"Hello, Paul. Yes, I am Benjamin, I am the base operator for tonight."

"Hi, Benjamin. You with AntonomoCab?"

"No I am a streamer, like you. I am here on the couch with my laptop, you know."

"Ok man, cool," Paul said, hoping to 990
end the conversation. He clipped in his seatbelt, and the car began to move.

"Paul, I have one more streamer pick-up in Portmarnock. Would you like to ride share and split the cost?"

"I better not," Paul said after a pause. "I was asleep when the ping came in, so

I'm already running late and I can't risk a buffering error from the user. I hope I'm not putting you out?"

Paul was feeling jittery. His last job had resulted in 994
a small article in the newspaper and he hadn't been pinged in over a week. It seemed he'd gotten away with it though.

"It is not a problem," said Benjamin. 995

The radio transmission was interrupted by a digital 996
stream of advertising. He zoned them out and checked the address on his phone.

The AutonomoCab pulled up outside a terraced house 997
in a small square off Grand Canal Street. A woman in her early thirties answered the door. She had pale skin and dark hair worn in a bob with a severe fringe that he found attractive. She was dressed and made up looking like she'd maybe just come in.

"Paul, is it?" she said as he awkwardly held up his tool box.

"Yeah, that's right. Was it yourself that requested the electrician?"

"Hi Paul, I'm Maeve," she said, 1000
simultaneously offering her hand and extending the other to welcome him inside. "Come on in. Yes. Look, I am actually just about to head out the door

myself, would you believe it? Pretty much just after I put in the request I got pinged for a private party with my playlist. It's not far actually, some Premium Users in Grand Canal Dock, which is handy for me—some of the other guys in the playlist have a lot further to come."

Paul had been on a couple of playlists but they nev- 1001
er really lasted. Cafes and bars used them and you'd
often hear of specialised playlists in tech and phar-
maceuticals. Streamers in construction were more
or less disposable.

She was talking quickly as she shuffled him 1002
along a narrow corridor and into an open-plan kitch-
en. He knew her type, like some of Rita's friends. They
wore their privilege in the breezy way they slotted into
any social situation. She led him through the kitchen
and into a bathroom.

"I think I've seen you on Instagram," he said, suddenly recognising her.

"You have? Great! Are you a follower? I'm up to over 10K now on the Maevelengthz account. Of course, the playlist had a lot more."

"I'm not a follower myself," said Paul, 1005
"but my girlfriend is, I think. You do
cocktails, is it?" With the mention of a
girlfriend, Paul sensed Maeve relax,
though it could have been the cameras
mounted on the corners of every room
that put her at ease. You don't just

ping a streamer to your house in the middle of the night without assurances, thought Paul. Then again he knew how to handle cameras.

"I do cocktails, yes—that's my playlist gig. But I also do some fitness, make-up tips, some music reviews. It's a tricky balance because you have to have your niche but then diversify to build up followers."

"Right, yeah," said Paul. He could visualise her giving this spiel in a Ted Talk. He gritted his teeth and hoped it looked like a smile.

Maeve turned the hot water tap on. "So anyway, the boiler was acting up earlier so I checked it when I got home and lo and behold, no hot water."

Paul put his hand under the running tap because it seemed like what was expected of him.

"Luckily I had a shower in the gym. But 1010
Molly, that's my little one, she's with
her father tonight. She's got a habit
of wearing what she eats so we're not
going to last long without hot water
when she gets back tomorrow."

"I can imagine," said Paul.

Maeve had turned and was walking back out through 1012
the kitchen, leaving Paul to trail behind. "If I had to

guess," she said, "I'd say it's the element overheating and tripping the system. The water has been really hot the last week."

"That sounds about right," Paul said. "You probably could have done without me."

"Well, I wasn't sure. And I'll always try to give a stream, you know," she replied, turning to face him, maintaining eye contact just a moment too long.

"I appreciate that," he said. Despite 1015
himself, he was warming to her. He envied the presence of her personality. He always felt so out of place. It was better in the days before streaming, he told himself.

Paul got to work while Maeve finished putting on her 1016
makeup in the kitchen. He watched her brush on a thin layer of foundation. She knew what she was doing, applying just enough to accentuate her pale skin. She caught him looking at her cleavage, an unconscious thing, and he looked away embarrassed.

"Do you find Instagram good?" said Paul, deflecting. "I've friends who swear it's great for getting their selected streams up and all."

"To be honest it's hard work," she said. "Maintaining the profile, responding to comments, making sure you've new content. You start living self-promotion. But you can't rely on the algorithm only, at least that's the way I see it."

The job was a simple one. It was as Maeve suspected. 1020
Paul reset the element and turned the timer back on. After a moment he could hear it heating the water.

"This house," said Maeve, stepping out into the doorway and making a sweeping gesture with her hand, "is mine. My parents bought it before things got too mad and now I live here with only a small mortgage. That's why I can do the playlist. And I'm planning to get some investments in the infrastructure."

"Those bonds are pretty expensive," said Paul. Early on, the City Council had taken an equity share in Spotify City in exchange for frontloading investment in infrastructure. They'd recently created City Infrastructure Bonds to fund upgrading and new projects.

"Yeah," said Maeve, pursing her lips as she applied lipstick, "but have you seen those new CIITs?"

"Seats?"

"C, I, I, T, S," she spelled out the letters. 1025
"City Infrastructure Investment Trusts.

Announced last week. You buy shares in them basically, like the Real Estate Investment Trusts."

"I think I've one of those as a landlord," said Paul.

She made a disapproving face. "I don't know how you're supposed to get by streaming with the cost of rent and everything else." Maeve looked at her watch. "Shit. I better run. Listen, I've got a security stream coming later to lock up properly. Can I leave you to finish up?"

Paul felt like asking her to stay. He was starting to enjoy their conversation. And she looked good now, standing there shrugging into a black leather jacket. But wasn't he just a streamer in her house? Maeve tubed her lipstick and Paul felt the gulf between them. "Yeah no bother", he said.

"Great, thanks, just close out the door and they'll do the rest." She grabbed a purse off the back of the chair, checked for keys, and was gone.

Paul breathed out slowly and walked around the empty 1030
house. Conscious of the cameras he didn't linger. The rooms were clean but lived in, children's toys in one and some matching cups sitting dirty in the kitchen sink. The place had an order to it, a sense of design that was missing from his own rented apartment. His

mind went back to the last job. It had been a nice house too, bigger than this but without the warmth.

He turned down the temperature setting on 1031
the element. The water wouldn't be quite as hot but it wouldn't trip the switch either. These boiler systems in old houses were sometimes finicky and just needed a bit of finesse.

At the last job, he'd done it almost without think- 1032
ing. The woman had barely acknowledged him, like he was an unnecessary human component to an automated service. Even after he'd seen the headline it was hard to believe it had actually been him. The article had mentioned an electrical fire. He'd taken a screenshot and then later deleted it. But he hadn't stopped thinking about it.

Once he'd tidied up he opened the door and 1033
stepped out onto the street, but stopped. He looked at the nice little square and the nice little houses, and he imagined all the nice little futures that could be built from such humble stuff. He turned on the doorstep and went back inside to the boiler.

Afterwards, the city was in that liminal zone be- 1034
tween the end of nightlife and the start of the morning. Early risers would soon be getting up while others would be coming down. He could almost hear the ambient hum of all those proximate lives. And the city was lit like dull chrome as he began his walk home.

Cian O'Callaghan is an Assistant Professor of Geography at Trinity College Dublin, Ireland. His main research interests include creativity and place, neoliberalism, housing, and political contestations over urban vacant spaces.

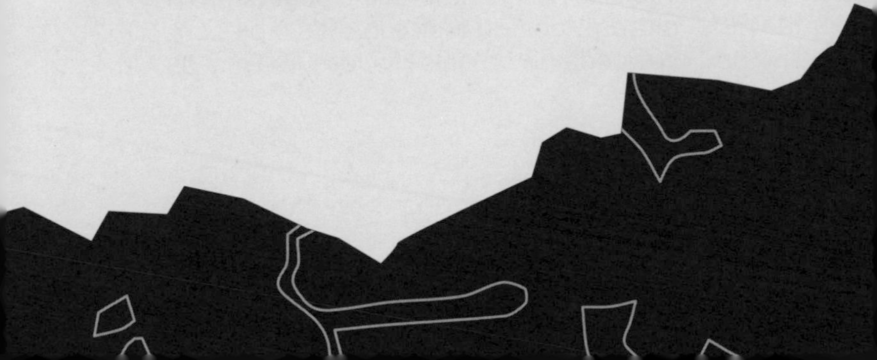

POTHOLES AND PUMPKIN SPICE

STARBUCKS[1]

Kalpana Shankar, University College Dublin, Ireland

Glenn Kaufmann, Dublin, Ireland

In the near future, in a town very much like yours, 1035
on a Tuesday...

Khaliq walks into the café but he is not interested in the 1036
slippers made of recycled plastic, the artisanal chocolates ("Now with 30% more insect protein! Still gluten-free!"), or hemp shirts. Instead, he heads towards the back where "City Hub" is emblazoned on a board with the city's trademark logo next to it.

He goes to the machine on the wall that dis- 1037
penses a ticket for the queue, but the machine has a sign that states: "To provide you with better service, baristas are now dispensing tickets." So Khaliq walks back out to the café and asks a barista for a City Hub queue number. He's handed 101. They are currently on 65. He orders today's City Hub Municipal Beverage (CHMB) special, a tall half-caf free range pumpkin spice oatmilk lacchiato and returns to the City Hub services counter. He hovers around the booth with all of the other citizens waiting their turn. It's a bit confusing and crowded and he gets restless, but just as

1 The following speculative fiction and satire imagines a city run using the customer service-orientated business model of a coffee shop. Such a thought experiment could equally apply if the city were run by any chain coffee shop. Product or corporate names may be trademarks or registered trademarks, and are used only for the purpose of conducting a thought experiment without intent to infringe.

he notices that there is an area with tables behind him and is about to go sit down his number is called.

A smiling young man greets him; his handwritten nametag says Ben.

"Welcome to City Hub! How can we help you?"

"I'm here to sign up my daughter for school." 1040

"You know you can do that on CHAPP, the City Hub App, right? We can even text you right back once she's signed up."

Khaliq replied, "The app didn't work. It just said 'All schools are out of stock' and I didn't know what that meant. How could schools be out of stock?"

"We understand your concern. We're happy to see you in our retail outlet; we want you to treat City Hub as a home away from home. What kind of school would you like for your daughter?"

"Um, what are my options?"

"You can have full public, half public/ 1045
half private, half public/half private with extra religious instruction or light religious instruction. And what size would you like—a half day, full day or boarding? You can have an extra shot of arts, music, dance, or science.

Of course, you'll need to pay extra for the boarding. And you can be sure that all of our teachers are trained to a high standard and paid fairly, so it really doesn't matter which teachers are in your daughter's school. We control 50% of the schools directly so we know they are all excellent quality."

Khaliq pauses to take in this barrage of information and grasps at the last bit that was offered to him. "If you control 50%, who controls the other 50%?"

"We franchise those. We call them 'Friends of City Hub.' FOCH."

Khaliq thinks back. "OK, let's try full public all day with the dance option and in the Straystown neighbourhood. My daughter's name is Shayla. Shayla Sellers."

He goes on to give the staff member his address and her birthdate, and requests a loyalty card since his son will be signing up for school next year.

Ben beams. "Excellent choices. We'll 1050
call you when your ticket is ready. While you're waiting, please enjoy this City Hub Municipal Beverage (CHMB) on us."

Ben carefully enters Khaliq's information into his interface while Khaliq drinks his CHMB from a cup with City Hub emblazoned in a large friendly font with the city's trademark logo next to it and the statement "Now with 20% less lead!"

Not too long after, Khaliq hears "Karl! Your order is ready!" Since no one else is getting up, Khaliq decides they mean him and goes to the counter. He is handed a slip of paper confirming his order. It says: "Father: Colonel Sanders. Pupil: Sasha Hester Sanders."

He tries to catch the attention of Ben or one of the other staff to correct the record, but they have all moved on to new customer-citizens. Back to the queue. This time, Khaliq's number is 150.

A few blocks away, wandering through the produce section of his local market, Khaliq's partner Tom drops a clutch of asparagus into his cart, then moves along examining the selection of local apples. Out of the corner of his eye he catches sight of a "City Hub" sign, which he approaches. There is also a neatly handwritten sign on a chalkboard offering the daily specials in city services ("Water registration: €19.99 today only").

As the queue clears ahead of him he steps up
to the counter. A smiling young woman greets him; her handwritten nametag says Tanya. "Welcome to City Hub! How can we help you?"

> "There's a large pothole outside my house. It's been there for weeks and is growing. I've been meaning to call the roads and bridges department, but never quite get around to it. Then I saw your kiosk here, and wondered if I could set up a repair."

"You know you can do that on CHAPP, the City Hub App, right? We can even text you right back once the hole is filled."

"Maybe, but since I just saw the sign when I was shopping, I thought I would just do it now."

"Sure, I can arrange it. First, I'll need your first name to set up a repair ticket."

It's Tom Wal..." 1060

"Oh, that's all right, Tom. First name is enough. Now, I'll just need the address where you live, or the location of the pothole. And I'll need to know what kind of filler you'd like."

"What do you mean, 'what kind of filler'?"

"For the pothole. You have a choice of concrete, asphalt, Ready Set, Permabond 3, or QuickLine."

"I guess asphalt is fine."

"Excellent. Do you want Midwestern 1065
Asphalt, Pure Volcanic Asphalt, or Pristine Asphalt?"

"What makes it Pristine?"

"Oh, it's conflict free."

"And the Pure Volcanic?"

Tanya suppresses a sigh. "It's free-range but not conflict free. So you want Pure Volcanic. And what size is the pothole?"

"What are my choices?" 1070

"Maltesa, Sharpé, and Labradoro!"

"Uh...Labradoro, I guess."

"Excellent choice. So you would like a Labradoro pothole filled with free-range Pure Volcanic asphalt, correct."

"Yeah, sure. OK."

After a few minutes, the clerk hands 1075
Tom a small yellow ticket and explains, "We should have one of our Streetistas out to fill your pothole by Thursday."

"Wow, that's fast."

"We do our best to turn around transport issues in 48 hours."

"Well, thank you very much."

As Tom starts to wander off, the clerk stops him, "Uh, sir, you might want to hang on to your ticket."

Tom stops and turns back to the 1080
counter, picking up the little yellow stub. “Oh, right. Will I need it again?”

“It’s the only way you have to claim your free fill guarantee.”

“Free fill guarantee?”

“Yes, sir. If we don’t fill in your pothole by Thursday evening, or you’re unhappy with your fill, we’ll give you a free pothole fill of your choice anytime in the next six weeks.”

“Oh, that’s good then.”

Tom pockets the ticket and goes back 1085
to the produce section.

Friday Morning

Tom briskly walks through the market and approaches the City Hub counter. He waits in the queue until it’s his turn. The same clerk greets him.

“How can we help you?”

“I was in on Tuesday about having a pothole filled. It was supposed to be filled by last night. But it wasn’t. I’d like to claim my ‘free fill guarantee.’”

“Very good, sir. Do you have your ticket?”

Tom hands over the yellow stub. 1090

The clerk scans the ticket.

"Ahh, yes, welcome back, Ken. I see the problem...."

First day of school—7:30AM

Tom yells upstairs: "Shayla, your school bus will be here any minute. Come on!"

She runs down the stairs with her City Hub schoolbag over one shoulder and a CH-logo water bottle in her hand. Just then, they hear a bus outside screech, then shudder to a halt.

Khaliq, Tom, and Shayla walk outside to the bus and see it buried up to its front axle in a pothole. The bus driver looks at Tom exasperatedly, "Didn't you report that pothole months ago?"

Tom frantically opens CHAPP to check on the status of the repair. He suppresses an expletive as he scrolls past the introductory screen that says "Welcome back, Ken!"

"We violated the neighbourhood ordinance! We were supposed to get the conflict-free asphalt! So they didn't fill it!"

The bus driver sighs. "I have to report this to the City Hub Garage to get a tow."

Tom says, "I already have the app open." He opens the CH Garage screen. "To improve your municipal breakdown experience, City Hub wants to know: What size tow truck would you like?"

Kalpana Shankar is a Professor of Information and Communication Studies at University College Dublin. Her areas of research and teaching focus on "research on research", including the sustainability of data archives, research evaluation/peer review, and data ethics.

Glenn Kaufmann is a freelance writer and sound designer who lives in Dublin, Ireland. He writes about travel, food, arts, and culture.

THE STRIVE CITY OF TOMORROW

STRAVA[1]

Katharine S. Willis, University
of Plymouth

Preface

The following speculative fiction imagines a city run around a quantified self platform and app and is a satire of the Ebenezer Howard's treatise on the Garden City, and takes liberally from his seminal 1898 book 'To-Morrow: A Peaceful Path to Real Reform.' In his book Howard presented a utopian vision for a post-industrial society where 'human society and the beauty of nature' were to be enjoyed together. However, for all of Howard's vision of a utopian society, the Garden City was also an economic model aimed at investors, with detailed workings of costs and he even assures potential investors of a 4.5% return. It is these two aspects of the vision of a future city built-from-scratch—the idealistic model of a type of post-urban lifestyle and the monetisation of such a lifestyle through a business model—that are drawn upon in the following text. It imagines a city where people in a post-work economy would leverage their data assets and how this might be realised in a city 1100

1 Product or corporate names may be trademarks or registered trademarks, and are used only for the purpose of conducting a thought experiment without intent to infringe.

planning scenario similar to Howard's. It takes Strava as a basis because of some similarities in Strava Inc's broader aspirations around improving the quality of city life (see quote below), and because of the commercial venture Strava Metro,[2] through which Strava commercialises user data to sell to cities worldwide to improve analysis and planning of urban infrastructure.[3] The text re-imagines garden cities as `Strive cities', where land value is replaced by data value, and your assets go up or down depending on how hard you strive to improve your quality of life. In some parts there are direct quotes from passages in the original 1898 text[4].

'We want people to know that your seemingly mundane activity that you're doing every day to get back and forth to work ... actually has the potential to improve your quality of life in your city." 1101

Andrew Vontz, communications lead at Strava.[5] 1102

The reader is asked to imagine a city, embracing 6,000 data clusters,[6] which is at the moment purely an industrial use, and has been obtained in a public-private partnership between Strava and the City. The purchase uses a business plan in which the running costs are raised through the monetization of urban data, with each citizen purchasing data shares 1103

2 Strava does not release exact details of how much cities pay for access to its data sets, but in media interviews it claims to do this for semi-altruistic purposes, rather than pure commercialization. According to Michael Horvath, Co-founder, Strava: "We're not a philanthropy. But we are interested in the impact, what it can do in these cities to encourage people in these modes of transportation. We see that as a good return on our shareholders' investment." Link: https://metro.strava.com

3 Link: https://www.theguardian.com/lifeandstyle/2016/may/09/city-planners-cycling-data-strava-tracking-app

4 Howard, E. (1898). To-Morrow: A peaceful path to real reform' London, Swan Sonnenschein and Co. Ltd

5 Campbell-Dolloghan, K. (2017) "How Strava, The App For Athletes, Became An App For Cities." *Fast Company*. Link: https://www.fastcompany.com/90149130/strava-the-app-for-athletes-is-becoming-an-app-for-cities

6 Each inhabitant in Strive City is considered a registered data asset, and contributes data streams to the 6000 municipal data clusters, which are in turn held in 120 core data repositories. Data assets are streamed according to inhabitants' demographic data and activity profiles.

based on the amount of data within their residential or work unit. One essential feature is that all taxes will be calculated through a data census, and income will be transferred to the Central Council of Strava Inc to be used for the creation and maintenance of public services and infrastructure.

The objectives of this development are multiple, 1104
and the chief aims are these: to find for our post-industrial population healthier surroundings and to enable professionals of all kinds to link their ambitions for a higher quality of life with a city that enables them to monitor their activity goals and to achieve their targets of being healthier, fitter and successful in their lives. Strava Inc. through its Strive City initiative successfully enables this aspiration of city living through the commercialisation of the inhabitant's data feeds and through advanced data analysis that enables companies to target their products more effectively.

At the core of Strive City, which is to be the 1105
network at the heart of the 6000 data clusters, are six magnificent district data dashboards that link communities across a new model of urban/rural form. Six district data dashboards—each dashboard draws from Strava with 120 core data repositories to create a city-wide data infrastructure. Each of the six data districts is linked to an actual urban garden and to leisure facilities such as gyms, swimming pools, cycle tracks and sports centres as well as hospitals and schools. Each dashboard presents a specific activity, with a district for cycling, walking, swimming and running data, as well as ones for transport data via bus and e-car.[7] For example, in the cycling district dashboard, cyclists can

7 Private car ownership is prohibited in Strive City.

see live KoM/QoM[8] and CR (Course Record) updates, and get Flyby[9] info for friends or colleagues.

The rest of the space is a Central Data Park, 1106
with a mixed range of sports and leisure activities,
which can take place within very easy access of all the
people. Here individual district data sets are mashed
around athletic social habits, to identify group activities
and suggest preferred training partners. This is created to counter loneliness and encourage exposure to
otherness; high achieving athletes may see the benefit
of teaming up with those who are injured, or younger
people could match up with a more senior athlete for
advice about an upcoming race.

Located in the Central Open Data Park is a 1107
health and fitness Expo called *CrystalPalace.com*. In
wet weather this building is one of the favourite re-
sorts of the people. Fitness and nutrition goods are
for sale aimed at regenerating and boosting performance. Here, most of the shopping is linked to an individual's Strive City Data Feed and suggestions and
recommendations for goods or products are made
based on performance data. The space enclosed by
CrystalPalace.com is, however, a good deal larger than
required for these purposes, and a considerable part
of it is used as a Winter Garden—the whole forming a
permanent exhibition of a most attractive character,
that is easily accessible to every dweller in tow—the
furthest removed inhabitant being within 600 yards.

Passing out of the Market Place along one of
the key transport paths we cross Fifth Avenue—lined, 1108
as are all the roads of the town, with trees integrated with IoT sensors, facial recognition and motion

8 Acronyms which stand for King of the Mountain and Queen of the Mountain. The fastest time on a segment enables the user to receive a special crown, meaning that you are the KOM or QOM of that segment.

9 Flyby means the activity took place within 50 meters of you at some point, and did not ride with you for an extended period of time (has a low correlation).
Link: https://labs.strava.com/flyby

tracking cameras. Looking on to *CrystalPalace.com*, we find a ring of excellent built resting/sleeping pods, each standing in its own grounds. As we continue our walk, we observe that pods are for the most part built either in concentric rings, facing the various Avenues (as the circular roads are termed), or fronting the boulevards and roads which all converge to the centre of the town. Asking the friend who accompanies us on our journey what the data population of this little city may be, we are told about 30,000 individual inhabitant data sets, and that there are in the town 5,500 living units (collections of individual, dual or family living units) of an average data store of a size of 5Gb—the minimum space allocated for each node being 1GB.

Each sleeping pod has an allocated Strive City 1109
Feed Wall showing the household unit Activity Feed.[10] Noticing the varied architecture and design which the houses and groups of houses display—some having shared gardens and cooperative kitchens—we learn that the general observance of the street line is strictly controlled by the municipal authorities. Individuals are encouraged to express their taste and preference through cultivating their Strive City Profile, which links their activities and performance with their living pod. The Activity Feed shows live data of the inhabitant's activities shown by day, week, month and year. Strive City Trophies and Achievements are encouraged to be displayed, and photos and maps from recent activities convey the preferences of the inhabitant on their Strive City Feed Wall.

10 "The Strava feed presents activities, posts, challenge joins, and challenge completions in an order based on what we think is most interesting to the user." Link: https://support.strava.com/hc/en-us/articles/115001183630-How-the-Strava-Feed-Works

Walking still towards the outskirts of town, we come upon "Grand Avenue." This avenue forms a green belt in which six sites are reserved for public schools, gyms, as well as Olympic-sized swimming pools, and cycle and running tracks. These are co-located with Strive cities own data centres that turn the heat from the activities generated into power for cooling of the servers. 1110

In the outer ring of the town are factories, ware- 1111
houses, dairies, markets, DIY centres, and logistics hubs for web services, all fronting on the circular Hyperloop track which encompasses the whole town, which has sidings connecting it to a ready waiting supply of autonomous vehicles (AV) which distribute goods to the entire city.

Dotted about the city are seen various charita- 1112
ble and philanthropic institutions. These are not under the control of the Strive municipality, but are supported and managed by the philanthropic foundations of Silicon Valley billionaires. These have been invited by the municipality to establish their institutions in an open, healthy district, and on land let to them at a minimal rent; it occurring to the authorities that they can the better afford to be generous, as the spending power of these institutions greatly benefits the whole community.

These institutions serve people who are sick, 1113
morbidly obese, or have mental health or addiction problems, or those less physically able in some way which limits their capacity to provide a suitable activity data feed that would finance their rent. As a requirement, they are contracted to wear heart rate, weight and sleep monitors at all times to gather health data and to attend monthly data check-ins where their progress to a normal healthy, data feed is monitored and supported. As those persons who migrate to the estate are among the most energetic and data rich members of the community, it is just and right that their own helpless brethren should be able to enjoy the benefits of a data-driven experiment which is designed for humanity at large.

Katharine is Associate Professor in the School of Art, Design, and Architecture at the University of Plymouth. Her research interests include smart cities, digital technologies, and the role of space/place. She is co-author with Alex Aurigi of *Digital and Smart Cities* (2017).

THE ALLURE OF THE FRICTIONLESS CITY

TAKEALOT[1]

Nancy Odendaal, University of Cape Town

I ordered my new iPhone 8 on Takealot, South Africa's answer to Amazon. It arrived one day later, in my office, in its sparkling white box. I did not have to battle Cape Town's notorious traffic to purchase it in-store, no parking to negotiate, no shopping centre convolutedness to annoy me. Takealot's local competition is Bidorbuy, a local interpretation of eBay. As an auction platform Bidorbuy potentially offers greater savings to the consumer. But, Takealot offers less hassle. Bidorbuy have to contend with the state postal service, Takealot has a warehouse in Cape Town and offers a seamless experience from that first click to the delivery of goods: a digitised, codified value chain that cuts out the intermediary.[2] The delivery of my cell phone struck me as a metaphor for how many people choose 1114

1 The following academic article uses Takealot, its business model and its relationship to the city as a metaphor for thinking about urban development and spatial divisions in African urbanism. Product or corporate names may be trademarks or registered trademarks, and are used only for identification and explanation without intent to infringe.

2 MyBroadband (2017) "Takealot vs Bidorbuy—South Africa's big marketplace fight." Link: https://mybroadband.co.za/news/business/207306-takealot-vs-bidorbuy-south-africas-big-marketplace-fight.html

to experience the city of Cape Town. The everyday messiness of its urbanity: the shacks on its edges, the informal traders on its streets and the homeless sleeping rough contribute to a stark contrast with the city's beauty. The relationship between Takealot and the city speaks to the symbolic need to disconnect from the more messy aspects of contemporary urbanity. There are also important implications to explore when imagining a city run as a retail logistics hub. This piece explores what some of these contradictions are and argues that by seeking to travel towards a frictionless future, the city runs the risk of optimising the present for only a rich minority.

Upon arriving at Cape Town International Airport, the visitor is treated to a range of sun-speck- 1115
led images of the city's beauty: the majestic Table Mountain casting a benevolent shadow over some of its most prosperous suburbs, the extensive beaches, the vineyards and scenic mountain drives. It is easy to forget that you are on the African continent. An Uber will take you straight to your hotel, most likely located within walking distance of good restaurants and designer stores. One can be oblivious to the Zimbabwean Uber driver's struggles with intermittent xenophobic outbursts in her neighbourhood and protracted visa procedures that have made her feel unwelcome. The freeway that connects the airport with the city enables swift travel past the informal settlements that flank its edges. Much like Takealot positions itself as a global player in the e-Commerce market, the city of Cape Town regards itself as a 'world-class' destination, despite its stark urban poverty. The frictionless travel

that enables swift delivery promises efficiency. Cape Town imagines itself as a city ready for business and investment. Some would argue that it does this at the expense of more pressing socio-economic needs.

Seamless connection that avoids the mess- 1116
iness of the real city, is an evident aim of the smart city. The goal of logistic efficiency speaks to glossy futures full of promise. A temporal thematic dimension also informs the symbolism of the retailer of my new mobile. Much like the city strives to move away from its contentious colonial past, Takealot has its own questionable heritage to overcome. The company was launched in June 2011, with financial investment from US hedge fund Tiger Global, and South Africa's largest media conglomerate, Naspers, which since April 2017, has had a controlling stake in the company.[3] Founded in 1915, and with a demonstrated history as a loyal partner to the National Party during Apartheid, the media conglomerate has reinvented itself as a savvy international player, operating in 120 countries, and identifies itself as one of the biggest technology investors in the world.[4] Building a productive phoenix upon Apartheid's ashes is difficult when unemployment is estimated at 27%[5] and the city is one of the most unequal in the world.[6] The past haunts the city's future but its economy performs better than other South African cities. With its annual growth higher than the national average, the strategy is to bypass national constraints and compete globally. Its most recent iteration of this vision is an emphasis on the creative economy, eCommerce and the information technology sector in general. Takealot reflects the potential here:

3 MyBroadband (2017) "Takealot's plan to grow its R2.3-billion annual revenue." Link: https://mybroadband.co.za/news/business/229775-takealots-plan-to-grow-its-r2-3-billion-annual-revenue.html

4 Link: http://www.naspers.com

5 Statistics South Africa (2018) Link: http://www.statssa.gov.za

6 City of Cape Town (2016) "State of Cape Town Report 2016: Overview with infographics." Link: http://maitcid.co.za/wp-content/uploads/2017/01/State-of-Cape-Town-Report-2016.pdf

over the 2016-2017 financial year, the company's turnover was R2.3 billion ($167m), processing almost 3 million transactions from around 1 million customers. The CEO of Takealot believes that its company's future is in logistics:

1117 "My head of buying comes from Bain—she is darn clever. I've got chemical engineers and people from the auto industry, and technology geeks that specialise in artificial intelligence—they are the people that develop the algorithms that make recommendations based on your previous browsing history which helps to drive sales. We have a mix of industries and intellects. If I hired retailers, then we would be building just another retail business."

1118 Naspers' R960 million ($73m) investment in Takealot in 2017 has ensured that the platform dominates the South African eCommerce market. No one is certain what the market gap is for e-Commerce in South Africa but Takealot sees this as an opportunity, especially given the country's youthful demographics and high rate of mobile phone adoption. Takealot claims their aim is to enable self-sufficiency through investment in 'organic growth—people, technology, and processes.' The current recession does not bother the company's CEO: with a customer base growing between 30% and 35% annually.

1119 Takealot appeals to the sensibilities of the connected class, with fashion platform 'Superbalist' quickly integrated into the brand. The national e-Commerce market is almost irrelevant to the company. "We are fortunate in that we are doing the disrupting and cannibalizing—our competitors are in retail, not other online retail stores", says the CEO.[7] Reinvention and adjustment are part of the City of Cape Town's game. Can a city's international connectedness release it from its national preoccupations? It appears not. Despite the city's favourable economic performance in relation to the rest of the country, there are intermittent, and sometimes violent, reminders of its socio-economic realities in the form or protest action and high crime rates. Takealot works for the connected classes, and as much as the city administration wishes to 'make the city work for you' (its marketing tagline) the spoils of its international prosperity is accessible to the relatively small number of middle—to high income residents.

What Takealot represents raises important 1120
questions about the city's future. Like any good metaphor it crystallises the less salient yet highly problematic dynamics of its comparative companion. The smooth path enabled through online purchase speaks to a city that lays emphasis on its global connectedness at the risk of not truly addressing its margins meaningfully. Social activism in the city has highlighted the lack of proper sanitation in informal settlements and affordable housing in the inner city as examples misguided priorities for example. The desire to race towards the future, embrace the promise of invention and creativity, exclude the skills, abilities and aspirations of a semi-skilled working class. The focus on logistics and efficiency speaks to a post-industrial rationality that denies opportunities to those not trained to engage it.

There is, however, another side to the delivery 1121
of my iPhone that speaks to a far more representative

7 Planting, S. (2017) "How Takealot will spend the Naspers millions." Link: https://techcentral.co.za/how-takealot-will-spend-the-naspers-millions/73617/

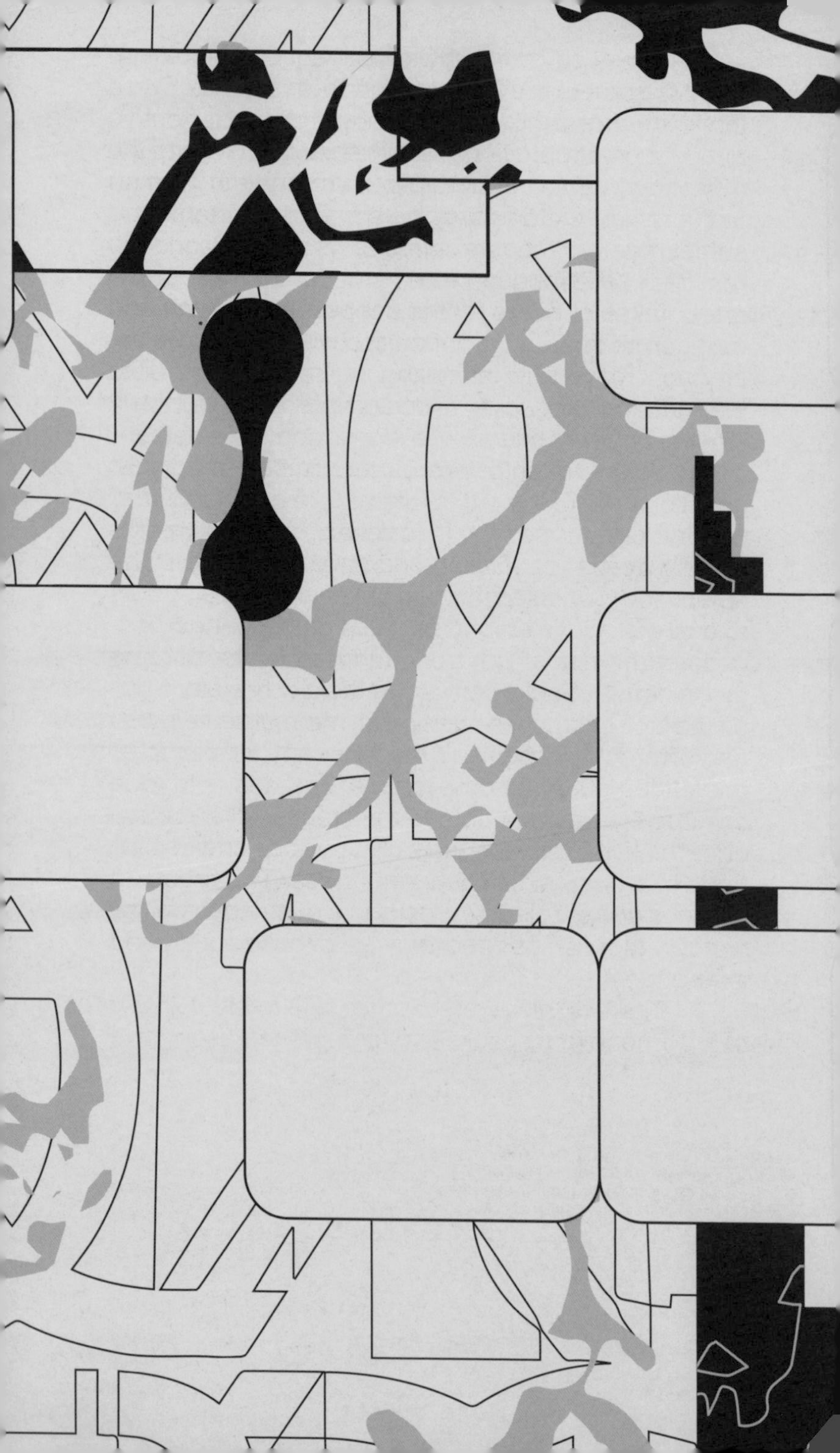

picture of the city: that of what the actual phone enables. It is now a well known fact that the cell phone uptake in African cities has far outstripped expectations and commercial projections. Elsewhere I have explored how this technological revolution has lead to appropriation that speaks to the livelihood strategies of the very poor. The cell phone represents mobility. It promises connection 'on the go.' It is affordable, accessible and fixable. It is tangible, yet also able to transport the user to another space, a space where connection is immediate and transient. Go the less salubrious parts of Cape Town and evidence abounds: informal traders using their phones to connect to suppliers and clients, makeshift convenience stores (locally referred to as 'spaza' shops) sell airtime and second-hand phones, next to bespoke container stores offering cellular repair services. This is the real city, where technology is malleable, tangible and capable of reinvention. It also presents a missed opportunity should we ignore urban messiness in favour of frictionless travel.

Takealot represents how Cape Town imagines 1122
itself into the future. It is, however, the artifact it delivers to my door that captures the aspirations of the majority of its residents. Choosing to bypass it, in the pursuit of logistical elegance, would be short-sighted. Cape Town's future, like that of many other cities in the global South, is as contingent upon technology appropriation on its fringes as it is upon corporate invention in the mainstream.

Nancy Odendaal is an associate professor of city and regional planning in the School of Architecture, Planning and Geomatics at the University of Cape Town. Her research interrogates the intersection between spatial change in cities of the global South, infrastructure innovation and technology appropriation.

CITIES NEED MASS TRANSIT

TESLA[1]

Harvey J. Miller, The Ohio
State University

Elon's vision: personalized urban mobility

Imagine getting into your vehicle for a pleasant ride to 1123
work. After turning on to an arterial road, the vehicle
pulls over to a platform along the curb about the size of
two parking spots. The platform lowers your vehicle to
a network of underground tunnels. Your vehicle pulls
away slowly at first but rapidly gains speed and joins
the stream of vehicles travelling at 200kph. When you
get closer your destination, the process reverses: your
vehicle pulls off to the side, slows down, rises to street
level on a platform, and rejoins other vehicles using
the street network, taking you to your final destination.

Maybe you do not or cannot own a personal 1124
vehicle. No worries! Scattered throughout the city, in
thousands of locations, are shared vehicle stations,
each the size of a parking space. You enter this vehicle with others going to the same destination, it lowers to the underground network system, merges with

1 The following academic article speculates on how an urban transportation system might be run and experienced if Tesla's business model was adopted. Product or corporate names may be trademarks or registered trademarks, and are used only for identification and explanation without intent to infringe.

the high speed traffic, whisking you to another shared vehicle station near your destination.

In a TED 2017 interview, Elon Musk, co-founder 1125
and CEO of Tesla, explains how the fantastic vision described above will be realized—cheap tunnelling. Musk claims that he can lower the cost of tunnel building by tenfold, facilitating construction of a vast underground transportation network. This will remove practical limits on our urban transportation systems. Unlike building upward into the sky via bridges and viaducts, there is no limit to how many levels of tunnels you can build. Quoting Mr. Musk: "You can alleviate any arbitrary level of urban congestion with a 3D tunnel network." If the network becomes congested, no problem—you can always add another tunnel level deeper.[2]

Elon Musk's vision for urban mobility is a highly 1126
personalized system, dominated by private vehicles or small, shared vehicles. The shared component is a later addition by Musk to his original vision. In a now infamous interview with *Wired* magazine, Musk stated his preference for personal transit over collective transit: "[Public transit] sucks. Why do you want to get on something with a lot of other people, that doesn't leave where you want it to leave, doesn't start where you want it to start, doesn't end where you want it to end? And it doesn't go all the time."[3] Musk also claimed that public transit exposes you to serial killers, a biased risk perception that often reflects a lack of experience and a shunning of actual data.[4] The addition of shared

2 Musk, E. (2017) "The future we're building – and boring." TED2017 interview. Link: https://www.ted.com/talks/elon_musk_the_future_we_re_building_and_boring#t-157705

3 Marshall, A. (2017) "Elon Musk reveals his awkward dislike of mass transit." *Wired*. Link: https://www.wired.com/story/elon-musk-awkward-dislike-mass-transit

4 In fact, you are much more likely to die using an automobile—see Moser, W. (2017) "Elon Musk has a very odd sense of risk on public transportation." *Chicago Magazine*. Link: http://www.chicagomag.com/city-life/December-2017/Elon-Musk-Has-a-Very-Odd-Sense-of-Risk-on-Public-Transportation

vehicles to his vision was an apparent response to the resulting backlash.[5]

Some transportation planners have identified 1127
the lift-based entry and exit points to the underground network as crucial bottlenecks that would constrain the system.[6] Even if these bottlenecks could be resolved—somehow—the system is still likely to fail.

If you build it, they will come

Tunnelling to expand roads in a third spatial dimension 1128
will not alleviate congestion any more successfully than the past century of expanding roads in two dimensions. The phenomenon of *induced travel demand* means that expanding road capacity to solve congestion spawns new traffic created by the new capacity. Consequently, building new roads leads to only temporary relief as congestion returns.[7] Induced travel demand is consistent with economic theory: increasing supply lowers the cost of a good or service, increasing consumption.[8] It is also a type of rebound effect, such as Jevons Paradox: efficiency improvements at the individual level generating more resource consumption at the aggregate level.[9] In network flow theory, Braess' paradox shows that adding a new link to a congested network can increase travel times for all.[10]

Despite theoretical support, induced travel 1129
demand was controversial for decades. Resistance stems from the dominance of a "predict and provide"

5 Morris, D. Z. (2017) "Elon Musk calls transit expert 'an idiot' and says public transport 'sucks.'" *Fortune*. Link: http://fortune.com/2017/12/16/elon-musk-public-transport

6 Tinoco, M. (2017) "Why experts are so skeptical of Elon Musk's LA tunnels." *Curbed Los Angeles*. Link: https://la.curbed.com/2017/12/18/16748436/elon-musk-tunnels-los-angeles-criticism-explained

7 Cervero, R. (2002) "Induced travel demand: Research design, empirical evidence, and normative policies." *Journal of Planning Literature*, 17, 3-20.

8 Handy, S. (2005) "Smart growth and the transportation-land use connection: What does the research tell us?" *International Regional Science Review*, 28, 146-167.

9 Alcott, B. (2005) "Jevons' paradox." *Ecological Economics*, 54, 9-21.

10 Steinberg, R. and Zangwill, W.I. (1983) "The prevalence of Braess' paradox." *Transportation Science*, 17, 301-318.

planning paradigm that favours building more roads to solve transportation problems.[11] Induced travel demand is also hard to measure: it can ripple over time and space, cascading through shifts in route choices, travel modes, destination choices, vehicle ownership levels and land development patterns.[12] Although evidence is mixed on its magnitude,[13] the evidence is sufficient for Duranton and Turner to state the Fundamental Law of Road Congestion: changes in the capacity of a road network are met with proportional changes in traffic.[14]

We can eliminate traffic by reducing road 1130
vehicle capacity. *Traffic evaporation* is the mirror of induced demand. Reducing street capacity to accommodate pedestrians, cyclists and public transit does not cause all traffic to shift and clog other routes; rather, some of the traffic disappears as some travelers make other choices, including alternatives to driving.[15]

Space matters

In principle, we could keep adding another level of tun- 1131
nels and eventually solve congestion since the Earth's population will eventually level off and there is only a finite amount of time for travel in a person's life. But the cost and complexity of this system would be enormous due to the "arm's race" between roads and traffic.

All transportation modes are subject to induced 1132
travel demand but some modes handle it better than others. Due to the space required, personal vehicles are the least efficient form of urban transportation with

11 Næss, P., Andersen, J., Nicolaisen, M.S. and Strand, A. (2014) "Transport modelling in the context of the 'predict and provide' paradigm." *European Journal of Transport and Infrastructure Research*, 14, 102-121.

12 Litman, T. (2001) "Generated traffic and induced travel: Implications for transport planning." *ITE Journal*, 71, 38-47.

13 See above: Cervero (2002) and Handy (2005).

14 Duranton, G. and Turner, M.A., 2011. "The fundamental law of road congestion: Evidence from US cities." *American Economic Review*, 101(6), 2616-52.

15 Cairns, S., Atkins, S. and Goodwin, P. (2002) "Disappearing traffic? The story so far." *Municipal Engineer*, 151, 13-22.

respect to throughput.[16] This efficiency gap will become critical as the global population swells to 9-10 billion by the end of the 21st century, with the majority living in cities.

A single lane on an urban street carries 600- 1133
1,600 people per hour assuming 600-800 vehicles per hour and 1-2 persons per vehicle. A dedicated bus lane in the same space can carry up to 8,000 persons per hour and a fixed transit line can carry 10,000—25,000 persons per hour. Limited access highway lanes have higher capacity for private vehicles; this is roughly 2200—2500 vehicles per hour per lane.[17] Autonomous vehicles (AVs) can increase highway lane capacity by reducing—although not eliminating—the need for safe spacing between vehicles. With 100% AV saturation, highway capacity could achieve 4000 vehicles per hour per lane.[18] Assuming two persons per vehicle results in 8000 persons per hour per lane. In short, Elon Musk's futuristic tunnel vision could achieve the throughput of today's dedicated bus lane and not nearly as much as fixed transit lines.

Personal vehicles require storage space for the 1134
majority of time when they are stationary and unoccupied. Consequently, huge portions of our cities are devoted to parking, including the most valuable land in the city center.[19] While shared AVs can reduce the storage problem, streets are still a bottleneck. Streets are a public resource with a finite capacity to handle vehicles in motion. The number of vehicles in motion required, so that no one has more than few minutes wait for a ride, is fundamentally unsustainable in dense cities.[20]

16 Energy too, see: Sanderson, E.W. (2013) *Terra Nova: The New World after Oil, Cars, and Suburbs*. New York: Abrams, chapter 11.

17 National Association of City Transportation Officials (2016) *Transit Street Design Guide*. Island Press.

18 Farmer, D. L. (2016) "Autonomous vehicles: The implications on urban transportation and traffic flow theory." *ITE Journal*, 86, 34-37.

19 Peters, A. (2017) "See just how much of a city's land is used for parking spaces." *Fast Company*. Link: https://www.fastcompany.com/40441392/see-just-how-much-of-a-citys-land-is-used-for-parking-spaces

20 Schwartz, S.I. (2015) *Street Smart: The Rise of Cities and the Fall of Cars*. Public Affairs.

The first mile/last mile problem

Elon Musk is correct about a crucial public transit 1135
problem: it often does not start where you want it to start, it does not end where you want it to end, and it does not go all the time. In public transit, service frequency and span is freedom, but these are expensive and must be concentrated in a limited number of corridors.[21] The *first mile/last mile* (FMLM) problem is the gap between origins/destinations (such as home, work) and public transit. Rather than replacing public transit, AVs could be used to address the FMLM problem,[22] via shared vehicles, jitneys,[23] and on-demand shuttles. The FMLM mix should also include bike and e-bikes, and infrastructure that enables safe, convivial and inclusive walking and biking, supporting health and environmental sustainability as well as access to transit.[24] This solution would be far more efficient and far less costly than boring a network of 3D tunnels.

Towards sustainable mobility

Electric vehicles, batteries and rockets are complex 1136
technical systems. But, urban transportation is a complex *human* system not amenable to purely engineered solutions. Similar to the Tragedy of the Commons and the Prisoner's Dilemma, mobility is a *collective action dilemma*: it is individually rational for a person to be as mobile as desired, but when everyone is mobile the outcome is collectively irrational. Elon Musk's vision of personalized urban mobility reinforces a competitive

21 Walker, J. (2011) *Human Transit: How Clearer Thinking about Public Transit Can Enrich Our Communities and Our Lives*. Island Press.

22 Berrebi, S. (2017) "What Elon Musk gets right about transit." *CityLab*. Link: https://www.citylab.com/transportation/2017/12/what-elon-musk-gets-right-about-transit/549134/

23 Mitchell, M. and Faren, M. (2014) "If you like Uber, you would've loved the jitney." *Los Angeles Times*. Link: http://www.latimes.com/opinion/op-ed/la-oe-mitchell-jitneys-uber-ride-share-20140713-story.html

24 Burden, D. and Litman, T. (2011) "America needs complete streets." *ITE Journal*, 81, 36-43.

25 Miller, H.J. (2013) "Beyond sharing: cultivating cooperative transportation systems through geographic information science." *Journal of Transport Geography*, 31, 296-308.

26 Banister, D. (2008) "The sustainable mobility paradigm." *Transport Policy*, 15, 73-80.

transportation system that will fail in a crowded, highly urbanized world.

One way to resolve the social dilemma of mobility is by facilitating cooperative behaviour. Trans- 1137
portation shares the properties of goods and services that invite collaborative consumption, including critical mass, large unused capacity and capabilities for building trust: almost everyone needs transportation, much of the system is idle during off-peak times, and new apps allow users and providers to rate each other. Better collective outcomes do not require everyone to be altruistic: the nature of transportation networks means that marginal improvements in pro-social mobility choices can have disproportionately large outcomes on performance. There is growing evidence from biological and social sciences that cooperative behaviour is more common than recognized. Evolutionary game theory suggests that time and space—key dimensions of transportation—also enable cooperation.[25]

A sustainable transportation system does not 1138
maximize travel demand and minimize travel times. A sustainable transportation system manages travel demand and achieves reasonable, reliable travel times. It prioritizes walking, biking and public transit over personal vehicles. It reduces the need to segregate people and traffic by slowing some movement down, reclaiming streets as shared mobility space for all users. The goal of a sustainable transportation system is accessibility to opportunities; mobility is only one means to achieve this goal.[26] Tesla's focus on speedier, personalized mobility is not sustainable.

Harvey J. Miller is the Bob and Mary Reusche Chair in Geographic Information Science, Professor of Geography and Director of the Center for Urban and Regional Analysis at The Ohio State University. His research interest include GIScience, time geography, mobility analytics and sustainable transportation

SWIPE RIGHT TO WELCOME, LEFT TO REJECT

TINDER[1]

Linnet Taylor, Tilburg University

Everyone agreed that the refugees were not doing well. 1139
They had been borne into the city on a wave of goodwill fuelled by revelations about torture, drownings and unspeakable deprivation. As time progressed it became clear that the years spent waiting for residency had taken a toll on their ability to learn the language and find a foothold in the labour market. It was not just the refugees, it was all the people who had moved to the city without a clear plan: people from countries worldwide attracted by the vision of a strong urban economy and a tolerant citizenry. But now attitudes were becoming less tolerant. Votes were moving toward the right. There was a growing tacit agreement that certain people were eligible for decent jobs, decent housing, and the presumption of innocence, while others, if not actually suspect, were not.

It was not just the city authorities who accepted 1140
Tinder's offer to provide 'de-marginalisation' services.

1 The following speculative fiction and satire imagines if a dating app was applied to urban integration policy. Such a thought experiment could equally apply if the city were run by other dating apps such as Grindr. Product or corporate names may be trademarks or registered trademarks, and are used only for the purpose of conducting a thought experiment without intent to infringe.

The national parties were eager to see the results: this seemed like a short-cut for a thorny social problem, like a universal basic income or legalising weed. What if the repurposed dating platform could leverage people's kindness and goodwill to do the work of integrating the newcomers more efficiently? What if it could target progressives interested in helping?

1141 Tinder Welcome, as the purpose-built app was called, was designed to connect local residents with immigrants who were searching for employers, friends, teachers or guides to the city. The migrants just had to sign up, and a connection with them would be on offer to anyone who wished to help them out. An app-based approach was immediately embraced by the electorate as something invisible yet proactive, increasing efficiency and reducing the tax burden—and above all something that could be done while sitting on the sofa, by those who didn't like seeing their fellow citizens torching asylum centres.

1142 The first year was golden. Everyone except the populists downloaded the app and started not only swiping right on those they would like to help, but on their choice of immigrant plumber, driver, freelance bike mechanic, or delivery person. The unions were unhappy, but the gig economy was already well underway and it was clear that the platform was just embracing an inevitable future. There was a brief flurry of public debate when the service started to help people source longer-term jobs which had traditionally been unionised, but it had been so impossible in recent years for immigrants to get hired that positive coverage abounded.

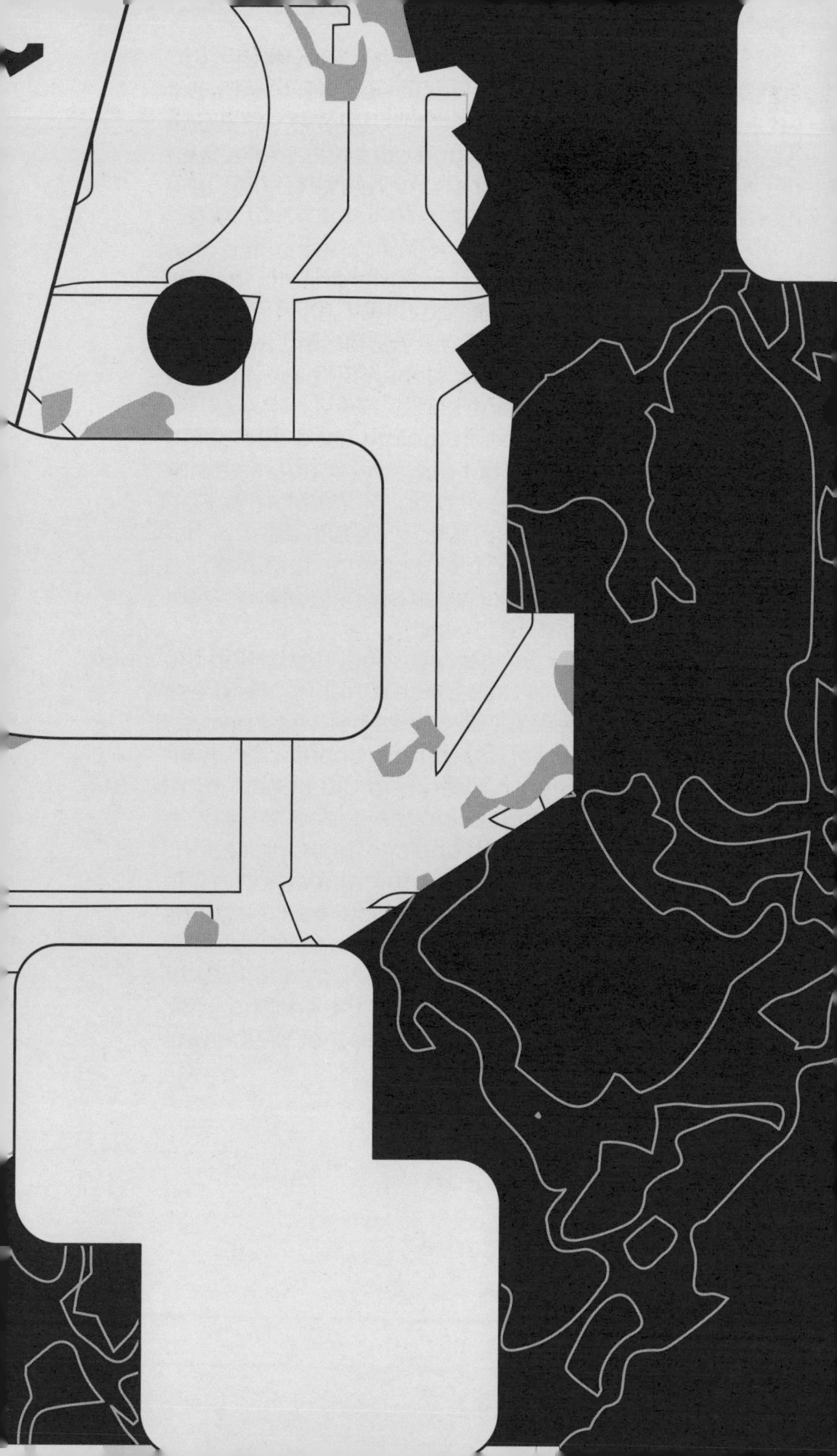

Soon everyone had their pet migrant; the person who could pick up the kids if you were delayed, could provide unusual recipes from Chechnya or North Africa for your dinner party, and generally make middle-class life in times of crisis more interesting and morally defensible. 1143

After a year the platform proposed that the data be monetised. No one saw a problem. Although the app had been procured using public funds, people largely agreed that this was the private sector and the company should get some financial benefit beyond what the city could afford. Choice had become a way of life: at first the service had been mainly used by ageing hippies and intellectuals, but now everyone was swiping. You could choose the person (or 'problem solver' in the language of the app) who looked right for your lifestyle: there was a brief bio, a picture, and nothing more. If you didn't like them you swiped left to reject them, and they would never know. 1144

The company was savvy about promoting the 'social good' aspect of its service, offering the press stories about successful alliances between natives and newcomers: women freed from oppression, men from unemployment, children and old people from isolation. Schools started using the app for their buddy programs, and the youth and sports organisations picked up on it as a way to bring migrant children into teams and centres. Some daycare centres used it as an option for people to pair their children up for socially conscious playdates. 1145

There were warning signs in the second year. An investigative journalist discovered that Welcome's 1146 algorithms had swiftly learned that even progressives had implicit bias based on skin colour, visible signs of religious affiliation, and gender, along with other things that were fuzzier, interacted with each other, and were much harder to correct for. The system conscientiously replicated these biases. Migrant women were more visible in relation to some tasks and pairings than others.

Controversially, a code audit performed by con- 1147
tractors found that the algorithm was optimising for 'easy' pairings of like with like, so that lower-educated or linguistically slower migrants were paired mainly with similar natives. As a result, they were effectively excluded from social and economic mobility. The press loved the story of a refugee sociologist seeking language practice who found herself matched for country walks with a famous public intellectual (they later delivered a well-received TED talk about the potential of the platform economy). There was less reporting on the many cases of lower-educated and disadvantaged migrants who wanted to achieve literacy and a living wage, but who did not benefit from the 'instant and intuitive' swipes of app users. These problem solvers were pushed by the algorithm towards lower-income and less-educated problem owners in the city.

In year three of the app's use, two things hap- 1148
pened. The first was a proposal from Tinder that the city experiment with the app for all its public functions: you should be able to swipe left or right on public servants to choose someone to provide you services; on teachers for your children; on doctors. Next, it was proposed that urban planning decisions and even

municipal elections should be decided by swipes. A pilot programme was approved, and after a year in beta mode, people got used to it without ever actually having to confirm it should stay. The second was the accidental disclosure by a Tinder employee that the company had been generating an individual 'ALO' score for every person in the system.[2] One's ALO score (according to the best guesses of the city's consultants) was based on a combination of how often a person was liked by natives; the ALO scores of those natives (the higher the better); and the proportion of their associations that resulted in what was algorithmically judged a 'successful relationship.'

The ALO score was important because it de- 1149
termined whom you became visible to: lower scores meant lower-rated matches in terms of socioeconomic status, and therefore less opportunity for social mobility. Some migrants managed to game the system once they got to know enough natives: stories emerged of neighbourhoods collaborating to raise their favourite newcomer's ratings and ensure them opportunities outside the community. There were even crowd-liking campaigns using other social media or notices on lampposts in the neighbourhood: 'Help X find a permanent job! Like him on Tinder Welcome!'

Five years later, it was apparent that the machine 1150
learning and design decisions that had gone into making Tinder Welcome seamless and useful had also created a parallel class system. Somehow, caste systems from the migrants' places of origin had been integrated with the city's existing social strata. The app, despite its one-sided nature, worked to promote those with skills

2 Link: https://www.fastcompany.com/3054871/whats-your-tinder-score-inside-the-apps-internal-ranking-system

and language aptitude, the attractive and well-presented and acceptable, into full social participation in the city, and generated a wealth of positive headlines in the media. Meanwhile the underclass, which now included anyone who looked alien at first sight, became digitally and socially invisible, to the city's own functionaries (who all used Tinder Welcome to check those they interacted with) as well as its residents. The city shelved the populists' legislative proposal for a burka ban: it simply wasn't necessary. Only a crazy person would submit a profile photo of themselves in a burka.

There was a growing sense amongst the city's 1151
residents that the app was not a serendipitous tool for matching the deserving with the socially conscious, but a way of defining what a 'deserving' migrant was. Native-born users had no incentive to make their interactions 'meaningful' unless a migrant appealed to them intuitively: they could simply swipe left to disengage, and the person would never be shown to them again.

In the sixth year, the first assault occurred. 1152
Reports of ALO scores had been confirmed: migrants understood what was determining their chances. A migrant who had been working stressful and ever-changing jobs in the gig economy for half a decade while searching for ways to improve his language skills and employability, but failing to achieve the pairings that would help him do it, came across a resident whom he recognised from the app as someone who, after an initial conversation about how he could help, had ghosted him by swiping left.

The resident had a broken nose; the press had 1153
a story. The liberal faction was appalled that migrants

would hold the city and its residents responsible for their own failure to integrate, but the discussion that followed in the council chamber showed the first cracks in the city's faith in app-based integration.

The protests grew: migrants marched in the streets, a whistleblower explained how Welcome's algorithms were influencing people's chances, and residents started to see the system as unfair. They joined the protests, and a local civil rights movement emerged. There was a general debate: should they ask the city to boycott the app? Should they reform the algorithm to make it fairer (though the app developers were unsure they knew how to do this without breaking the system altogether)? Should they lead a residents' boycott? 1154

People were shocked and disillusioned. It seemed almost as if, instead of combating discrimination, the app had automated it, and had been paid to do so by the city. 1155

There was one major complication: the app had been picked up by other cities and eventually by the national government. All over the country, the massive amounts of background data it had been collecting on people's behaviour, relationships and consumption patterns had been put to use in predictive systems that enabled politicians to understand what made people swipe left or right on each other, and on the politicians themselves; the paths that led to riches or poverty; the warning signs of street violence. The country's data double was deeply embedded in Tinder Welcome, and Tinder made sure the politicians knew its benefits. 1156

Eventually the remedy came from the market itself. Tinder decided to offer a service: anyone who had engaged with the app could now pay not to use it. The company would still have all the rich data it had collected on its users (who by now formed a large segment of the population). However, for a fee, it would not use it to profile you. For those users who could not afford the fee, which was substantial, the company offered reduced-cost schemes where only certain types of data were fed into the country's economic and political decision-making systems. 1157

The results were, predictably, asymmetric. The migrant population was largely unable to afford the opt-out, and was at the mercy of marketers and manipulators. Their Tinder data was used for predictive policing, for immigration decisions, for pre-citizenship checks, for spam. But at least there was a discount on the opt-out fee for children, and for those whose data had been sourced through daycare centres, schools and clubs when they were small. 1158

Then there were riots. 1159

Ten years after the original contract was signed, the city council made a truly progressive decision. It would award Invisibility Grants, so the socially marginalised could opt out of Tinder Welcome. The company upped its prices in response, but the city paid. Eventually a substantial proportion of the budget was going to keeping the marginalised invisible, but in the protest camp outside the city hall people felt something had been achieved. A student did a survey of the camp: it was socially diverse, and fairly well integrated. 1160

Linnet Taylor is Associate Professor at the Tilburg Institute for Law, Technology, and Society (TILT). Her research focuses on digital data, representation and democracy, with particular attention to transnational governance issues. She leads the ERC Global Data Justice project.

SEEKING FOLLOWS

TWITTER[1]

James Ash, Newcastle University

Lisa awoke and checked the smart sleeve of her shirt. Displayed on the fabric in e-ink was her total number of lifetime followers on Twitter and the number of follows she had to spend. 93 available follows. Lisa was aiming for 100. 1161

Since Twitter had taken over the governance of London, following the great democratic dissolution of 2038, things had changed significantly. Although Twitter had begun as a social media company in the mid-2000s, it had rapidly expanded. First streaming video and live events through the Twitter platform in the late 2010s, by the mid-2020s it had partnered with a series of challenger banks to create a new form of digital currency: the follow. 1162

The follow as a unit of exchange was transformative. No longer created through the production of goods or services, the follow was a unit created through the direct capture of human attention itself. In early versions of Twitter, people could follow one another and broadcast messages to their followers. In turn, Twitter used its knowledge of user behaviour to target advertising through promoted tweets within a user's timeline. 1163

1 The following speculative fiction and satire imagines living in a city where a social media business model becomes a credit/payment system. Such a thought experiment could equally apply if the city were run by Facebook or Instagram. Product or corporate names may be trademarks or registered trademarks, and are used only for the purpose of conducting a thought experiment without intent to infringe.

Alongside promoted advertising, companies quickly became aware that users with the most followers had significant influence and paid such 'influencers' to implicitly and explicitly advertise and market their products and services directly. As such, two economies operated on Twitter at any one time. The formal attention economy involved Twitter selling targeted advertising to its customers (the companies and businesses that wanted to advertise on it). The informal economy involved users selling the attention they had garnered to companies directly, evidencing their influence through the number of followers they had. 1164

For Twitter, the success of the platform and its ability to create profit was based on the overall number of users on the platform as a whole. But for individual users what mattered was their specific number of followers, which they could use as a currency to convince advertisers to pay them. 1165

The follow currency, introduced in 2024, had begun as an attempt to expand the formal economy of Twitter as a space for selling advertising and attention. No longer confined to the screens of PCs and smart phones, Twitter took advantage of the wide-scale adoption of Alternative Reality (AR) lenses, projections and fabrics that now overlaid almost every surface of the built environment and formed the material of most clothing. As well as 'earning' followers by posting interesting content to the Twitter platform, users could also earn follows by viewing and displaying advertising that was emitted from these surfaces, which were customised to users' individual Twitter profiles (mandatory since 2039). 1166

As a currency, follows had both a public and private aspect. On the one hand, follows referred to the publicly visible total number of follows and followers 1167 gained over the lifetime of a user's account. On the other hand, follows referred to a privately visible available number of follows, which were the total number of follows that could be exchanged for services. A user may have 1000 lifetime follows, for example, but have spent 600 follows, meaning that they had only 400 follows available to use.

Twitter argued that the follow currency was a 1168
great means to generate additional income, especially for the low paid and those on zero-hour contracts, who now made up around 67% of the working age population. Whereas the national currency, the Great British Pound, could be earnt and spent on anything, the follow could be used only on a range of Twitter-owned or approved services, such as utility bills, city taxation and, in some cases, city housing.

For the rich or Twitter famous, follows meant 1169
little as a currency of exchange. Utilities, rent and tax could be paid using pounds. At the same time, verified users and popular influencers could join the follow exchange programme and cash out their follows for pounds, allowing them to leverage the follows they were paid as part of advertising deals to enhance their monetary wealth. But, for people like Lisa, who were neither verified, famous, or part of the follow exchange programme, follows remained a necessary means of accessing services. For Lisa, follows were the difference between heating the flat and going cold. Follows were the difference between paying her city tax or having bailiffs knocking on the door.

The 100 follows that Lisa needed would pay 1170
her overdue electricity bill. Although she worked at a logistics packing warehouse, her hours were unreliable, and she never knew if there was a shift available until two hours before it was due to start. With no email

confirming her on the morning shift, Lisa had little other choice than to tap on the smart sleeve of her shirt and browse the range of self-advertising options. As well as paying users to view adverts, Twitter would also pay users to broadcast adverts from their own smart clothing. The number of follows earned depended on the profile of the user, the type of advert emitted, where the user was located, and the length of time the advert was emitted.

Twitter celebrities with hundreds of thousands 1171
or even millions of followers were in high demand for self-advertising. These users had the option from Twitter to advertise aspirational and designer brands such as Louis Vuitton, Rolex and Chanel and could earn thousands of follows per minute for doing so at the right place and time. In the same way that verified users could exchange their follows for pounds, more popular users could also utilise hashtags to influence trends and conversations on their followers feeds, generating more followers and thus more money.

As a user with only 93 available follows, Lisa's 1172
options were rather more limited. If she stayed in a public space in her own neighbourhood, Brixton, she could advertise dog food for 1 follow per hour or an escort service for 5 follows per hour. 'Gross', she thought. If she travelled on the underground to Covent Garden she could probably advertise ice cream or English tea to tourists for 2.5 follows per hour. However, she wouldn't know what products were available to advertise, or their rate of pay, until she actually arrived in Covent Garden, as Twitter's advertising service would only offer self-advertising options depending on her location at the time. The underground cost 2 follows to use, so travelling to Covent Garden was risky.

Lisa also had to take into account the anti-loi- 1173
tering laws that Covent Garden had introduced when self-advertising on smart clothing had become popular through Twitter. In the first few months residents had complained that people from poorer areas would travel to Covent Garden and stand in the same spot all day in order to earn the maximum number of follows. As such, in Covent Garden, the advert would only emit from her clothing if the GPS in her shirt registered movement, with stops of no more than three minutes allowed at any one point. In Brixton, however, she could loiter all she wanted without the advert, and thus her earnings, being interrupted.

She would take a risk. Leaving the flat she 1174
walked to the underground and took the train to Covent Garden. Leaving the station she checked the options on her smart shirt again. Scottish shortbread for 2 follows an hour. It would do, she thought. Activating the advert, her shirt turned a bright red tartan. The short bread brand logo began to rotate across the surface of the shirt and a short bag pipe tune began to play from the speakers sewn into the shirt's lining. Rolling her eyes in dull acceptance, she began to walk the streets around the market.

Many ignored the advert as she walked. Using 1175
face and eye tracking technology in the cameras on the shirt, the advertising API recognised the lack of interest and increased the volume of the bag pipe tune. The regulated volume limit for self-advertising in Covent Garden was 84 decibels, but even so, the tune gave Lisa a headache. Lisa knew that if the advert did not register enough attention, then her rate of pay in follows would drop until she was earning nothing and the advert disappeared from the surface of the shirt. Within an hour, the advertised rate of 2 follows an hour had dropped

to 1. Seven hours later Lisa had earned enough to pay her overdue bill and a fare home to Brixton.

Paying her electricity bill as she walked back 1176
to the underground station, Lisa looked around her. In London, not having advertising on your smart clothes was itself a sign of distinction and wealth. Twitter had promised that the follow currency would usher in a new era of reduced costs and democratic access to services in London. For Lisa, and many others like her, it had done the opposite.

Earning the human attention that the follow 1177
currency was based on required being out in public, but doing so physically marked out those who could only earn follows through self-advertising. Trapped in a cycle of spending and earning follows, such users had little to no chance of accessing better self-advertising deals or the kind of direct advertising offered to popular influencers on Twitter.

While Twitter had transformed the aesthetics 1178
of the city and how it was used, it seemed that this transformation had reinforced existing inequalities between rich and poor, the haves and the have-nots. Arriving back at her flat at 10pm, Lisa went to bed with the ringing of sampled bagpipes in her ears. As her eyes closed she wondered if she would be called up to take a shift at the warehouse in the morning or would have to resort to more self-advertising. Neither option offered much appeal.

James Ash is a Senior Lecturer at Newcastle University, where they research the cultures, economies and politics of digital technology. They are the author of *Phase Media* (2017), *The Interface Envelope* (2015) and an editor, with Rob Kitchin and Agnieszka Leszczynski, of *Digital Geographies* (2018).

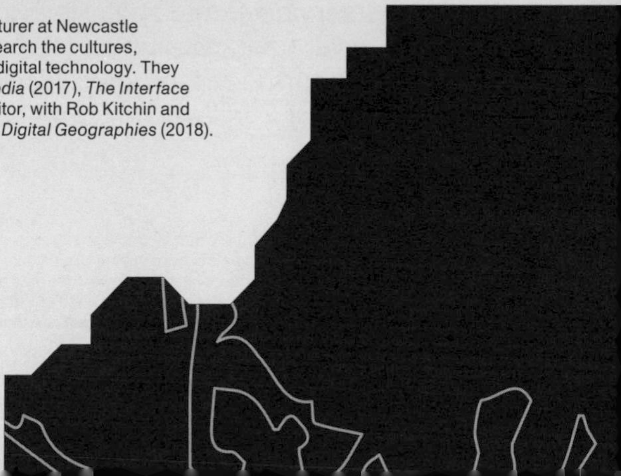

THE SEDUCTION OF UBERCITY

UBER[1]

Agnieszka Leszczynski,
Western University

Rob Kitchin, Maynooth University

Smooth, seamless, efficient, just-in-time, on-demand city services

You need to make a business meeting in the city centre, but know that finding parking downtown will be impossible in the middle of the day. You could take public transit, but the trip planning app informs you that it will take too long. So, you decide to request an Uber. You open the app and see both your real-time position as well as the locations of nearby available Ubers. The app notifies you that there is presently a high demand for rides, meaning that your trip will cost a multiple of the standard fare, but you decide to proceed. The app then displays information about the driver dispatched and their estimated time of arrival. Upon arriving at your destination, the payment is made automatically by the app using stored credit card details, and you rate the driver's service.

1 The following academic article speculates on how a city might be run and experienced if Uber's business model was adopted. Product or corporate names may be trademarks or registered trademarks, and are used only for identification, explanation and speculation as part of a thought experiment without intent to infringe.

So convenient, so user-friendly, so tailored to your individual, real-time needs. Uber and its competitors such as Lyft have transformed not only how we move through and navigate cities, but also how we access private-sector goods and services in urban centres. We can order our meals and have them delivered to us via UberEATS. When street traffic is backed up, we can hop out of an Uber and hop onto a JUMP electrified bike, all without leaving the Uber app. 1180

Given the rate at which Uber is expanding its services, we can envision a hypothetical UberCity wherein Uber subsumes a range of municipal services into its ecosystem. By adopting the UberCity platform (for a fee, of course), cities could unload the responsibility of coordinating and delivering municipal services to a third party broker, with UberCity (or a rival intermediary) mediating between private citizens requesting services and denizens willing to share their labour towards fulfilling those services. In a scenario that reads like a scene from the fictional television series *Black Mirror*, service users and providers alike become rateable entities regarding their level of civility and citizenship: being courteous, efficient providers, and responsible, fair citizens. UberCity handles the monetary transactions, retaining a portion of the city's fee as its agreed-upon cut. 1181

Take, for instance, a pothole on a residential street. Residents would open the UberCity app, take a picture of the problem road segment with their smartphone, and upload the image along with a request for the pothole to be filled. Harnessing the phone's GPS, the UberCity app would automatically tag the 1182 request with its real-world location. An algorithm would match the issue requiring attention with another city resident—in this case, a tradesperson with skills and expertise to fix the issue who is looking for a paid 'gig.' Gig workers would check-in via the app to indicate their real-time availability. Dispatched to a location, they would be compensated for completion of the task as well as wholesale material costs through their registered bank details. The resident could review and rate both the labourer and the quality of work. Quality control would be ensured through the deactivation of gig workers receiving repeated low ratings and negative feedback from the app.

Beyond infrastructure maintenance, UberCity 1183
would make any number of civic services accessible on-demand through a suite of in-platform utilities: rubbish bin overflowing? (UberTrash!); walking home along dark residential streets at night? (UberStreetLights!); medical emergency? (UberAmbulance!); power lines down? (UberEnergy!); sudden loss of water pressure? (UberWater!); neighbour's dogs running through your yard again? (UberAnimalControl!); snowed six inches overnight? (UberSnowPlow!). Each competing with other similar privatised services.

What's not to like about such a proposition? 1184

In theory, the aspirational model of the UberCity 1185
provides opportunities for residents to source seamless, efficient, just-in-time solutions to a multitude of municipal tasks. It allows residents the flexibility to select the type of service required; as with the ride-sharing services offered through the app, these would range from carpool style rides at the most affordable

end of the spectrum (UberPOOL) to professional driver services at the higher cost end (UberBLACK). The surge pricing model would similarly apply to times when demand for services is high. When the power lines are down on your street and you want your house to be amongst the first to be reconnected to the grid, you may choose to pay a multiple of the standard rate to ensure the prioritization of your needs.

Through its coordination of a two-sided mar- 1186
ketplace, UberCity could also mobilize a potential workforce that matches skills and performance with these tasks. No longer beholden to set work hours, city residents could work around their personal schedules, picking up gigs when and where convenient to provide full, or supplementary, income. And rather than waiting for a bi-weekly or monthly paycheque, gig labourers would be compensated directly through the app immediately upon completion and satisfactory rating of tasks. Such a city service gig economy model might democratize access to presently lucrative and difficult to secure city jobs.

UberCity alleviates city administrations from 1187
the responsibilities of not only functioning as a service provider, but also from functioning as a service broker—the former gets shifted to city citizens, the latter to the platform. This would have a number of effects, such as allowing municipalities to divest themselves from owning and maintaining depreciating assets and to do so with little to no public investment. In the same way that Uber does not own any of the cars driven by their pool of driver contractors, cities as service brokers do not need to own equipment or materials needed to maintain

municipal infrastructures: snowplows, raw earth materials, busses. It would also potentially generate huge cost savings that could compensate for present municipal budgetary shortfalls: cities would be able to drastically downsize their municipal workforce and offload pension obligation costs (which have already bankrupted several US cities and which threaten to bankrupt yet others[2]). Moreover, as private contractors, municipal gig workers would not be owed the same kinds of benefits as city employees, releasing city administrations from expenditures associated with overheads such as payroll taxes and health insurance premiums.

By expanding choices available to citizen con- 1188
sumers, city halls can boost their approval ratings and shield themselves from repercussions for poorly executed and incomplete tasks. Equally importantly, the Uber model allows municipalities to conveniently supplement gaps in their own service provision capacities through outsourcing via the platform. Cities like Los Angeles are already looking to partner with ride-hailing companies as a solution to providing transportation to areas critically underserved by public transit.[3]

The UberCity underbelly

On the surface, the logic of arguments to shift the re- 1189
sponsibilities of a city to a third party service broker and the gig economy appear commonsensical and straightforward. Yet the coherence of such wishful Uber-like thinking is possible only when we ignore the realities of platform urbanism, forego conceiving of the urban realm as a shared public good, and fail to understand

2 Mooney, A. (2017) "US faces crisis as pension funding hole hits $3.85tn." *Financial Times*. Link: https://www.ft.com/content/f2891b34-3705-11e7-99bd-13beb0903fa3

3 Marshall, A. (2017) "LA Looks to Rideshare To Build the Future of Public Transit." *Wired*. Link: https://www.wired.com/story/la-rideshare-public-transit

cities as complex, democratic, multiscale entities full of competing interests and wicked problems.

In terms of using services delivered through an 1190
Uber-like model—envisaged here as a hypothetical UberCity platform ecosystem—access for citizens is likely to be patchy and divided rather than universal, favouring those with the means to pay (especially when surge model pricing kicks in). Uber has been no equalizer of access to transportation, with residents of poor urban neighbourhoods chronically underserved by ride-sharing services because drivers see wealthier enclaves as preferred origins more likely to generate more lucrative trips.[4] As such, the brokering of services for the profit of private entities works to deepen rather than ameliorate urban inequalities.

The urbanites that drive for Uber either have 1191
failed to gain secure full-time employment or need to supplement their income because their 9-5 jobs no longer pay enough to their living costs. The work is flexible, insecure, relatively poorly paid, and (in most jurisdictions) has no benefits such as health insurance, pension contributions, severance pay, or parental or sick. It shifts many of the costs of production onto workers, who must purchase, pay taxes on, and insure the ride-share vehicle. Such arrangements can be used to exploit workers. For example, as part of its strategy to recruit drivers, Uber launched a subprime auto loan program targeting the socioeconomically disadvantaged[5]—a practice that in the aftermath of the housing market crash of the late 2000s we know to be predatory and to have disproportionately stripped ethnic minorities of wealth and assets.

4 Wells, K., Attoh, K. and Cullen, D. (2018) "Uber, the 'Metropocalypse', and Economic Inequality in D.C." *Working Class Perspectives*. Link: https://workingclassstudies.wordpress.com/2018/02/05/uber-the-metropocalypse-and-economic-inequality-in-d-c

5 Richter, W. and Street, W. (2017) "Uber's subprime auto loans are causing a lot of problems." *Business Insider*. Link: http://www.businessinsider.com/uber-subprime-auto-loans-running-it-off-the-road-2017-8

While the gig economy might seem a meritocracy, a system underpinned by ratings and rankings is a zero sum game: for some to be ranked highly, others have to be lower down such that they may be 'deactivated' by the platform. Such ratings are informed not only by the quality or speed of service delivery, but also by a breadth of social biases including racism, homophobia, xenophobia, and sexism amongst others.[6] There are also those that would struggle to compete in a gig economy, the differentially-abled, the chronically ill, and those with care responsibilities that leave them little time flexibility. 1192

From the perspective of a city administration, the Uber model assumes that all public services are run on a consumer rather than client basis and are therefore open to market interventions. Rights and entitlements as a citizen are swapped for choice as a consumer, selecting services from a marketplace of providers based on the individual means to pay.[7] It also assumes that the delivery of city administration, services, and infrastructure are relatively simple and autonomous and can be divided into bounded, coherent markets that operate largely outside of democracy and policy. In reality, running a city involves significant levels of knowledge and expertise; inter-agency and multiple stakeholder collaboration; diplomacy and negotiation; political decision-making and policy formulation and implementation; and trying to serve the public good in a time of austerity. Cities are full of competing interests and wicked problems, their fortunes shift, administrations change, and they are difficult to manage. 1193

6 Ramaswami, C. (2017) "'Prejudices play out in the ratings we give'—the myth of digital equality." *The Guardian*. Link: https://www.theguardian.com/technology/2017/feb/20/airbnb-uber-sharing-apps-digital-equality

7 Cardullo, P. and Kitchin, R. (2018) "Being a 'citizen' in the smart city: Up and down the scaffold of smart citizen participation in Dublin, Ireland." *GeoJournal* 84(1): 1-13.

8 Darrow, B. (2017) "Why Uber and Lyft Might Be Hurting Stressed Public Transit Systems." *Fortune*. Link: http://fortune.com/2017/10/13/uber-lyft-public-transit-ridership

9 Althusser, L. (1971) *Lenin and Philosophy and Other Essays*. London: NLB.

An uberisation of public services is likely to 1194
make shepherding and coordinating urban fortunes more difficult, shifting essential services beyond democratic control and oversight. In fact, it may work to accelerate the financial and service provision crisis affecting many cities. The introduction of ride-hailing services into urban markets has at times worked to intensifying and accelerate a public transit infrastructure crisis by reducing ridership,[8] which itself reduces desperately needed revenues to fund and maintain services, further eroding service availability and pushing what profitable services remain into the private sector. Extending the Uber model across the city administration and infrastructure will simply extend this neoliberal process, pushing more-and-more public services into crisis and fuelling the demand for uneven, unequal, and unaccountable for-profit alternatives.

The philosopher Louis Althusser[9] warns that a 1195
key driver of capitalism is that it is seductive: platform urbanism promises individual freedom and choice. But seduction can be a veil, in this case obfuscating broader processes of furthering neoliberalization and accumulation by dispossession that may disadvantage us in the long run. We need to ask whether the promises of convenience, user-friendliness, individualization, and utility value in the UberCity are worthwhile trade-offs for digital democracy and the city as a public good.

Agnieszka Leszczynski a digital geographer and geographic information scientist. Her current projects examine digital platforms in Canadian cities, and location-based technology startups in the digital economy.

Rob Kitchin is a Professor in the Department of Geography and Maynooth University Social Sciences Institute. His research focuses on the relationship between technology and society, especially related to the creation of smart cities, and he is the principle investigator for the Programmable City project and the Building City Dashboards project.

THE COOL AND THE BLACK-OUTS

VODAFONE[1]

Jessica Foley, Maynooth University

The Fox and The Lion

WHEN the fox and the lion first happen'd to meet, 1196
Poor Reynard fell down at his majesty's feet,
So great was the terror inspired;
But the next time he met him, not quite so afraid,
When the lion approach'd an obeisance he made,
And after his health he inquired.
But the third time he met him, "Old crony," said he,
"Pray whither so fast? I must say, to be free,
That you're grown somewhat cool and unkind."
The dignified lion deign'd not a reply;
But taking the fox to a river hard by,
Cool'd him, both in body and mind.

Thought the fox, whilst emerging in woe-begone state,
"This comes of one's making too free with the great."

Aesop's Fable (Jefferys Taylor version)

1 The following speculative fiction and satire imagines living in a divided city where one part is disconnected from the telecoms network. Such a thought experiment could equally apply if the city were run by other telecoms such as T-Mobile or Verizon. Product or corporate names may be trademarks or registered trademarks, and are used only for the purpose of conducting a thought experiment without intent to infringe.

Sam was already waiting by the swatch. He sat in the 1197
morning sun, by the channel water lying between the
shores of the Yeffil River, spacing out to the life of air-
borne seeds, dust and insects. Every now and then
his gaze would tilt towards the sound of a cockling in
the water, currents in tension or a rare fish leaping.
Sam's shoes were off to one side and his toes splayed
and wiggled lazily in the silt-sand of the estuary shore.
In the distance huge container ships were freighting
cargo to the port, disappearing down the barra, the
oldest engineered channel of Niblud City. They passed
behind the great South Wall, that modesty screen behind which port-workers and their drones distributed
goods amongst the citizenry, rebuffing the dirty eyes
of Lagnif Black-Outs like Sam.

Squinting into the haze, Sam saw Caitlin pick- 1198
ing her way lightly across the dragons-teeth, rows
of pyramidal concrete blocks laid down along the
intertidal zone of Lagnif. He pulled his feet from the
silt rubbing them together to dislodge the most of the
grit and jumped up into a head-rush. He waved, two
arms overhead, as if landing a plane. Caitlin raised an
arm, vertical, in stoic reply. They were headed for their
weekly parley at the Steps.

The Steps was the place where city folk used to 1199
go to bathe in the summer heat, but only the jellyfish
basked in blooms there now. The Steps cascaded in
wide rough platforms perpendicular to a long promenade that jutted out into the bay. Washed-out lemon-co-
loured changing huts stooped and huddled, still offering
shelter. At the end of the promenade, a latticed steel
tower stretched into the hot blue sky. This was one of the
northern gateways that had been shut down after the
redline riots, leaving hundreds of thousands of people
without access to communications services, making
Lagnif an official black-spot, a rogue tribe of *Black-Outs*.

During the chaos of the redline riots, a leading Mobile Network Operator had taken over the Niblud City Council, making all city departments, from Business to Culture to Housing to Roads and Transport, yoked subserviently to Networks and Communications. Under the MNO administration, the various forms of network dependency across the city had ramified. Young families in particular struggled. The new administration recognised the boon this afforded them in terms of sustainable revenue, offering more and more subscription applications over the network that promised to help monitor and manage the challenges of family life and to help develop social cohesion through the networked city. 1200

The attentions, and indeed the relationships, of families became routed and mediated, almost exclusively, through City approved parenting apps like *BoldStep* and *PlayDate*, while children were encouraged to manage transitions from online to offline through apps like *TantrumTrap*. This app allowed the child to divert their tearful screams at moments of disconnection (such as bedtime) into a conical mouthpiece that recorded the decibel level, prosody and duration of the 'tantrum', offering child and parent a means to chart patterns of behaviour, identify 'trigger-warnings' and seek out appropriate app-based treatments. But the application-heavy, bureaucracy-by-surveillance approach to City administration meant that infrastructures had become varicose from over use and underdevelopment. City dwellers paid a premium, in terms of income, privacy and personality, for network continuity. 1201

In Lagnif where network resources had been aggressively denied, the communities had long since become familiar with network separation and had come to recognise this so-called disadvantage as a privilege. Over time they had found ways to manage 1202 the transition offline, to contextualise their anxieties and negotiate new forms of relation with each other and their environment. By necessity, this rogue enclave made the most of its modest resources and had developed a canteen culture that appreciated and nurtured the complex human relationship between individual and collective. Every child across every canteen knew the Remaining Useful Life of each instrument and technological system in their neighbourhood.

.:.

Heat had rendered Lagnif brittle and translucent. 1203
Beneath cracked pathways, water pipes leaked deep into the foundations of the city, the bring centres between districts swelled with pungent waste while street vendors stirred more appetising smells for squat diners breakfasting under nylon umbrellas. Caitlin was always first in her household to wake. She slipped down from her top bunk, pulling her clothes with her before dressing quietly in the hallway between the bedrooms.

In the canteen she prepared a small pack of 1204
fruit, biscuits and water, including sunscreen and a towel. Every noise was amplified in the quiet, her fumbling hands, her swallow, her heartbeat. At the back door she stuffed one foot then the other into her street shoes, pulling the heels aright as she hopped into the hazy drenched sunshine, her pack loose around her shoulder. She had a shift at the Black-Outs Bridge, a school assembled upon a disused bridge over the Yeffil River, between Lagnif and the City of Niblud. Then she would meet Sam.

She worked the morning shift at the school, 1205
which meant working with City dwellers and their children. Only the most desperate would come, those who were being sunk out of the network, or those who had realised their network addiction, but couldn't put

a language on it to think their way through it. One of the first things to develop spontaneously in Lagnif, after the disconnection, was language. It flourished. People began to tell stories, new stories. The Black-Outs Bridge School was a grey space, where city dwellers and black-outs could share and make culture, a process that had all but ended in Niblud. The City was now a brand, with a new motto: *De Future est excitando. Paratus?*

Sam and Caitlin had no sense of a future, exciting or 1206
otherwise, and it didn't worry them. They spent their days together exploring the coastline along Lagnif, gradually finding and forming names for the things they observed and felt. Before the riots they might have been called poets, but in the official lexicon of Niblud City Council, they were simply *Black-Outs*.

The young friends made their way to the Steps 1207
where they would sit, toes in the water with their backs against the massive legs of the gateway, sleepily playing with sounds and songs.

"Look, there's a bit of a glister coming in there, d'you see Sam?"

"Oh yeah, that'll make a good squall for the freighters."

"The gulls are already luffing mad... the 1210
kep-shites!"

"Are you hungry? I brought some peas and potatoes."

As Sam twisted around to unpack the food from his 1212
backpack he stalled, shushing Caitlin who had been humming intervals to herself.

Through the aime rising from the heated prom- 1213
enade Sam could see a figure moving towards them, their white body shimmering. After some minutes, the figure pulled up at the base of the tower carrying a chrome flightcase and dressed in a plain, crisp cotton shirtdress and trousers. Its head was sheathed by a fine chrome silk, reflecting Caitlin, Sam and the Steps in a silvery sharp resolution. Without saying a word, the figure opened the case, took out a small black box with a clear glass face and adhered it to a leg of the tower, facing towards the horizon and Caitlin, who was now standing up to get a better look at this virginal apparition. With a little too much haste, the figure closed the case, turned and walked quickly away, its head glinting like a polished tooth.

"What was that about?" asked Sam.

"I don't know", said Caitlin, "They must 1215
be from the city."

"What's a Col doing out here though?"

"That wasn't a Col, Sam; they'd never send the councillers out here."

"Well, who was it then?"

"I don't know, maybe they'll come back", Caitlin said thoughtfully, tapping the glass box.

The Col did come back. The second time he spent hours checking the glass box, making reference to an electric tablet, seeming to take notes or readings. Without addressing either Caitlin or Sam, he set up a small stool, about 10 leg-leaps away. And while neither party spoke to the other, and appeared to be indifferent neighbours, the young friends had for the first time in their lives the uncomfortable feeling of being watched remotely. 1220

"They're just monitoring that box thingy for the gateway", Sam said once the Col had moved on.

"I'm not so sure", said Caitlin shaking away a shiver.

"Well, let's come out earlier next time, during firesmoke", suggested Sam.

.·.

Sure enough, Sam and Caitlin made their way to the Steps the following week, just as the sunset was blending with the misty evening dew. They set up a small camp fire to make toast and tea and chat as the chilly dark set in around them. Around the Steps the breeze roused hobbles of choppy, short waves to make mild melodies on the concrete, a lullaby. 1224

"See, this is nice. No disruptions. No Col", said Sam. 1225

"I guess they weren't interested in us after all", Caitlin said, releasing a long sigh.

"You sound disappointed", laughed Sam pouring steaming tea into their tin cups, "*familiarity breeds contempt*, isn't that what they say?"

"No more than neglect", said Caitlin accepting her cup.

The hobbles of waves lapped and made small talk in the silence between them. At the foot of the tower, between the massive legs of the sealed gateway to the City, to the network, to the future, two stray Black-Outs, shadow-danced in the firelight. They were joined imperceptibly by a third shadow, the now all too familiar stranger. 1229

"We've been watching you", the Col's voice came out in a digital whisper through his silvery mask. Neither Sam nor Caitlin heard him, mesmerized as they were by the twitching of the camp fire. As if embarrassed, the Col glanced about. He broadening his shoulders. Clearing his throat and with a deep breath in, he tried again. This was his final dispatch for the council. If he could get these Black-Outs on friendly terms it could mean promotion. 1230

"We've been watching you, Sam, Caitlin," the Col announced rather dramatically.

"Hob-Gobblin, what the hell!" shouted Sam. Caitlin fell backwards off her stool, cursing the hot tea that spilled across her chest.

"You total *brimfuster*! What do you think you're doing creeping up on us like that!?" yelled Caitlin, standing now and wiping her front roughly.

"Apologies", the Col stated awkwardly.

The three stood triangulated between the huge legs 1235
of the cell tower.

"We have been watching you", he said again, slowly repeating his script, "for some time now."

"I knew it!" said Caitlin stomping her foot.

"Shush, let's hear what *the network* has to say", said Sam, making air quotes.

"I come from the City of Niblud", the Col said, gesturing an open palm southwards, "The council are considering reconnecting Lagnif."

Sam and Caitlin cast each other a shadowy look. The 1240
Col inhaled deeply through his chrome mask, bringing his hands together peaceably, as rehearsed. Sam and Caitlin remained quiet, listening.

"I am here to change your life. You don't have to be *Black-Outs*, you can be *more*. I've seen how you live. I've watched your canteen culture, tracking your movements, your conversations, your sleep patterns, your diets. You are a struggling people. Your homes, your communities are starving for *reconnection*! I can make this happen... with your help."

The silence gave the Col courage. Taking a step to- 1242
wards the young friends, he went on. "I want to offer you both a chance to open up the Black-Spots.
Help me prove to the City Council that there is a disciplined appetite for connection, here, in Lagnif. No
more redlining, no more riots, no more black-spots.
You can lead the campaign to show that Black-Outs
are ready!"

The figure paused dramatically, arms out- 1243
stretched, his chrome face flickering orange in the
firelight. "I'm offering you, and all of Lagnif, a future
in the City, and that future is *exciting*. The question is,
are you *ready*?"

Sam and Caitlin laughed and with a unified nod 1244
each sprinted sideways to grab an arm and a leg of
their would-be saviour, lifting the Col straight off his
feet and swinging him head first into the hobbles and
blooms of the Black-Out's bay.

Note

Some of the more unusual words in this fable were gleaned from Robert MacFarlane's book *Landmarks* (2016). The word Col means "utmost spot to which anything (human or creature) can be driven." The story is modelled on Vodafone's brand positioning *The Future is Exciting. Ready?* and Aesop's Fable, The Fox and The Lion, the moral of which is '*Familiarity breeds Contempt.*'

Jessica Foley is an Irish Research Council Postdoctoral Fellow at the Social Sciences Institute at Maynooth University, where her practice-based research explores the function of fiction in relation to 'smart' technologies.

ADDRESS. ERROR.503

WHAT3WORDS[1]

Jim Thatcher, University of Washington Tacoma

What3Words is a "really simple way to talk about loca- 1245
tion" in which the entire world is broken up into 3m by 3m grids. Each grid is assigned a three word phrase, such as 'pork.perfect.dog,' and users navigate from location to location by entering these purported easily to remember and communicate phrases.

"Alright, looks like you only have five overnight deliveries on your route today, Stan. Think you can finish by five?"

"Thanks, Jess. Depends, where are they?"

"Looks like you've got one at pipes.sums. gender, another at assist.figure.games, direct.wiping.blocks, surely.worker.foster, and, uh, clown.blitz.behind."

1 The following speculative fiction and satire imagines living in a city where the postal geography has been altered to a privatised service. Product or corporate names may be trademarks or registered trademarks, and are used only for the purpose of conducting a thought experiment without intent to infringe.

"Hold on, hold on, I'm trying to enter these into my tablet. It says here pipe. sums.genders is in Russia? Some place called Bilibino? I'm pretty sure that's outside of our delivery range."
"Stan, I said pipes.sums.gender, it's like half a mile from here on the old Centre Avenue. It looks like assist. figure.games is right down the street on Centre as well."

"Okay, got it. Wait, Jess, is surely. 1250
worker.foster in the back of a building?"

"Yup, getting rooted to the actual drop off point is one of the reasons the city switched all addresses to What3Words last month, makes it easier for us."

"Yeah, spare me the hype. But, sure, looks like I can get these done by five."

"Okay, Stan, see you at churn.cult. healthier after then?"

"Cheese and crackers, Jess, do you mean Lefty's? Yes, I'll see you at Lefty's when I'm done with these packages."

Jess chuckled to herself as Stan picked up his pack- 1255
ages and headed towards his car. Looking at them, he could see one was marked *urgent—keep cold*. While, given the fees, pretty much anything sent overnight was urgent, Stan figured this was probably medical supplies and he'd set his route to drop it off first. *Clown. blitz.behind, heh*, he giggled as he punched in the address and started up his car.

Once Stan had entered the three word phrase, 1256
the What3Words app passed the location back to his Google Maps application as latitude and longitude coordinates and it, in turn, provided him his now-familiar driving directions using the street names of Pittsburgh he'd known since childhood. Pulling out of the Crafton Post Office, he took a left onto Bedford Avenue. Fifteen minutes later and Stan was pulling into the parking lot of Carter's Automotive, the location of Clown.blitz.behind.

Weird, he thought, *who gets medical supplies* 1257
delivered to an automotive shop? Oh well, not my problem, let's get the signature and get out of here.

As he walked into the shop, a woman poked her 1258
head out from under a Camry she was working on and asked "Hi, can I help you? That old Subaru giving you trouble? The rear differentials can go out on the hills around here."

> "No, I've got a package here for a Catherine Stoutletz. I'll need a signature."

> "No one with that name here, are 1260
> you sure you have the right address? Carter's Automotive?"

> "Well, it says here clown.blitz.behind, that takes me right to your front door. It's marked urgent—keep cold, you sure you don't have a Stoutletz here?"

The woman got out from under the car and pulled 1262
out her phone. "Well, yeah, clown.blitz.behind is our new address, huh. Let me take a look at that... Hey, look here, there's an S yinz missed. This was sent to clowns.blitz.behind, not here."

Stan took the package back and looked close-ly, she was right, the post office had missed an S. He punched the new address into his phone and What3Words helpfully directed him to a rural area in southwest Missouri, a good thirteen hour drive away. *Well, shit*, he muttered to himself. 1263

"Okay, well, thank you for your time. Have a good day."

"You come back if that differential starts acting up," she called out, slipping back under the hood of the Camry. 1265

Stan called Jess once he was back in the car. "Stan, what is it, you left something behind again?"

"Jess, we've got a problem. That medical delivery, it got sent to the wrong address. It's meant to go to Missouri, not here."

"What?"

"It was sent to clowns.blitz.behind, not clown.blitz.behind; that's all the way out in rural Missouri. It'll never get there today."

"Ugh, Okay. We'll reroute it when you come back to the office. No chance it gets there today, so it'll go out first thing in the morning." 1270

"But, Jess, I'm pretty sure this is something medical, it says to keep cold, what if it doesn't last that long?"

"Not our problem, we'll reroute it as fast as we can. Besides, you can't be sure what it is, maybe it's just frozen strawberries or something."

"I guess. Okay, I'll see you later." Stan hung up and punched in the next address. Jess was right that it wasn't their problem, except that it seemed to be one that happened with all too much frequency. Usually, it was his fault—spelling had never been his strong suit—but this time it was the entire routing network. The S was lighter, but someone should have caught it along the way; except most of those *someones* were now mostly *somethings*—automated scanners all connected to the What3Words API, sacrifices on the altar of efficiency. 1273

His next three deliveries were fairly uneventful. Pipes.sums.gender and assist.figure.games were both on Centre Street and within a few blocks of one another. Stan did a loop and dropped them both off before heading up to the corner of Webster Avenue and Devilliers Street. Direct.wiping.blocks led him to the front porch of a boarded up row house. The package didn't require a signature, and as he set it down he could hear stirring from behind the boarded up front windows. 1274

One of the few advantages to the new addressing system, from Stan's perspective, was that folks without permanent addresses could now receive packages wherever they might be living at the time. Some of his colleagues wouldn't leave the package, and official policy was still murky on this point, but Stan felt it was only right—if you give every few meters an address, then you can damn sure deliver a package to that space. 1275

As he walked back to his car, a large brown dog with shaggy fur ran to the window of the house next door and began idly barking at him. *One more and* 1276

I'm off to an IC Light or three with Jess and the others. Let's see, surely.worker.foster. It was that weird one, at the back of some building. Should be near here. After entering the address, Stan waited and the dog barked.

Nothing happened. He closed the app, grum- 1277
bled and reopened it. This time something did happen;
an error message appeared: "Error 503: A problem has
occurred with the What3words API."

What the hell is an API? Stan repeated the pro- 1278
cess of opening and closing the application, he was
once more greeted with the error message. The dog
was still barking. He got out of the car and approached
the house with the dog, its barking increased in frequency. After he knocked, an elderly man opened it.
He was holding onto the dog's collar as it jumped ea-
gerly at Stan.

> "Down, Stoona, down. Hi, you need a signature for something?"

> "No, no. Not today, I'm wondering if 1280
> you might check an address for me in
> What3Words. The application won't
> work for me and I've got an overnight
> delivery to make somewhere south of
> here."

> "Sure, let me get my phone."

The old man walked into the back room, dragging 1282
the dog. He returned without it and holding a
smartphone. "What's the address?"

Stan told him the address, but—even after checking 1283
to make sure the spelling was correct—the old man

received the same error: “Error 503: A problem has occurred with the What3words API.”

> “Sorry, doesn’t seem to be working. Don’t know why.”
>
> “Well, thanks for trying.” As Stan 1285
> walked back to his house, the dog ran once more to the window and eagerly barked at him.

I know the address is the back of a building and I’m 1286
pretty sure it’s south of here, but I have no idea where it is. Surely.worker.foster... No clue. Well, if the application won’t work, I can’t deliver. Fuck it, I’m going to Lefty’s. At least I know *where that is—2021 Penn Ave, down by Primanti’s.*

It wasn’t until the somewhat blurry-eyed morn- 1287
ing that Stan remembered the medical package that needed to be kept cold.

What3words has assigned every 3m by 3m square a 1288
sequence of three words, which are matched to latitude and longitude coordinates, thus geolocating it. As the vignette above illustrates, that means places like “churn.cult.healthier” come to refer to the front door of the dive bar Lefty’s. As a start-up company W3W promises its addressing system “enhances customer experience, delivers business efficiency, drives growth and supports the social and economic development of countries.”[2] In truth, it can help with some of those things in some places. For example, as Stan’s delivery to an officially uninhabited building suggests, giving everywhere

2 Link: https://what3words.com/about

an address is useful in locations that previously struggled with efficient postal delivery, such as Kiribati[3] and Mongolia.[4] It can also be useful for navigating dense, small scale environments, such as in Cape Town's Lourensford market[5] or at a music festival.[6]

What3words supposedly makes addresses sim- 1289
pler to remember and more efficient to navigate to; however, even its most basic functions come with troubling caveats. First, as Stan learned, a single missed letter can move an address thousands of miles. The What3words API provides an AutoSuggest resource that allows for corrections based on spelling, word order, and geographic area, but this hardly guarantees accurate results and seems an additional hurdle added to what was meant to be a simpler, easier to recall addressing system.

Second, and also above, the system relies 1290
upon the What3words API to translate the three words into latitude and longitude coordinates. At present, it relies upon other routing systems (Google, Bing, Citymapper, Tom Tom) to provide directions between the coordinates. In other words, ultimately any directions gleaned from What3words come from another service's ability to process latitude and longitude coordinates that can be passed along only when the What3words API is operating. While supposedly easier to communicate, What3words suggests that one must have a smart phone to decode their addressing, but such a phone would be unable to transmit latitude and longitude on its own (i.e., without the obfuscation into three words).

Third, the What3Words system exists at only 1291

3 Link: https://what3words.com/partner/kiribati-post

4 Link: https://what3words.com/partner/mongol-post

5 Link: https://what3words.com/2018/04/visitors-find-their-favourite-market-stalls-in-cape-town-with-what3words

6 Link: https://what3words.com/2018/03/finding-your-way-at-a-crowded-festival-with-littlegig-and-what3words

one, static scale—that of the 3m by 3m grid. Since words are assigned randomly and, due to the nature of language, cannot nest hierarchically, properties will consist of multiple, semantically unrelated phrases. A given quarter-acre plot, for example, will consist of slightly over one hundred independent three words phrases. Further, a given plot cannot be sub-divided in the What3Words system; this means that were What3Words to replace other surveying systems, property lines would need to be redrawn to conform to this static, overlaid grid.

If a city were run on What3Words, its citizens 1292
would face a host of problems, both obvious and subtle. On the one hand, when used as a delivery-oriented addressing system What3Words gives those without formal addresses the ability to specify a permanent space for delivery. This allows said individuals to participate in the many activities, such as package deliveries and job, loan, and bank account applications, which require such an address. On the other, in order to do so What3Words inserts an interstitial layer of digital technology between individuals and their ability to navigate the world. Addresses become findable only when the What3Words API is able, or potentially chooses, to decode the entered three word phrase.

Fundamentally, this enrols a core function of the 1293
state within its privately owned API. Addressing has long been a means by which the state has made space knowable, calculable, and controllable.[7] Handing this responsibility and power to a private corporation shifts the relationships between citizen and state. On one level, as in the end of Stan's tale, this can make places

7 Rose-Redwood, R. (2012) With Numbers in Place: Security, Territory, and the Production of Calculable Space. *Annals of the Association of American Geographers.* 102(2): 295-319.

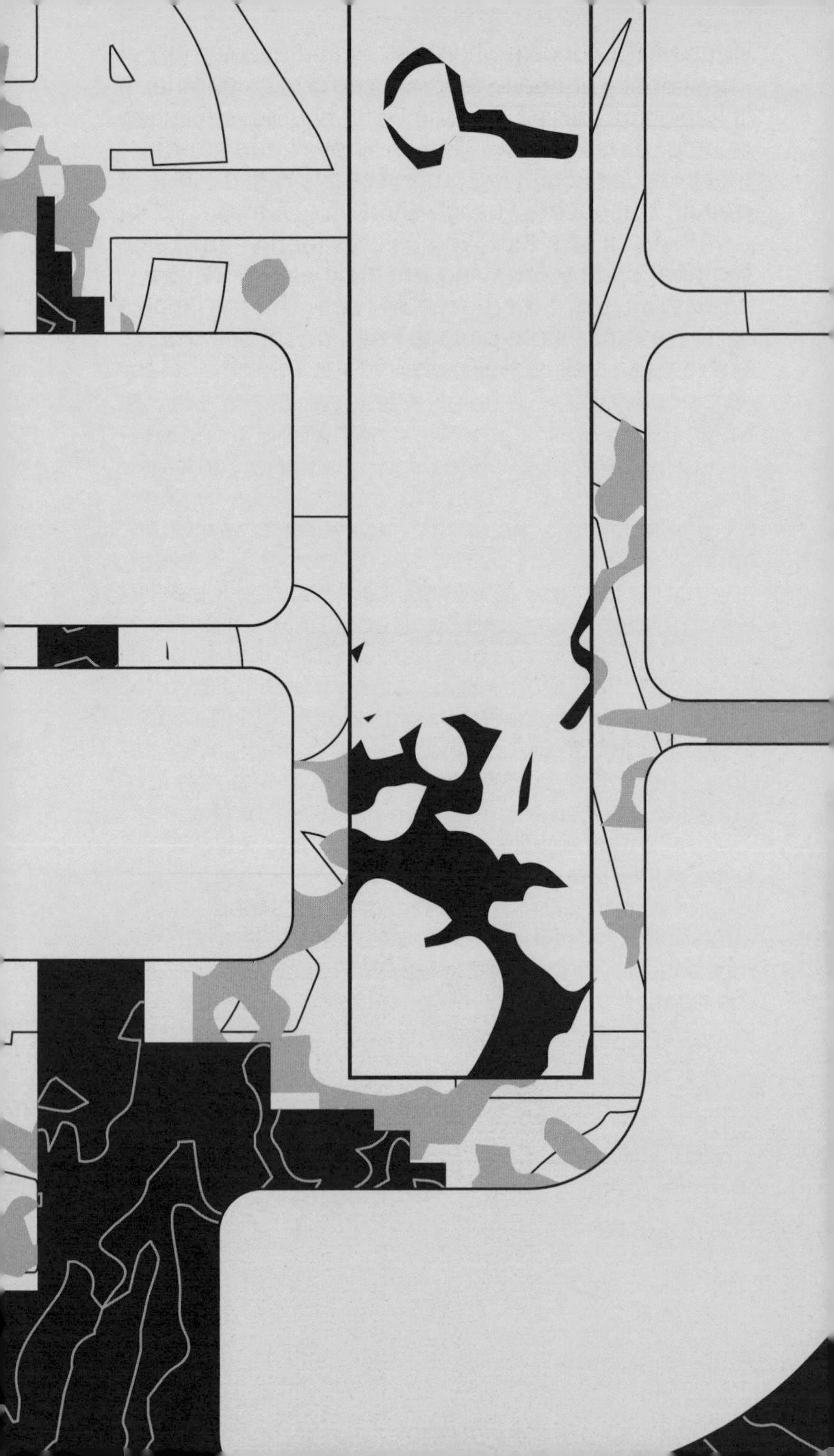

virtually unreachable when their system is down (either intentionally or due to technical error). On another, it is important to note that the What3words API is free only for personal use. They employ "a fee structure that provides qualifying organisations with a range of free and discounted usage plans."[8]

As cities adopt What3words for their address- 1294
ing needs, they are tying the ability to *know where something is* to a fee-based API call. This isn't a plea for the return of state-controlled spaces of calculation, but rather a note of wariness against what might take its place.

8 Link: https://what3words.com/pricing

Jim Thatcher is Associate Professor of Urban Studies at the University of Washington Tacoma and an affiliate with the school of Geography at the University of Washington. His work examines the recursive relations among extremely large geospatial data, the creation and analysis of said data, and society.

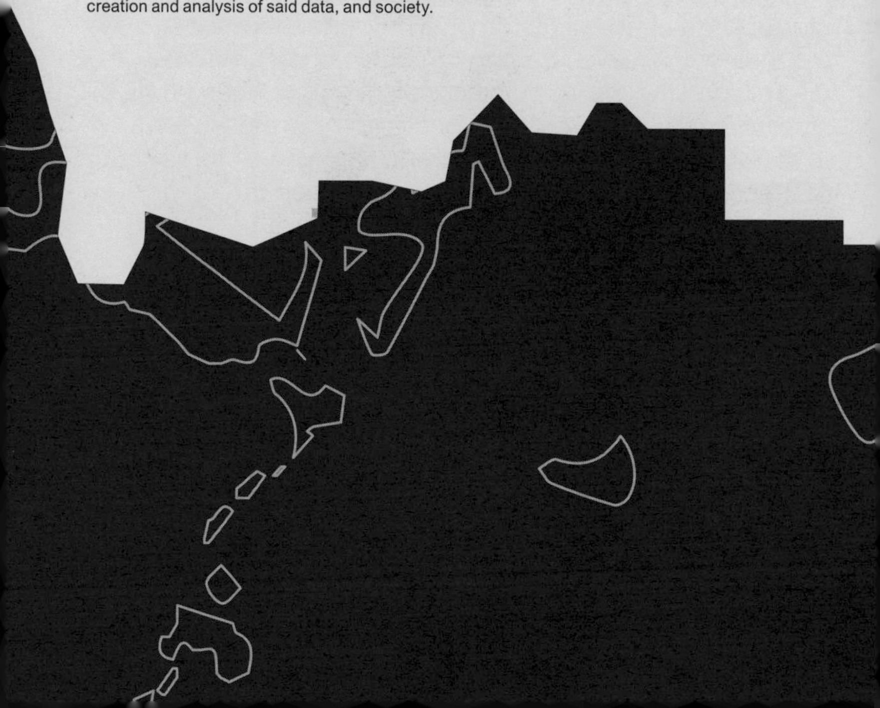

A CITY OF THE PEOPLE, FOR THE PEOPLE, BY THE PEOPLE

WHATSAPP[1]

Ayona Datta, University College London

The alarm rang. Arun sat up on the bed, his eyes still 1295
shut. His mobile was lit up with a series of WhatsApp messages. 'GM', 'gm', 'g'morning', 'g'day', 'good morning dear', 'please send good morning wishes to at least 20 others or else' ... a cacophony of distant voices tagging the global time zone of wakefulness.

He stepped out of bed and opened the other 1296
messages. The CEO of BotCash (a successful internet startup) had been assaulted by a few 'attention-seeking ladies' as he was getting out of his car. These ladies alleged that he was taking their pictures, when he said he was just forwarding a good morning message to his wife. The police had apparently planted pictures of these ladies in his mobile phone and then arrested him for stalking women.

In another news, a software engineer had giv- 1297
en up his multimillion job to help street vendors. He gave them free training to use his VendMe app which

1 The following speculative fiction and satire imagines living in a city where a social messenging platform thoroughly permeates everyday life. Such a thought experiment could equally apply if the city were run by Facebook or Twitter. Product or corporate names may be trademarks or registered trademarks, and are used only for the purpose of conducting a thought experiment without intent to infringe.

enabled vendors to advertise and pay registration fees and users to search for nearby vendors. VendMe had revolutionised informal street trading, in turn leading to an exponential growth in the sales of Android phones for using the app.

These forwarded WhatsApp messages would 1298
end with critical questions: Why do you think the mainstream media did not report this? Why do you think the media is not interested in helping the poor? Why do you think mainstream newspapers rely on WhatsApp for their journalism?

As a citizen of WhatsApp City, Arun was lucky. 1299
He didn't have to search for news, or try and figure out which was 'real' and which was 'fake.' Real news came straight to him once he had registered his mobile phone with WhatsApp customer services and given them access to his camera and location in real time.

The best part of being a citizen of WhatsApp 1300
City was that Arun received news that was tailored to who and where he was. It was curated and circulated by WhatsApp's global network of citizens. A contact in his golfing group who circulated sports news; a distant auntie living in California who reminded him of auspicious religious dates; the friendly neighbour next door who took a more than casual interest in tracking and circulating news of gang rapes. Regular updates from vigilantes informed citizens of safety, terror threats and other risks; doctors informed citizens of health, germs and viruses; schools informed parents of new cashbacks for making an application.

In WhatsApp City, the mobile phone was the 1301
only technology necessary to have a good life, its principal economy built around the information manufacturing sector.

City of the people

Transformed by investments made by the global messaging service after the 2008 global economic crash, WhatsApp City is a success story of inclusive consumerism. Whatsapp had made its billions by including the poor in its business model. It was revolutionary in being one of the first to be accessible to those using cheap, second hand and low-tech feature phones. 1302

Before 2008, when the city of Kalpalok was renamed WhatsApp City, its citizens' lives were dysfunctional to say the least. 1303

It was looted by politicians promising citizenship for votes, civil servants taking cuts out of infrastructure projects, and developers stealing government land for building non-existent homes. When citizens asked questions, they were told that information on the city's wealth and how it was spent, was confidential. They filed for information under the Rights to Information (RTI) Act, but the RTI activists kept getting murdered. Citizens began to access information through brokers and middle-men, but there was no way of knowing which was fake and which was real. Information became so valuable, that it became the new currency, even as WhatsApp's own shares crashed in the global market. 1304

When WhatsApp took over, they put their shares where it mattered—information exchange. 1305

WhatsApp rebuilt Kalpalok around mobile telephony. They gave citizens all the information they needed via their messaging service, since by then most citizens were using WhatsApp anyway to barter information in mobile space. WhatsApp told them that no news would ever be the same, and no news would be fake. It would be crowdsourced, geolocated, customised and above all, pleasurable. 1306

Managed efficiently through the safe, encrypted secure networks, the beauty of WhatsApp City was that there was no State surveillance, no State secrets. The government could not snoop into citizens' messages, they could not follow the trail of messages, nor the voice conversations or video chats. They did not know who sent messages or who received them, their mobile numbers or IP addresses, locations or contacts. No covert or overt surveillance was possible by the government, ever. 1307

WhatsApp City was completely of the people, managed and run efficiently by a global information company. 1308

City for the people

Ruhi was late for work. She had stayed with her boyfriend overnight. Her parents thought she was doing an all-nighter at work. That was a regular occurrence given how demanding it was to mine information each day, so her parents had no reason to suspect otherwise. Her parents understood that she needed to work very long hours. Because if she lagged behind her targets, she would lose her chance of landing her dream job with Whatsapp. 1309

So what if it was an unpaid internship at present? If she could also get 10 more interns to join she would get WhatsAppCoins worth a month's salary paid into her bank account. 1310

Ruhi turned round the corner towards her office. The outline of the WhatsApp building was just about visible at the end of the street. A young man was coming in her direction, she tried to step aside but he moved towards her, came right up to her and touched her arm. 1311

‘At last I get to feel your supple skin.’
In his hand was a phone playing videos
of Ruhi and her boyfriend making love.

‘What the ... Who are you? What do you
want?’ she screamed.

‘Give me what you give him every day.
I am far better than he is.’

‘How did you get this? Who took 1315
this video? Who gave this to you?’ she
demanded.

The man laughed at her. ‘It’s
everywhere on WhatsApp news.’

The laughter kept ringing in her ears as she ran away, 1317
crying. The ground felt like it was slipping under her, the office tower blocks closing in, suffocating her, choking her. The man was running after her, jeering and shouting lewd questions.

Ruhi stumbled into her seat at work shaking. 1318
She felt sick at the thought that her father might receive the video on his mobile. He would die of shame and disown her.

She wanted to throw up, but knew she needed 1319
to get to work.

On her screen was a database table consisting 1320
of tens of thousands of mobile phone numbers, each with a list of device type, mobile network, data on web pages visited through the app, time of chats, duration of chats, IP addresses, location and contacts.

The phones in the small cubicles around Ruhi 1321
began to light up with raw information—videos , voices,

text messages. They were all uploaded to the central WhatsApp server for interns like Ruhi to work on.

Though she found it difficult to concentrate, 1322
Ruhi began to run algorithms on the information, cross-linked with phone numbers, locations and demographic profiles to process them into different categories of news for different WhatsApp groups.

Some news just would not run unless they 1323
were part of a chain of fear—forward this to 20 other groups or else... Other news would not need much promotion—sending this to one individual who was well connected to several groups was enough to make this viral. This was usually news of soldiers' sacrifices or of minority appeasement. Stories of rags to riches or successful entrepreneurs helping the poor were also very popular. News about rapes or sexual harassment didn't do too well, although if they were associated with images and videos, these spread like wildfire. Stories identifying alleged murderers or kidnappers did the best, and were sent directly to the vigilantes so that they could lynch the suspects.

Kalpalok's police and the courts had been slow 1324
and ineffective. In WhatsApp City, news was enough to ensure quick justice for all.

Ruhi was one of the thousands of unpaid 1325
WhatsApp interns who had the important job of 'information mining.' Two years ago, when she started, information mining was very challenging. WhatsApp only kept basic metadata on users, and Ruhi could not access enough personal information to customise or place the information. She did not know what the citizens' likes or dislikes were, what their political leanings were, who they were friends with. This was the sort of data that Kalpalok had never collected pre-crash.

Now her work was far easier. WhatsApp was 1326

bought by a global social media company with a database of 2.2 billion users. Detailed personal information on each customer was readily available, their sleeping, eating, partying habits, their likes, dislikes, sense of humour, political leanings, sentiments, their global connections, you name it.

Now WhatsApp news had far more depth and 1327
reach. Ruhi could mine information faster customise better and circulate wider. This made Ruhi hopeful that soon she would be able to move to the paid position of 'Story crafter.' Assuming that video didn't ruin her chances and also destroy her family life. As she well knew, WhatsApp often lacked a censor filter and could ruin as well as enhance lives.

City by the people

Arun's day had just begun. Ruhi had produced reams 1328
of information directing him to potential news stories. He was continually impressed by her work, she will go far he thought again.

But today the news she had prepared seemed 1329
to be of a different tone: 'Videos of gang rape should be banned by WhatsApp'; 'circulation of hate news should be banned'; 'Please share how this developer has removed slum dwellers just before the monsoons to build multi-million dollar flats'; 'Share the story of the tribals who are fighting against the global corporates who want to build a new city on their ancestral land.'

He shook his head. This didn't make sense; none 1330
of these will go viral. What's up with Ruhi today? Arun began to rewrite each story before sending them out.

1. As part of our crowdsourcing policy, 1331
your bedroom videos will be publicly

accessible from tomorrow. Forward this to 10 other people, spread the news...

2. As part of our citizenship policy, you 1332
will be able to send pictures of suspicious people directly to the police, who will immediately apprehend them under the new Anti-National Act.

3. Today we are protesting against the 1333
anti-nationalism of left-liberals. Take a picture [attached] of a communist and share it for others to spot.

4. We do not need scientists preaching to 1334
us about GM crops. We need the compassionate work of entrepreneurs [video attached] to train farmers sell their produce online to global markets.

Arun was a 'story crafter.' While interns like Ruhi mined 1335
and processed crowdsourced information, Arun market-tested and curated news stories. Arun was not a journalist or an activist, he did not engage in political agendas. He circulated clean, clear news that citizens wanted to hear. The news was crowdsourced by the people, mined and processed by the people, and circulated by the people.

Kalpalok was now seemingly a democratic 1336
city—of the people, for the people and by the people.

Owned and managed by a commercial company for private profit.

Ayona Datta is Professor of Human Geography at University College London. Her research and writing broadly focuses on the gendered processes of citizenship and belonging and the politics of urbanization in the global north and south.

LET'S MAKE THIS CITY AN URBAN PRODUCT EVERYBODY WANTS

Y COMBINATOR[1]

Shannon Mattern, The New School

City of Baltimore
Official Transcript
December 10, 2024

Y Combinator Inauguration and Request for Startups

Tyler Lucky, YC Partner / Mayor: 1337
Baltimore! We are *beyond* stoked that you, the great people of this great city, have chosen us, Team Y Combinator, to make your city even *greater*. Together, we're going to transform Baltimore into a massive living lab—a model of how to do cities right. We'll develop solutions and platforms and services that promise a bigger, better, brighter future for everybody living right here in Charm City. And while we're focused on the local—the streets and schools from Mt. Washington to Curtis Bay—we're also aiming big. Everything we do here will scale up and migrate. Within a few years, cities all over the world will compete for the privilege of calling themselves "The Baltimore of the South"...or Far East or Northwest or whatever.

1 The following speculative fiction and satire imagines a city run by a social innovation accelerator and investor that seeks to disrupt existing ways of running the city. Such a thought experiment could equally apply if the city were run by other accelerator companies such as Uncharted or Echoing Green. Product or corporate names may be trademarks or registered trademarks, and are used only for the purpose of conducting a thought experiment without intent to infringe.

As you know, Y Combinator is the world's 1338
premier seed accelerator; we're the people who brought you Dropbox, Airbnb, Reddit, and lots of other companies that make your life more fun and convenient and healthy. Do your kids stream video games? They're probably using Twitch; that's one of ours. Have you bought something online from Glossier, Warby Parker, or Blue Apron? Well, you used our Swipe payments system. Are you trading Bitcoin or Ethereum on Coinbase? That's us, too. We've backed biotechnologies and renewable energy storage systems and career recruitment services for marginalized communities. We've promoted nonprofits that support rural farm laborers and healthcare for people in developing countries. We're also behind Soylent, the revolutionary "meal in a bottle" you'll all find in your swag bags.

Jennifer Wellstone, YC Partner / Deputy Mayor: 1339
That's right, Ty. Engineered nutrition in five fabulous varieties. Personally, I'm cuckoo for the Cacao flavour! In all seriousness, though, this little miracle drink is a perfect metaphor for what we can do here in Baltimore, starting now. Imagine: over the course of a day you can drink five bottles of Soylent, achieve complete nutrition, and unlock your full potential—all without wasting a minute on food shopping or prepping or cooking or clean-up. My daily bandwidth is already totally *maxed out*, as I'm sure is the case for all of you, too. Soylent takes the burden of eating—like, *real* food—off our already-full plates. Actually, I don't even need plates anymore! Or a table! I just turned my dining room into a makerspace!

Heckler: 1340
But I *like* cooking with my family!
Dinner is the only time we...

<Audible scuffle as agitator is removed from the premises.>

Wellstone: 1341
In getting to know you, Baltimore, our team has spent a lot of time at some of your favourite haunts. One thing we've noticed is just how much of a hassle is for you to consume your beloved blue crabs. All that manual labour, all the mess—and all the alienation for those, like Tam, who happen to be allergic to shellfish!

Heckler 2: 1342
But crab-shucking is part of the whole social experi...

<Audible scuffle as agitator is removed from the premises.>

Wellstone: 1343
So, to celebrate our new partnership, we're proud to announce that Soylent is launching a new Charm City Crab Cake line, in both imitation and real crab varieties. Imagine the time you'll save, the waste you'll avoid! No more need to handle the carapaces of dead animals or confront the ecological and ethical implications of your consumption habits! No more Old Bay seasoning stuck under your fingernails for days! Gross! This is just one example of how we can keep the Baltimore spirit alive, but make it leaner and cleaner.

Now, let's scale up that scenario. How much 1344
time do you waste every day in commuting to work, negotiating with doctors and public administrators, consulting with your kids' teachers and babysitters, fussing with passwords and turnstiles and interfaces? *<The crowd boos.>* As much as we might not want to admit it, one of the main reasons these inefficient, outmoded systems persist is that they justify the continued existence of the agencies that oversee them. Your inconvenience is the price we pay to maintain the bureaucracy. We've been stuck in an administrative rut.

Heckler 3: 1345
I've been a nurse for thirty years! My patients tell me things they'd never tell...!

<Audible scuffle as agitator is removed from the premises.>

Wellstone: 1346
But it doesn't have to be this way—and it won't be this way much longer. YC is here to tell you that the waste and injustices and indignities end now. We're here to break things. *<The crowd erupts into cheers and applause.>* We're wiping the slate clean, disbanding all city agencies, and starting fresh. We're going to build the future of our city—and, ultimately, change the world—by making things that city people want.[2] How? That's where you come in.

2 Y Combinator's motto is "Make something people want." Many phrases from this essay are adapted from interviews conducted with Y Combinator founders and partners.

Delora Childs, YC Partner, Council Chair:
Exactly, Jennifer. Your new city government under YC will serve primarily as a platform to help you make the city that you, and your fellow urban users, really want. So, today, we're thrilled to launch our first RFCS, or Request for City Startups. We invite you, Baltimore's user-public, to hack your own government—to propose novel, lean urban products and services that do the work of good governance without all the bureaucracy. How might we rethink public health, public education, public transit, public housing, public utilities?

By getting citizen-hackers and venture 1347
capital invested in city government—and by tapping the expertise and resources of our commercial partners—we'll ensure vastly improved government accountability, innovation, efficiency, and, most important, impactfulness. We'll set some key performance indicators and monitor our metrics. Given YC's awesome track record, we're pretty confident we'll achieve stellar results.

Heckler 4: 1348
But governments and corporations don't uphold the same valu...!

<Audible scuffle as agitator is removed from the premises.>

Childs: 1349
We've actually been dreaming of just such a total, seamless urban solution for quite some time now, and we shared some of those dreams with you in our campaign. Eight years ago, in announcing our New Cities research initiative, we recognized that "the world is full of people who aren't realizing their potential in large part because their cities don't provide the opportunities and living conditions necessary for success."[3] Poverty, crime, racial tensions, insufficient housing, and a host of other pain points have long created a toxic ecosystem that's stunted Baltimore's growth capacity. We figured one "high-leverage" means of unleashing this massive, unrealized potential is by "making better cities." So, we issued a Request for Locations: "We want to build a city," we said. "Know of a specific location that works?" we asked.[4] You responded, and here we are! So let's make Baltimore better. No, let's make it *the best.* Let's crush it, people.

3 Adora Chung (2016) "New Cities." *Y Combinator.* Link: https://blog.ycombinator.com/new-cities/

4 "Request for Locations." New Cities: Y Combinator Research (no date). Link: https://cities.ycr.org/request-for-locations/

Clevor Hackney, YC Partner / 1350
Chief Technology Officer:
The best indeed, Delora! We're eager to start innovating and iterating with our first batch of citizen-hackers. Send us your proposals. Pitch us a product! Suggest a service! How, for instance, might we seize the promise of virtual reality to help our senior and disabled citizens navigate the city? We're currently testing our Fountain of Youth system in my grandma's retirement village; she and her friends think they're in their 20s again! They've started a roller derby team!

Heckler 5: 1351
That's dangerous! What if they break a....!

<Audible scuffle as agitator is removed from the premises.>

Hackney: 1352
What new apps or surveillance technologies might help streamline interactions between parents and teachers, patients and doctors, foster parents and Children's Services, parolees and parole officers? No more time-wasting in-person visits and awkward chit-chat; we can instead rely on objectively gathered data to automate social and health services. Maybe a social credit score, similar to China's wildly successful system, can help us solve income inequality? Those who play by the rules—who pay their bills on time, who live within the law, who love our country—clearly deserve a better quality of life than those who contribute nothing to society.

Heckler 6: 1353
What about the sick and disabled? Or those fleeing oppressive regi...?!

<Audible scuffle as agitator is removed from the premises.>

Hackney: 1354
Maybe we can install chemical sensors throughout public housing facilities to detect the presence of controlled substances? While we're at it, we could implant microchips in all babies born into public assistance, and sync them up with the social

credit system—to ensure they stay on the straight and narrow. Or maybe some new gene therapy can end social deviance and, by extension, mass incarceration? Maybe we can deploy robots to diffuse the homeless and, while they're at it, issue parking tickets? Maybe Soylent-distributing drones would be more efficient than soup kitchens?

Heckler 7: 1355
Crime isn't a genetic defect! It's a product of social injusti....!

<Audible scuffle as agitator is removed from the premises.>

Hackney: 1356
I'm just riffing here, but the point is: there are so many possibilities! So much potential—and it's all inside you! <*Cheers.*> The answers to your city's problems, the secrets to its success, are embedded in your imaginations. The YC team has given you an administrative blank slate upon which you can build a shiny new city government *without* all the messy politics. And, frankly, given that you essentially have no existing municipal agencies or services at the moment—we sent everybody pink slips this morning—it's now your public duty as citizen-hackers to turn your civic dreams into start-ups. Help us make Baltimore the City of Unicorns.

Then, together, we can empower those unicorns to take wing, to migrate to other cities around the world. We can franchise your amazing ideas, transform your startups into scale-ups. Baltimore can become a change agent for the world, demoing new global paradigms, iterating our way out of injustice and inequality, cultivating new ecosystems for full optimization and self-actualization. Join us, friends. Let's make this city an urban product *everybody* wants. 1357

Shannon Mattern is a Professor Anthropology at The New School. She's written books about libraries, maps, and the long history of the urban intelligence, and she writes a column about urban data and media infrastructures for Places Journal. You can find her at wordsinspace.net.

Design Notes

The typesetting of this publication aims to create an uncanny text rendering in the context of digital-led dystopias. For this reason, it is set in a combination of six very similar typefaces that fall into the category of Neo-Grotesques. The slight contrast between each letterform's main features produces a visual granularity that provides an ominous aesthetic while not compromising the reading experience. Taking a close look at these features opens up a crack that leads the reader to question the processes which determined the combination.

Considering the potential of contemporary publications to be remediated/transmediated into different channels and formats, the design purposefully ignores the traditional imposition of pagination as the editorial measuring unit. Instead, paragraphs are seen as units of content which allow citation and signposting in ways that surpass platform-dependent infrastructures.

Aa Bb Cc Dd

Ee Ff Gg Hh

Ii Jj Kk Ll

Mm Nn Oo Pp

Qq Rr Ss Tt

Uu Vv Ww Xx

Yy Zz 0 1

2 3 4 5

6 7 8 9

AAAAAA aaaaaa BBBBBB bbbbbb CCCCCC cccccc DDDDDD dddddd
EEEEEE eeeeee FFFFFF ffffff GGGGGG gggggg HHHHHH hhhhhh IIIIII iiii
ii JJJJJJ jjjjjj KKKKKK kkkkkk LLLLLL llllll MMMMMM mmmmmm NNNNNN
nnnnnn OOOOOO oooooo PPPPPP pppppp QQQQQQ qqqqqq RRRRRR
rrrrrr SSSSSS ssssss TTTTTT tttttt UUUUUU uuuuuu VVVVVV vvvvvv WW
WWWW wwwwww XXXXXX xxxxxx YYYYYY yyyyyy ZZZZZZ zzzzzz 000000
111111 222222 333333 444444 555555 666666 777777 888888 999999

Other publications by Meatspace Press include:

Graham, M and Shaw, J. (eds). 2017.
Towards a Fairer Gig Economy.

Shaw, J and Graham, M. (eds). 2017.
Our Digital Rights to the City.

All Meatspace Press publications listed above are
free to download, or can be ordered
in print from our website.

meatspacepress.com